The Fabric of GEOLOGY

The Fabric of

FREEMAN, COOPER, & COMPAN

CLAUDE C. ALBRITTON, Jr., *Editor*

GEOLOGY

*Prepared under the direction of a Committee
of The Geological Society of America, in
commemoration of the Society's 75th Anniversary*

Box 3050 · Stanford, California

Preface

During the years immediately following World War II, many geologists became dissatisfied with the training that was being given to students of the earth sciences. Accordingly, the Council of The Geological Society of America, in December of 1946, named a committee to investigate the state of geologic education, and to offer suggestions for its improvement. The report of this committee appeared in the *Interim Proceedings* of the Society for 1949. Of the recommendations presented, the one emphasized most strongly urged that, at all levels of instruction, "only those inferences be presented . . . for which the essential observational data and the logical steps leading to the inference have also been presented."* Before this criterion could be satisfied, the committeemen asserted, the logical structure of geologic science would have to be re-examined—"from the ground up."

When the time came to make plans for the Society's seventy-fifth anniversary, the Councilors, recalling this last recommendation, decided that the theme for the anniversary meetings should be the philosophy of geology. A committee was asked to produce a book of essays on the fabric of geologic thought, and to arrange a program on the same subject for the annual meetings in 1963.

The very lack of any modern book on the philosophy of geology is justification enough for this work. The members of the Anniversary Committee will have achieved their purpose if this collection, despite any shortcomings it may have, serves as a focal point for discussions of our role as scientists.

The book begins with a toast to James Hutton, as founder of modern geology. McIntyre seeks out the origin of the ideas which shaped Hutton's fruitful theory of the earth, and he finds some likely sources in some unlikely places—including steam engines, organisms, and the all but forgotten work of George Hoggart Toulmin.

Does geology have laws and theories of its own? What is to be understood when geology is called historical science? These questions are considered in a sequence of three essays. Bradley identifies the history and constitution of the earth as the two principal subjects of geologic investigation. Simpson goes on to develop the differences between the historical and the nonhistorical aspects of the science, which he finds in their respective concerns with the *configurational* as opposed to the *immanent* properties of matter and energy. If "laws," in the

---

* Hubbert, M. K., Hendricks, T. A., and Thiel, G. A. (Chairman), Report of the Committee on Geologic Education of The Geological Society of America: Geol. Soc. Am., Int. Pr., 1949, pt. 2, pp. 17–21.

usual sense of this term, apply to the immanent and not to the configurational in nature, then the laws of physical and dynamic geology are the laws of physics and chemistry. Kitts concludes that the theory of geology is likewise the theory of physics and chemistry—used by geologists, however, as instruments of historical inference.

Laboratory experiments have played a less important role in geology than in chemistry or physics. And yet, as H. H. Read has observed, "Any man looking out of any window sees a geological laboratory in constant and full-scale operation." McKelvey develops this theme by showing how geologists have the unusual opportunity to observe the results of complex natural experiments that involve larger masses and longer periods of time than can be handled in the laboratory.

The six essays forming the middle section of the book treat of geologic thought within the framework of some particular branch of earth science. Woodford critically examines the proposition in stratigraphy that fossils may be used to order strata in chronologic sequences. McIntyre investigates the reliability of certain methods for obtaining the absolute ages of rocks that are used to calibrate the stratigraphic column described by Woodford. McIntyre's essay also illustrates a trend toward the quantitative in geology, and this is the theme of Mackin's comparison of the rational and empirical methods of investigation. Mackin draws his examples from geomorphology, the same field which Leopold and Langbein use to illustrate the association of ideas in geologic thought. Structural geology provides Hill with an example which he uses to develop rules of geologic nomenclature and classification. Anderson also turns to structural geology for examples to show how the geologist uses the logical principle of simplicity.

Three essays are concerned primarily with the communication of geologic data and ideas. Betz examines the documentary tools of communication and suggests how these might be better used to contend with the "information problem" which is of growing concern to all scientists. Gilluly shows how G. K. Gilbert, in his scientific memoirs, took pains to disclose the chains of reasoning that linked his observations to his conclusions. Harrison discusses the interpretative character of the geologic map, and illustrates the way in which theory may influence mapping, and vice versa.

The last two essays in the book identify contrasting areas of geologic thought and work which are in need of further development. Hagner urges that more attention be given to the history and philosophy of geology, while Legget points to the increasing opportunities of putting geology to work in the service of man.

A bibliography of writings that reflect upon the character of geologic thought concludes the volume.

The planning of this book has been the responsibility of a committee of eight persons, who, in addition to the Editor, are Messrs. Frederick Betz, Jr., James

Gilluly, J. M. Harrison, H. H. Hess, Mason L. Hill, Luna B. Leopold, and W. W. Rubey.

The members of the Anniversary Committee thank the Trustees of The Graduate Research Center, Inc. for sponsoring a conference on the scope and philosophy of geology, which was held in Dallas in October of 1960. At this meeting, members of the Committee presented their tentative thoughts on the logical foundations of geology. Three philosophers—Nelson Goodman, Carl G. Hempel and John H. Kultgen—served as critics, and were especially helpful in drawing lines between real problems and false issues. William E. Benson and Eugene Herrin were guests of the conference and active participants in discussions which did much to shape the contents of the book.

The idea of bringing philosophers and geologists together for the conference in Dallas belongs to Mr. W. H. Freeman. As the Publisher's Editor for this book, he has, moreover, arranged to have most of the essays read by Professors Morton Beckner and Michael Scriven, whose forthright criticisms are gratefully acknowledged.

Mrs. Robert R. Wheeler prepared the special index for the annotated bibliography and also the general index for this book. Mrs. Jacquelyn Newbury typed much of the manuscript and obtained permission to reproduce the numerous quotations in the bibliography and text.

"When 'Omer Smote 'is Bloomin' Lyre," by Rudyard Kipling, is reprinted from *Rudyard Kipling's Verse* (Definitive Edition) by permission of Mrs. George Bambridge and Doubleday & Company, Inc.

Dallas, Texas   C. C. A.
July 1, 1963

Contents

DONALD B. McINTYRE

Pomona College

James Hutton and the Philosophy of Geology

"When 'Omer smote 'is bloomin' lyre,
    He'd 'eard men sing by land an' sea;
An' what he thought 'e might require,
    'E went an' took—the same as me!

"The market-girls an' fishermen,
    The shepherds an' the sailors, too,
They 'eard old songs turn up again,
    But kep' it quiet—same as you!

"They knew 'e stole; 'e knew they knowed.
    They didn't tell, nor make a fuss,
But winked at 'Omer down the road,
    An' 'e winked back—the same as us!"

KIPLING

Prior to Hutton, geology did not exist, and I think it is generally agreed that the science was created in the fifty years between 1775 and 1825. In 1775, Hutton's close friend, James Watt, constructed his first working steam engine, and Werner, who was to become the leader of the Neptunists, began teaching at the Mining Academy of Freiburg. By 1825, the first passenger train was in operation, and Lyell, who was born the year Hutton died, was at work on his "Principles of Geology"—"the coping stone" of the new science.

1

The same years saw the American War of Independence, the Industrial Revolution, the French Revolution, and the Napoleonic wars. It was the age of Wordsworth and Coleridge, Byron and Shelley, Goethe and Schiller, Scott and Burns.

During this period the necessary foundations for petrology, and the study of the materials of the crust, were laid by the work of Haüy on crystallography, Werner on the physical properties of minerals, and Joseph Black on their chemical composition. Stratigraphical paleontology and the technique of field mapping were initiated by William Smith, but it was Hutton, and Hutton alone, who provided geology with a dynamic scheme—a theory, in the original sense of "something seen in the mind." Thus Hutton plays the same role in geology as Newton in astronomy, or Darwin in biology. Comprehension is the power of the mind to understand, and these intellectual giants have given us comprehension of the great processes which go on around us. For this reason, Hutton truly deserves the title "Founder of Modern Geology."[1]

Fortunately for posterity, Hutton had a most eloquent biographer in John Playfair, Professor of Physics and of Mathematics at the University of Edinburgh, and one of the finest writers of scientific prose the English language has known. If the history of science is to be the study of the origin and development of ideas, then the history of geology needs to give attention to Playfair's remark: "It would be desirable to trace the progress of Dr. Hutton's mind in the formation of a system where so many new and enlarged views of nature occur, and where so much originality is displayed."

But how can anyone, other than the author himself, possibly hope to follow the sequence of ideas that unconsciously have been at work in a creative mind? The classic answer to this question has been given by John Livingston Lowes in his study of the process of creation in the mind of Coleridge, entitled "The Road to Xanadu"—one of the most remarkable works of detection ever written. Coleridge kept a notebook in which he recorded facts and phrases which had caught his attention, and Lowes was able to use this book, along with library records, to follow Coleridge through his reading and hence "to retrace," as he said, "the obliterated vestiges of creation." The result is astonishing: the origin of almost every phrase and analogy in "The Rime of the Ancient Mariner" can be identified; and quite an assortment these sources are,

---

[1] On the 150th anniversary of Hutton's death it was my good fortune to attend, in Edinburgh, a memorable lecture by S. I. Tomkeieff. The effect it had on me was profound and, because my present subject concerns the unavoidable and indeed laudable practice of borrowing of ideas, I have not hesitated to adopt Tomkeieff's title—and a little more besides. The extent of my indebtedness may be gauged by reference to Tomkeieff's paper (1948).

including as they do such unlikely works as Burnett's "Sacred Theory of the Earth," Maupertuis' geodetic study on "The Figure of the Earth," Father Bourges' "Luminous Appearances in the Wakes of Ships," and the Astronomer Royal's paper in the Philosophical Transactions of the Royal Society entitled "An account of an appearance, like a star, seen in the dark part of the moon."

Hutton, we are told, "was in the habit of using his pen continually as an instrument of thought," and he left behind him what is described as "an incredible quantity of manuscript"; unhappily almost none has survived, so we are deprived of the clues his notebooks would have afforded.

Coleridge himself was keenly aware of the pattern: "the imagination, the true inward creatrix," constantly working on "the shattered fragments of memory, dissolves, diffuses, dissipates, in order to recreate." And elsewhere he wrote that the "hooks-and-eyes of memory permit a confluence of our recollections." The analogy is reminiscent of Poincaré's image of mathematical discovery, in which he pictures ideas as hooked atoms ploughing through space like the molecules as conceived in the kinetic theory of gases. The number of possible combinations is so vast that even in a lifetime they couldn't all be examined, and Poincaré concluded that esthetic sensibility, the appreciation of the beauty of an elegant solution, acts in the subconscious like a delicate sieve to catch combinations worthy of the attention of the conscious mind. Thus, the creation of a poem and the discovery of a mathematical law may have much in common. Perhaps a geologic theory also is born in the same manner.

A long time ago that giant of American geology, Grove Karl Gilbert, elaborated this theme in two masterly presidential addresses: one was entitled "The Inculcation of Scientific Method by Example" (1885) and the other "The Origin of Hypotheses" (1895). Gilbert, himself no mean deviser of brilliant and ingenious ideas, made a practice of trying to analyze the methods he and his associates used in geologic research.

He wrote: "Just as in the domain of matter nothing is created from nothing, just as in the domain of life there is no spontaneous generation, so in the domain of mind there are no ideas which do not owe their existence to antecedent ideas which stand in the relation of parent to child. It is only because our mental processes are largely conducted outside of consciousness that the lineage of ideas is difficult to trace . . . To explain the origin of hypotheses" wrote Gilbert, "I have a hypothesis to present. It is that hypotheses are always suggested through analogy. Consequential relations of nature are infinite in variety, and he who is acquainted with the largest number has the broadest base for the analogic suggestion of hypotheses." I believe it was H. H. Read who affirmed that "the best geologist is he who has seen the most geology." At any rate, there is undoubtedly some truth in the remark.

The conclusion we reach seems to be that the equipment necessary to devise hypotheses includes:

First, an excellent memory and an extensive knowledge of the relevant material;

Second, the ability to form associations of ideas, and to reason by analogy; and

Third, the possession of an unusually high degree of esthetic feeling for an elegant solution, and a burning enthusiasm for the subject.

Now Playfair (1805, p. 98) informs us that Dr. Hutton:

> ... had acquired great information; and an excellent memory supplied an inexhaustible fund of illustration, always happily introduced. He used also regularly to unbend himself with a few friends, in the little society ... known by the name of the Oyster Club... The original members of it were Mr. [Adam] Smith [the author of "The Wealth of Nations"], Dr. [Joseph] Black [the discoverer of latent heat and of carbon dioxide, and who introduced quantitative methods in chemistry], and Dr. Hutton, and round them was soon formed a knot of those who knew how to value the familiar and social converse of these illustrious men. As all the three possessed great talents, enlarged views, and extensive information, without any of the stateliness and formality which men of letters think it sometimes necessary to affect; as they were all three easily amused, were equally prepared to speak and to listen, and as the sincerity of their friendship had never been darkened by the least shade of envy; it would be hard to find an example where every thing favourable to good society was more perfectly united, and every thing adverse more entirely excluded. The conversation was always free, often scientific, but never didactic or disputatious; and as this club was much the resort of the strangers who visited Edinburgh, from any object connected with art or with science, it derived from thence an extraordinary degree of variety and interest.

Hutton, then, was peculiarly well placed for the accumulation of diverse information and ideas, and he had an excellent memory. What of his ability to reason by analogy? Playfair records that Hutton possessed "the experienced eye, the power of perceiving the minute differences and fine analogies which discriminate or unite the objects of science, and the readiness of comparing new phenomena with others already treasured up in the mind."

What then of his appreciation of the beauty of an elegant solution, and what of his enthusiasm?

> A circumstance which greatly distinguished the intellectual character of the philosopher of whom we now speak, was an uncommon activity and ardour of mind, upheld by the greatest admiration of whatever in science was

new, beautiful, or sublime. The acquisitions of fortune, and the enjoyments which most directly address the senses, do not call up more lively expressions of joy in other men, than hearing of a new invention, or being made acquainted with a new truth, would, at any time, do in Dr. Hutton. This sensibility to intellectual pleasure was not confined to a few objects, nor to the sciences which he particularly cultivated: he would rejoice over Watt's improvements on the steam engine, or Cook's discoveries in the South Sea, with all the warmth of a man who was to share in the honour or the profit about to accrue from them. The fire of his expression on such occasions, and the animation of his countenance and manner, are not to be described; they were always seen with great delight by those who could enter into his sentiments, and often with great astonishment by those who could not.

With this exquisite relish for whatever is beautiful and sublime in science, we may easily conceive what pleasure he derived from his own geological speculations. The novelty and grandeur of the objects offered by them to the imagination, the simple and uniform order given to the whole natural history of the earth, . . . are things to which hardly any man could be insensible; but to him they were matter, not of transient delight, but of solid and permanent happiness. (Playfair, 1805, p. 91)

Elsewhere Playfair remarks that both Hutton and Black were "formed with a taste for what is beautiful and great in science, with minds inventive and fertile in new combinations." Clearly, Hutton had all the qualities we have suggested as necessary in a great scientific synthesizer—and he possessed them to a remarkable degree. We must now look at the most likely sources of his ideas: his immediate background and the achievements of his friends.

Hutton's first serious studies were in chemistry and medicine, first in Edinburgh, then in Paris, and finally in Leyden, where he took his M.D. degree at the age of 23. However, he never practiced medicine, for, on his return to Scotland, he took charge of the small farm which he had inherited from his father. Hutton, who never did things by halves, immediately applied his scientific training to agriculture. He introduced new methods to Scottish farming, and he traveled to Norfolk and the Low Countries in search of the best techniques and practices. While on these journeys he became increasingly interested in the origin of soil and in the processes of geology.

After 13 years of successful farming, he moved to Edinburgh, where his principal income was from his ammonium chloride plant—the first in Britain. His time was spent in reading, in chemical experiments, often together with Black, and in the company of his illustrious and stimulating friends. He was a member of the Council of the newly organized Royal Society of Edinburgh, and for the first volume of the Society's Transactions he prepared his paper on the "Theory of the Earth, or an investigation of the laws observable in the composition, dissolution, and restoration of land upon the globe." The paper was read at two successive meetings of the Society in 1785. Illness prevented

Hutton from attending the first of these meetings, and the first part of his paper was read by his friend Joseph Black.

In addition to his studies of medicine, agriculture, chemistry, meteorology, and geology, he published a three-volume work on philosophy and a dissertation on the Chinese language.

The accomplishments of his friends are so extensive that we can afford only a catalog. His intimate acquaintances were responsible for the discovery of carbon dioxide, nitrogen, oxygen, and strontium, and he himself was the first to extract sodium from a silicate. The list includes the discovery that water has a point of maximum density and that latent heat is needed to change its state. His friends included men responsible for the development of the steam engine; for the founding of iron works and a sulfuric acid plant; for the use of chlorine in bleaching; the author of the first book on agricultural chemistry; the author of the "Wealth of Nations"; the man to whom Sir Walter Scott dedicated "Waverley"; and that remarkable man who, never having been to sea, devised a system of naval tactics which won the British fleet several victories, and which was quoted in Nelson's battle orders at Trafalgar.

With this background we are now equipped to examine Hutton's Theory, and we will also draw somewhat on the unpublished manuscript of his "Elements of Agriculture" on which he was working at the time of his death. Insofar as is practicable, I will give you Hutton's own words.

First of all we need to know that for Hutton, "A theory is nothing but the generalization of particular facts; and, in a theory of the earth, those facts must be taken from the observations of natural history." For Hutton, a phenomenon (what he termed an "appearance") was "explained" when it had been "comprehended" by a theory, that is to say, incorporated into the structure of the theory.

Second, Hutton remarked that "It is with pleasure that man observes order and regularity in the works of nature, instead of becoming disgusted with disorder and confusion. If the stone which fell today were to rise tomorrow, there would be an end of natural philosophy, our principles would fail, and we would no longer investigate the rules of nature from our observations."

This, of course, is the doctrine of uniformitarianism, but it wasn't original with Hutton. Before Hutton went to Leyden, the Professor of Astronomy there wrote: "When, as a result of certain observations, we anticipate other cases which we have not directly observed, our prediction is based on the axiom of uniformity of nature. All action would be impossible if we could not assume that the lessons of former experience would be valid in the future."

For Hutton it was clear that, in his own words, "We must read the transactions of time past in the present state of natural bodies, and, for the reading of this character, we have nothing but the laws of nature, established in the science of man by his inductive reasoning. For man is not satisfied in seeing things which are; he seeks to know how things have been, and what they are to be." However, it was Sir Archibald Geikie and not James Hutton who crystallized this concept in the memorable dictum: "The present is the key to the past."

In Hutton's own opinion, it was agriculture that had been the study of his life; geology had been incidental. Accordingly he looked on the world as a well-run farm, designed to sustain plants and animals, and with rotation, necessary to maintain fertility. Indeed, the secret of Hutton is that he thought of the world as a sort of superorganism. His was not the mind of a narrow specialist. For him the biological sciences were completely integrated with the physical. "Here," he said, "is a compound system of things, forming together one whole living world."

> The most solid rocks moulder and decay upon the surface of the earth, and thus procure a soil, either immediately upon the place which, thus, had given it birth, or remotely upon some other place where it may be transported by the water or the wind. For this great purpose of the world, the solid structure of the earth must be sacrificed; for the fertility of the soil depends upon the loose and incoherent state of its materials; and this state of the fertile soil necessarily exposes it to the ravages of the rain upon the inclined surface of the earth.
>
> From the tops of the mountains to the shores of the sea, all the soils are subject to be moved from their places, and to be deposited in a lower situation; thus gradually proceeding from the mountain to the river; and from the river, step by step, into the sea. If the vegetable soil is thus constantly removed from the surface of the land, and if its place is thus to be supplied from the dissolution of the solid earth, . . . we may perceive an end to this beautiful machine; an end arising from . . . that destructibility of its land which is so necessary in the system of the globe, in the economy of life and vegetation. It may be concluded that the apparent permanency of this earth is not real or absolute, and that the fertility of its surface, like the healthy state of animal bodies, must have its period and be succeeded by another. (Hutton, 1788, p. 215 *et passim*)

"We have now considered the globe of this earth as a machine, constructed upon chemical as well as mechanical principles, . . . But is this world [he asks] to be considered thus merely as a machine, to last no longer than its parts retain their present position, their proper forms and qualities?" And here we see Watt and his steam engine in Hutton's mind.—"Or, [he asks] may it not be also considered as an organized body such as has a constitution in which the necessary decay of the machine is naturally repaired . . . [Is] there, . . . in the constitution of this world, a reproductive operation by which a ruined constitution may be again repaired?" (Hutton, 1788, p. 215) And here we see the physician and the farmer.

"From the constitution of those materials which compose the present land, we have reason to conclude that, during the time this land was forming, by the collection of its materials at the bottom of the sea, there had been a former land containing minerals similar to those we find at present in examining the earth . . . A habitable earth is made to rise out of the wreck of a former world." And this is Hutton the geologist.

The whole spirit of Hutton's geology is contained in his statement that "The matter of this active world is perpetually moved, in that salutary circulation [a good medical expression!] by which provision is so wisely made for the growth and prosperity of plants, and for the life and comfort of the various animals."

Now it is a most remarkable fact that, immediately prior to the publication of Hutton's Theory in 1788, there was a man, today almost completely forgotten, who viewed the earth just as Hutton did. His name was George Hoggart Toulmin. No one familiar with Hutton's writings can read Toulmin's "The Antiquity of the World" without being impressed by astonishing similarities. For my own part, I find it impossible to avoid the conclusion that Hutton had read it prior to writing his own paper.

Like Hutton, Toulmin took a remarkably comprehensive view of the earth, referring to "the beautiful order and disposition of the several parts that compose the stupendous whole." Like Hutton, he adopted a fundamental uniformitarianism: "Nature is always the same, her laws are eternal and immutable." Like Hutton he believed that slow changes, long continued, can produce far-reaching results: "These immutable truths should never be forgot," he writes, "that animals and vegetables flourish and decay; that earths are formed by slow degrees; that they too change by time; that stone is formed, is decomposed or altered in its composition; that mountains now are elevated; now depressed;—that nature lives in motion."

Like Hutton, he recognized the significance of sedimentary rocks as proof of the circulation of matter. But to me it was of particular interest that Toulmin's very words and phrases echoed what I knew in Hutton: "The continual formation and decay of every existing substance, the unceasing circulation of matter, produces no disorder. A continual waste in every part is necessary to the incessant repairs of the whole. The closest sympathy and connection is preserved throughout the entire system of things."

Now Hutton wrote: We are "led to acknowledge an order in a subject which, in another view, has appeared as absolute disorder and confusion. . . There is a certain order established for the progress of nature, for the succession of things, and for the circulation of matter upon the surface of the globe. . . We must see how this machine is so contrived as to have those parts which are wasting and decaying, again repaired . . . the necessary decay is naturally repaired."

"We are," says Hutton, "thus led to see a circulation in the matter of the globe, and a system of beautiful economy in the works of nature. This earth, like the body of an animal, is wasted at the same time that it is repaired. It has a state of growth and augmentation; it has another state which is that of diminution and decay. This world is thus destroyed in one part, but it is renewed in another."

The last sentence of Toulmin's book ends: "We have by no means been led to contravene . . . the existence of infinite intelligence and wisdom." And elsewhere he refers to "nature, whose every operation is stamped with wisdom and consistency." The last paragraph of Hutton's paper begins, "We have now got to the end of our reasoning; we have the satisfaction to find that in nature there is wisdom, system, and consistency."

Toulmin wrote: "there has ever been a succession of events, something similar to what is continually observed . . . a vast succession of ages. . . We have been induced to conclude that the whole system of things," and so on. Hutton put it thus: "having seen a succession of worlds, we may from this conclude that there is a system in nature."

Toulmin said: "In the circle of existence, in vain do we seek the beginning of things." And Hutton, intimating that he had reached the limit of his vision into the past, wrote: "It is in vain to look for anything higher in the origin of the earth."

Toulmin's main point is that "through the whole of this enquiry we have endeavoured to demonstrate . . . that, as there never was any beginning, so will there never be a conclusion. . ." And he repeats, "the whole system of things never had any beginning, nor will have any termination." And the final sentence of Hutton's paper is: "The result, therefore, of our present enquiry is, that we find no vestige of a beginning, no prospect of an end." Are we not, like John Livingston Lowes, "retracing the obliterated vestiges of creation"?[2]

In 1749 Hutton was granted the M.D. degree at Leyden for his thesis on "The Blood and Circulation in the Microcosm." The title reminds us that, from the beginning of speculative thought, philosophers have pondered the concept that man, the microcosm, is the epitome of the macrocosm or the world in which he lives. Attempts were constantly being made to find analogies or correspondences between aspects of the anatomy and physiology of man, and the structure and workings of the universe. One of the oldest was the analogy between the sun, as the ruling power of the macrocosm, and the heart, the governing power of the microcosm. Now at a medical school with the reputation of that at Leyden, Hutton could not have taken the circulation of

---

[2] I trust that the significance of these words will be understood; no reader of Lowes is likely to accuse Coleridge of plagiarism.

blood as his subject without becoming very familiar with Harvey's classic book "On the Movement of the Heart and Blood," published in 1628.

Harvey began his dedication, to King Charles I, thus: "The animal's heart is the basis of its life, its chief member, the sun of its microcosm; on the heart all its activity depends, from the heart all its liveliness and strength arise. Equally is the king the basis of his kingdoms, the sun of his microcosm, the heart of the state." And in his text Harvey wrote:

> I began to think whether there might not be a motion, as it were in a circle, in the same sense that Aristotle uses when he says that air and rain emulate the circular movement of the heavenly bodies; for the moist earth warmed by the sun evaporates; the vapors drawn upwards are condensed and fall as rain to moisten the earth again, so producing successions of fresh life. In similar fashion the circular movement of the sun gives rise to storms and atmospheric phenomena. And so, in all likelihood, is it in the body, through the motion of the blood. . . The heart deserves to be styled the starting point of life and the sun of our microcosm just as much as the sun deserves to be styled the heart of the world.

That the suggestion I am hinting at is not far-fetched is made clear by the following quotation from Hutton: "The circulation of the blood is the efficient cause of life; but life is the final cause, not only for the circulation of the blood, but for the revolution of the globe: without a central luminary and a revolution of the planetary body, there could not have been a living creature upon the face of this earth." Now this quotation is not from his medical thesis, but from the "Theory of the Earth," written 46 years after he left Leyden! And twice, in that geologic classic, does Hutton refer to the "physiology" of the earth— a most significant phrase, and one reminiscent, incidentally, of Thomas Robinson's book, "The Anatomy of the Earth," published in 1694, which proclaimed that the earth was a superorganism with "a constant circulation of water, as in other animals of blood."

Analogy of microcosm and macrocosm, analogy of celestial spheres and atmosphere, analogy of heart and sun, analogy of blood and rain: this is the heredity of Hutton's Theory—of our theory. And the heart of the theory (if I may use the analogy) is the concept of circulation of matter in the macrocosm. One of the famous teachers at Leyden, just before Hutton's time there, wrote that "the author of nature has made it necessary for us to reason by analogy." I know that Grove Karl Gilbert would have approved of this. The moral seems to be that analogies are so important in the genesis of scientific hypotheses that even false analogies are sometimes extremely fertile.

In closing I should like to report to you on the Circulation Club which was founded in Edinburgh three years before Hutton's paper was read to the Royal Society. Its object was, and here I quote from the Constitution: "to commemorate the discovery of the circulation of the blood by the circulation of the glass." Let us adopt and adapt that old tradition; let our hearts beat faster and our blood thrill as we commemorate the discovery of circulation in the macrocosm, and drink to the immortal name of the founder of geology, James Hutton, M.D.

BIBLIOGRAPHY

BAILEY, Sir E. B., 1950, James Hutton, founder of modern geology (1726–1797): Roy. Soc. Edinburgh, Pr., vol. 63, sec. B., 1947–49, pp. 357–368.

GILBERT, G. K., 1885, The inculcation of scientific method by example, with an illustration drawn from the Quaternary geology of Utah: Am. J. Sci., 1886, 3rd series, vol. 31, pp. 284–299.

———, 1896, The origin of hypotheses, illustrated by the discussion of a topographic problem: Science, n.s., vol. 3, pp. 1–13.

HARVEY, WILLIAM, 1628, Exercitatio anatomica de motu cordis et sanguinis in animalibus: Tr. from original Latin by Kenneth J. Franklin for the Royal College of Physicians of London, 1957, Oxford, Blackwell Scientific Publications, 209 pp.

HUTTON, JAMES, 1788, Theory of the earth; or an investigation of the laws observable in the composition, dissolution, and restoration of land upon the globe: Roy. Soc. Edinburgh, Tr., vol. 1, pt. 1, pp. 209–304.

———, 1795, Theory of the earth, with proofs and illustrations: Edinburgh, Facsim. reprint 2 vols., 1959, New York, Hafner.

LOWES, J. L., 1927, The road to Xanadu; a study in the ways of the imagination: Boston, Houghton Mifflin, 623 pp.

PLAYFAIR, JOHN, 1802, Illustrations of the Huttonian theory of the earth: Edinburgh, Cadell and Davies, and William Creech (Facsim. reprint with an introduction by George W. White, 1956: Urbana, Univ. of Illinois Press), 528 pp.

———, 1805, Biographical account of the late Dr. James Hutton, F.R.S. Edin.: Roy. Soc. Edinburgh, Tr., vol. 5, pt. 3, pp. 39–99. Reprinted in The works of John Playfair, Esq., 1822, vol. 4, pp. 33–118, Edinburgh.

POINCARÉ, HENRI, 1908, Science et méthode: Translated by Francis Maitland, reprinted 1952: New York, Dover Publications, 288 pp.

TOMKEIEFF, S. I., 1948, James Hutton and the philosophy of geology: Edinburgh Geol. Soc., Tr., vol. 14, pt. 2, pp. 253–276. Reprinted 1950, Roy. Soc. Edinburgh, Pr., vol. 63, sec. B, 1947–49, pp. 387–400.

———, 1950, Geology in historical perspective: Adv. Sci., vol. 7, pp. 63–67.

TOULMIN, G. H., 1780, Antiquity and duration of the world: (cited by Tomkeieff).

———, 1783, The antiquity of the world, 2d ed.: London, T. Cadell, 208 pp.

———, 1785, The eternity of the world: (cited by Tomkeieff).

W. H. BRADLEY

U. S. Geological Survey

Geologic Laws[1]

Students of the philosophy of science agree that general laws are numerous and widely accepted among physicists and chemists. Indeed, they seem to regard these laws as the *sine qua non* of science, and some even go so far as to say that if there are no general laws, we are not dealing with true science but with something of a lower order—something more amorphous. Some philosophers have also observed (though rarely in print) that, in geology, laws of general scope are either rare or perhaps as yet unrecognized and therefore unformulated.

General laws are indeed rare in geology. Why is this so? Is geology not amenable to such generalizations or are geologists too little concerned with the universal aspects of geology? Is geology perhaps still too immature to produce generalizations of wide applicability or have geologists found that, for their purposes, general laws are intellectual traps? Or do geologists, because of their subject matter, have to reason somewhat differently from chemists and physicists? Perhaps we, and the biologists who also must perforce travel a comparable, or even more complex, network of paths, have something different in the way of disciplined reasoning to offer the philosophers of science. Just possibly, the philosophers of science err in judging the goals and caliber of a science by the traditionally rigorous sciences of physics and chemistry. May there not be goals other than the general laws of physics with their undeniably beautiful simplicity and vast inclusiveness?

[1] In writing this essay I have, as usual, had the benefit of generous criticism and suggestions from a number of my colleagues in the U. S. Geological Survey. Of these, I want to thank particularly W. T. Pecora and Dwight Taylor because, among other things, they persuaded me to throw away the first draft and start afresh.

Besides this aid from my colleagues, I am especially grateful to Donald B. McIntyre, of Pomona College, and Allen M. Bassett, of San Diego State College, for constructive suggestions. Professor McIntyre also raised a number of provocative questions not dealt with in my essay. Fortunately, most of his points are discussed and satisfyingly answered by Simpson in his chapter.

One wonders whether full understanding and satisfactory explanation of a continuously operating dynamic process, such as the building and sculpture of a mountain range or the division of living cells, are not as desirable goals and as valuable rungs in the ladder of knowledge as the discovery of Gay-Lussac's law. This is not to derogate Gay-Lussac's law; I merely wish to raise for serious consideration a matter of long-term values in the realm of knowledge. Actually, I wonder whether physicists, chemists, and indeed scientists in general, are not today much less concerned with formulating laws than they are with gaining deeper understanding of phenomena and the relationships among all kinds of phenomena.

It is pertinent to examine first what is meant by a law in science and then take a brief look at geology itself. After that we shall be in a better position to consider what laws there are in geology, what are some of the laws being formulated today, and why laws are in fact rare in geology. But before we get to these we shall consider briefly the more speculative aspects of the mental tools geologists use in reasoning. These speculations involve an analogy with modern biologists, whose problems of explication and law formulation seem to have somewhat the same pattern as ours, and for similar reasons.

Of the many explanations of the term "law" in science, probably none is more plainly stated than that of Karl Pearson (1900, pp. 86–87, 99):

> Men study a range of facts . . . they classify and analyze, they discover relationships and sequences, and then they describe in the simplest possible terms the widest possible range of phenomena . . . We are thus to understand by a law in science . . . a resumé in mental shorthand, which replaces for us a lengthy description of the sequences among our sense impressions . . . Such laws simply describe, they never explain . . .

Classical examples of natural laws are, of course, Newton's laws of motion and the laws of thermodynamics. Some of the most fundamental relationships in nature, such as the equivalence of mass and energy, are stated in the form of general laws. They express concisely a group of more or less complex interrelationships that have repeatedly been observed to be consistent. They are convenient packages of knowledge—bench marks of a sort. They simplify our efforts to explain the phenomena we study. But all such laws are man-made, and for that reason reflect man's range of experience. They differ in degree of generality. Some, like the laws of thermodynamics, are apparently valid for all earthly phenomena over every yet conceivable range of values. Others are valid for all ordinary conditions, say of pressure and temperature, but do not hold strictly over extreme ranges, e.g., Boyle's law.

Natural laws that state more limited relationships are commonly referred to as specific laws or empirical generalizations. They too are convenient small bundles of knowledge. "Principle" is a word we, and other natural scientists,

use freely, yet I have found no satisfactory way of discriminating between specific laws or empirical generalizations on the one hand and principles on the
other. Perhaps they are equivalents. If so, it is odd that geologists react so
cautiously toward one and so casually toward the other. A suitable illustration
of a "basic principle" is given by Gilluly, Waters, and Woodford (1951, p. 146)
in discussing the contribution Cuvier and Brongniart made to stratigraphy,
"Each formation (closely related group of strata) contains its own characteristic assemblage of fossils."

Earlier in this essay I suggested that possibly geology has goals that are
somewhat different from those of physics and chemistry and has different
means for reaching them. If our ways of reasoning do in fact differ, the cause
must lie within the science of geology itself.

What are the properties of geology that set it apart? Geology is commonly
thought of as a derived science because it draws so much of its substance from
other sciences, notably chemistry, physics, and biology. But it has a hard core,
or spine, which is quite independent. It is this spine that gives geology its
distinctive qualities, and that determines in large measure the manner in
which its problems must be tackled. Geology's spine is the history and constitution of the earth—each term to be understood in its broadest sense. Running through this spine is the thread of time—a thread connecting all terrestrial
events. The succession and relationships between these events, together with
the dynamic processes that have operated, make up the science of geology.
Geology's task is to reconstruct these events and explain their direct and indirect consequences. When we say "constitution of the earth" we mean to
include not only its elemental chemical composition but also its mineralogical
and lithologic constitution, the internal structures of minerals and rocks, and
the structural relationships these have with one another, i.e., the architecture
and ornamental features of the earth.

Long ago, Lyell's simple definition of geology (1832, p. 1) said much the
same thing:

> Geology is the science which investigates the successive changes that have
> taken place in the organic and inorganic kingdoms of nature; it inquires into
> the causes of these changes, and the influence which they have exerted in
> modifying the surface and external structure of our planet.

Indeed, everything we find in or on the earth came to be what it is, and where
it is, by geologic processes. Perhaps this should be qualified in the case of
organisms, but life also had its evolution in geologic history and certainly all
of life that has gone before us, and left any trace of itself or its activities, is of
concern to geologists.

To implement our understanding of geologic phenomena, we make use of
the dynamic earth processes of weathering, erosion, sedimentation, volcanism and deformation—all of which are assumed to have operated throughout

the vast expanse of geologic time essentially as they do today. Nevertheless, much of our understanding must come from completed "experiments": from the results of processes that required thousands or, more usually, millions of years to form, or that have formed and lain dormant millions or billions of years. The interpretation of such completed experiments is further complicated by the fact that the same rocks may have been repeatedly deformed, and have been reconstituted both chemically and mineralogically. Given immense spans of time and immense forces acting for these long intervals, elements become mobile and substances that are hard and brittle yield, flex, and flow. As McKelvey points out elsewhere in this volume, most of these experiments were of such a scale and involved forces and spans of time so enormous that we probably cannot achieve adequate similitude in laboratory models designed to test our explanations.

An additional difficulty is omnipresent, as only nongeologists need be reminded, and that is the impossibility of seeing all of most geologic features by reason of their size and depth below the earth's surface, or by reason of a partial cover of soil or younger rock, or by reason of the fact that parts of the features have been eroded away. Therefore geologists are forever faced with the task of reconstructing events that happened on a vast scale and in the remote past from the partial remains of the products of those events. This compound problem puts a premium on the capacity to reason analogically, inductively, and with imagination.

Reasoning by analogy is not only common, it has probably been with us as long as man has reasoned. Sir D'Arcy Thompson (1961, p. 6) refers to analogical reasoning as another great Aristotelian theme. Indeed, he thus led into the following footnote, "Hume declared, and Mill said much the same thing, that all reasoning whatsoever depends on resemblance or analogy, and the power to recognise it." G. K. Gilbert, apparently quite independently, expressed exactly the same concept to account for the way scientists originate hypotheses (1896, pp. 2–3). I want to amplify Gilbert's specific point a little and add a small homily for geologists. We can often say that the unknown phenomenon resembles another phenomenon whose explanation is already known or can be determined from experiment or from observation and study. We are, in fact, often aware of present-day processes in nature which may provide valuable analogies, only to find that the processes themselves are still without adequate explanations. But these processes operate where we can observe and measure them. Adequate explanations are within reach, if we will but reach.

Because a geologist must use fragmentary data—the incomplete results of long-completed experiments—he must use inductive reasoning to reconstruct a whole from the parts. The virtue and value of inductive reasoning have been extolled and used effectively by many. Others who have trod the same paths have been equally eloquent in pointing out the dangers inherent in the use of inductive reasoning. Valuable and necessary as inductive reasoning is, a geologist must keep at least one foot on the tangible earth which he seeks to explain.

Many people equate imagination with the tendency to conjure up fanciful, unreal things without restraint—a faculty to be used either for amusement or for escape from reality. And so it is, but in a more literal sense it is the power of having mental images. Again, because a geologist can see only parts of the features he studies and must forever deal with partial information (he constructs geologic maps primarily to bring large features down to a comprehensible scale at which he can integrate the parts and visualize the whole), it is most essential that he be able to visualize, in three dimensions and with perspective, processes that may have gone on that will help to reconstruct the events of the past. Indeed, all the better if his imagination permits him to visualize processes as they may have operated with time—a sort of vision in motion. Although I have mentioned imagination last of the three essential elements in the thought processes of geologists, I am inclined to place it first in importance. A geologist who has no imagination is as ineffective as a duck without webs between his toes.

Perhaps such a long discursion on how geologists reason is out of place in an essay on geologic laws. Nevertheless, by these mental means, I believe geologists have made significant contributions. They have brought forth a satisfying, though far from perfect, image of the earth on which we live and a satisfying account of the long sequence of events that provided the changing environments in which all life evolved. Such images and concepts have value in human affairs and fill a significant niche in the realm of knowledge.

If this appraisal of the geologist's contribution is valid, it is pertinent to enquire how much of this edifice was built on what kind of a foundation of natural law. As W. M. Davis (1926, pp. 465–466) said, most of it is built on inference—the inference that the processes we observe today operated in the same way in the remote past. But the events and the sequence of events are none the less valid, for they have so far met all the tests we can apply to them for the great expanse of time we can actually measure. For absolute measurements of geologic time, however, we rely mostly on the physicists and their laws.

We might consider first how far geologists have gone and can go if they stay within what we have defined as the core of geology—that part which borrows little or nothing from other disciplines. We can, with confidence, explain the stratigraphic succession of any series of beds, and tell which way is "up" in most such sequences, using purely geologic evidence. Indeed, the oft-repeated verification that in any such sequence (not upset by tectonic movements) the youngest beds are on top, gave rise many years ago to the law of superposition: "In any pile of sedimentary strata that has not been disturbed by folding or overturning since accumulation, the youngest stratum is at the top and the oldest at the base" (Gilluly, Waters, and Woodford, 1951, p. 73). This was first clearly stated by Nicholas Steno in 1669. Steno also stated another law, recognized by all geologists as generally valid, namely, the law of original horizontality, thus: "Water-laid sediments are deposited in strata that are not far from horizontal, and parallel or nearly parallel to the surface on which they are accumulating" (*idem*, p. 73). We can tell the geologic ages of such sequences from the fossils they contain, and we can correlate such sequences of beds even though their outcrops are discontinuous. This follows the "basic principle" established by Cuvier and Brongniart, already mentioned, and this principle seems to have as good a claim to be one of our established laws as those of Steno.

If we are granted the use of mathematics, we can, still within the framework of pure geology, determine the sequence of events in complexly folded and faulted areas, and can explain how we can predict where the various parts are to be found beneath the surface. Furthermore, much of the sculpture of the earth's surface can be explained without borrowing anything from other sciences. (See, for example, Gilbert, 1877 and Hack, 1960.) Such explanations must be based on analogy with present-day processes. Volcanic cones, ash beds, lava flows, and mud flows all have ready explanations from what has been observed in nature.

It was the analysis of a vast volume of such descriptions and explanations, wholly within the realm of pure geology, that led Bucher (1933) to formulate 46 laws, each of which stated some generalization about the observed relationships of deformational features of the earth's crust. Whether such generalizations (specific laws as we saw earlier in this essay) have served the purpose he visualized, I leave to students of structural geology. Perhaps it will be regarded as another homily if I observe that another natural science, biology, has formulated many such specific generalizations, or laws, and apparently has used them to good advantage.

Except for Bucher's formulation of a goodly number of specific laws in 1933, geologists of the present century have shown relatively little inclination to formulate laws. But this was not always so. Seventy-five to 100 years ago geologists were more prone to formulate generalizations and to state them as laws. A few illustrations will suffice to make the point. In G. K. Gilbert's Henry Mountains Report (1877, pp. 108–124) he analyzes the processes that sculpture the land surface and speaks often about laws, although he explicitly formulates only three: the law of declivity, "In general we may say that, *ceteris paribus*, declivity bears an inverse relation to quantity of water"; the law of structure, "Insofar as the law of structure controls sculpture, hard masses stand as eminences and soft are carved in valleys"; and the law of divides, "The nearer the watershed or divide the steeper the slope."

L. V. Pirsson (1905, p. 43) stated the following generalization as a "General law of the province". "The petrographic province of central Montana is characterized by the fact that in the most siliceous magmas the percentages of potash and soda are about equal; with decreasing silica and increasing lime, iron and magnesia, the potash relatively increases over the soda, until in the least siliceous magmas it strongly dominates." Today such a generalization would not be stated as a law. This example, and those cited above from Gilbert, reflect a tendency of those times—a striving for generalization and for fixing generalizations in the form of laws. From our present vantage point, realizing now how complex nature actually is, we probably would be right in saying that such a tendency reflected a then unrecognized immaturity of our science.

If geology was too immature 75 or 100 years ago to warrant the formulation of general laws, what is our status today?

Actually, if one were to make an exhaustive census, which I have not, we probably would find more generalizations being expressed now than there were a generation or two ago. Three illustrations with which I happen to be acquainted will serve to characterize the current effort, though none is called or thought of as a law.

One is the principle of dynamic equilibrium in the evolution of landscape elaborated by Hack (1960, pp. 85–96) from earlier statements by G. K. Gilbert, W. M. Davis, and A. N. Strahler. According to Hack (p. 86):

> The concept requires a state of balance between opposing forces such that they operate at equal rates and their effects cancel each other to produce a steady state, in which energy is continually entering and leaving the system. The opposing forces might be of various kinds. For example, an alluvial fan would be in dynamic equilibrium if the debris shed from the mountain behind it were deposited on the fan at exactly the same rate as it was removed by erosion from the surface of the fan itself.

Another generalization was expressed by T. B. Nolan in his presidential address before the Geological Society of America (1962, p. 277). In discussing the grade of mineral resources he pointed out that in making estimates of future resources one should keep in mind not only the fact that we have been able over the years to use progressively lower-grade ores, but "that the tonnages of material available in the earth's crust increase geometrically with decreasing grade."

Still another generalization or, more accurately, a group of generalizations, was presented by James B. Thompson (1955, pp. 65–103) in his treatment of the thermodynamic basis for the mineral facies concept.

He considers the following four limiting cases and then discusses certain geologic applications.

CASE 1. The mobile component in question is present as a pure phase at the same temperature and pressure as the surrounding rock. This is the assumption implicit in current hydrothermal experimental work and in calculated equilibria such as that of Goldschmidt for calcite-wollastonite. It yields a maximum equilibrium temperature at any given pressure (depth).

CASE 2. The rock is in chemical equilibrium with a fissure system containing a dilute aqueous solution. This method is applicable only when the mobile component in question is water itself. It indicates a decrease in most dehydration temperatures with depth.

CASE 3. The vertical gradient of chemical potential of the mobile component has reached a value such that there is no longer any tendency for vertical diffusion of this component. This method also suggests (not without reservations) a slight decrease of most devolatilization temperatures with depth.

CASE 4. The chemical potential of the mobile component is sufficiently low that no phases containing it are stable.

For simplicity, we will refer to these limiting cases as cases 1, 2, 3, and 4, respectively. It now remains for us to consider the extent to which these may be applicable to some specific geological problems. (p. 96)

Thompson's treatment of the various mineralogical changes under the assumed conditions goes far toward quantifying these geologic processes and therefore constitutes an important advance in the science of geology. Given adequate data on the environments and thermochemical data on the minerals involved, it appears that similar generalizations can now be made about such processes as diagenesis, weathering, and the formation of ore deposits.

Thus far (with the exception of Thompson's work just mentioned) we have deliberately kept within that sphere of geology which is purely geologic, that is, not borrowed from any other science. We have seen that we can explain many of the phenomena of geology within this frame of reference. But such explanations leave unanswered virtually all questions of "how." How can hard rocks bend and flow; what caused this mineral to change over into that, what permits it to do so and what are the conditions that determine the change; how do we account for the fact that the ratios of oxygen isotopes change progressively with distance from a certain focus; how can such things as amino acids be preserved in fossils for millions of years; what must have been the conditions to permit the preservation of the color pattern in a fossil or a chloroplast within a plant cell? How can we account for the mobility and rearrangement of elements and compounds within the earth's crust; how does it come about that certain elements aggregate to form deposits of commercial value and that some minerals are piezoelectric? One needs only to begin asking "how" in geology and the list grows like weeds after a warm rain.

We cannot begin to answer these queries without the help of chemistry, physics, or biology. In every problem of this broad class of problems we realize that minerals, the fundamental units of geology, are chemical compounds and that they are what they are and came to be where they are by chemical as well as geologic processes. Moreover, they have optical, electrical, magnetic, thermal, and mechanical properties, and atomic structures that belong just as much in the realm of physics as the properties of any man-made material or man-designed experiment. In short, we can scarcely look to a deeper understanding of any of our geologic problems without coming face to face with the realization that all the materials we seek to understand and whose behavior we seek to understand have the properties, structures, and behavior of all matter. The answers we seek must come from the same kinds of sources that the chemist, the physicist, and the biologist study to get their enlightenment.

We are utterly dependent on chemistry, physics, and biology for understanding, yet the problems we bring up from the earth do not in any sense thereby lose their geologic character. Geologists must and will continue to observe, measure, and analyze geologic phenomena and, more importantly, they will continue to formulate the problems—to ask exactly how and exactly why. This is the province and the responsibility of geologists, and no one can be expected to do it better. Important as chemistry and physics are to the solution of geologic problems, neither chemists nor physicists are going to take over the role of formulating the problems that arise out of geologic work unless they themselves become geologists. This is not to say, of course, that the geochemists and geophysicists will not generate questions of their own about earth processes.

We have considered what natural laws are, what properties give geology its distinguishing marks, something about the way geologists reason, and lastly the growing realization of the great complexity of geology and the growing dependence of geology on the disciplines of chemistry, physics, and biology. Let us consider next the steps in the development of generalizations in geology. At least in part this can be expressed graphically (Fig. 1). The concept of such a graph evolved in a discussion with my colleague V. E. McKelvey, after he had returned from the Brookings Institution's Conference for Federal Science Executives at Williamsburg, Va., where he had heard Henry Margenau of Yale discuss the development of natural laws in general. Margenau's diagram, as I understand it, consisted of three ordinates, labeled Primary observations, Concepts, and Propositions (laws). These are used also in Fig. 1. McKelvey and I added the boundary curve to indicate the philosophical field of activity of geologists. The great bulk of geologic activity hovers close to the observational ordinate. When enough observations have been related and explained, the activity moves right into the field of concepts. This move comes

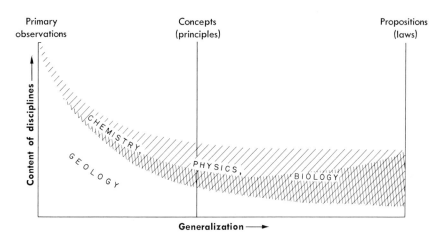

Fig. 1. Diagrammatic representation of the field of geologic activity and thought plotted against Margenau's three ordinates: Primary observations, Concepts, and Propositions (laws). The shaded field above represents a reservoir of the combined disciplines of chemistry, physics, and biology in an unsorted mixture—the position of the names, therefore, has no relationship to Margenau's ordinates. The crosshatched part of this field indicates progressively greater assimilation by geology of chemistry, physics, and biology. Ideas in geology move out along the generalization abscissa in proportion to the number and significance of the verified observations and theories that are unified into broader concepts or principles.

about from inductive reasoning and results in a concept or principle, i.e., a generalization, which we repeatedly test against more observations. Parenthetically, we also use these principles to explicate other geologic phenomena, thereby nourishing a sort of feedback mechanism, which is present in the reasoning operations of all sciences. But I am inclined to think that such feedback operations are especially important in geology because we deal so much with fragmentary data and with working hypotheses.

The theory of isostasy, the origin of igneous rocks, and organic evolution are examples of such concepts or principles.

Most geologists are happy to explore and describe. Fewer are unhappy until they are able also to explain what they have found. And very few seem interested in trying to integrate the explanations into more general concepts or principles. Just possibly this derives from the patent fact that it is a lot more fun to do field work than it is to put the pieces of explained phenomena together, especially if the pieces were constructed by someone else.

Casual inspection of this curve (Fig. 1) prompts one to ask why (with the exception of Steno's two laws formulated long ago) we have not, or do not, push our concepts or principles still farther to the right into the realm of laws? I believe there are several reasons for this. One is the growing realization that the earth's history and the processes involved in shaping it are vastly more complex than was thought even a generation or two ago. We have, so to speak, become more conscious of the number of variables and the magnitude of the gaps in our knowledge. Another reason is the growing realization that we can press our effort for deeper understanding of geology only with the aid of progressively more chemistry, physics, and biology. As we progress with our reasoning toward the right in the diagram, the content of these borrowed disciplines must increase. I hazard the guess that the area under the curve in the region of the "concept" and "laws" ordinates will increase with time in proportion to geology's assimilation of chemistry, physics, and biology.

In conclusion, it seems to me that wherever we look there is a striving for deeper understanding of ever more complex problems and a corresponding realization of how much more we must learn, especially in geochemistry and geophysics, in order to gain this fuller understanding. Such phases of rapid expansion of the frontiers of any science, I suggest, are not conducive to thinking about the formulation of general laws. Everything is too new, too pregnant with the possibility of growth and change—too much is clearly missing or imperfectly understood—for us to become preoccupied with reflective thinking about that which is already known. The new and unsolved problems are much more worth the candle, are more exciting, more rewarding. Reflection is crowded out in the excitement of the day.

The biologists appear to find themselves in pretty much the same situation. Paul Weiss (1962, p. 470) stated it thus:

> Biology . . . is destined to retain its autonomy, which means that to be known and understood, biological mechanisms will have to be studied and formulated in their own right and full diversity. And this explains why in biology so many generalizations must stop far short of the vast inclusiveness of laws of physics, hence, why the range of validity of each must be determined empirically. It is this inherent feature of biological nature, rather than backwardness or extravagance, then, which necessitates testing over a far wider spectrum of variables . . . than would seem necessary or even pardonable in most of physics.

But this situation we find ourselves in is no cause for lament; rather is it a source of inspiration, a cause of exhilaration. It seems to me geology is now at the beginning of an explosive stage of development comparable to that which occurred in the biological sciences when biochemistry and biophysics came into full swing. Let the philosophers of science revel a bit in the yeasty ferment that is geology today and tomorrow. Some day we may grow old and have more laws; right now we are busy exploring, experimenting, and trying to understand more of the "how" of those processes that have produced the features of the earth, its crust beneath, and all it contains.

REFERENCES CITED

BUCHER, W. H., 1933, The deformation of the earth's crust: Princeton, Princeton Univ Press, 518 pp.

——, 1936, The concept of natural law in geology: Ohio J. Sci., vol. 36, pp. 183–194.

DAVIS, W. M., 1926, The value of outrageous geological hypotheses: Science, vol. 63, pp. 463–468.

GILBERT, G. K., 1877, Geology of the Henry Mountains: U. S. Geog. and Geol. Survey of the Rocky Mountain Region, Washington, D. C., Government Printing Office, 170 pp.

——, 1896, The origin of hypotheses, illustrated by the discussion of a topographic problem: Science, n.s., vol. 3, pp. 1–13.

GILLULY, J., WATERS, A. C., and WOODFORD, A. O., 1951, Principles of geology: San Francisco, W. H. Freeman, 631 pp.

HACK, J. T., 1960, Interpretation of erosional topography in humid temperate regions: Am. J. Sci., vol. 258-A, pp. 80–97.

LYELL, Sir CHARLES, 1832, Principles of geology, 2nd ed.: London, John Murray, vol. 1.

NOLAN, T. B., 1962, Role of the geologist in the national economy: Geol. Soc. Am., B., vol. 73, pp. 273–278.

PEARSON, KARL, 1900, The grammar of science, 2d ed.: London, Adam and Charles Black, 548 pp.

PIRSSON, L. V., 1905, The petrographic province of central Montana: Am. J. Sci., vol. 20 (whole no. 170), pp. 35–49.

THOMPSON, Sir D'ARCY W., 1961, On growth and form (abridged edition, edited by J. T. Bonner): New York, Cambridge Univ. Press, 346 pp.

THOMPSON, J. B., 1955, The thermodynamic basis for the mineral facies concept: Am. J. Sci., vol. 253, pp. 65–103.

WEISS, PAUL, 1962, Experience and experiment in biology: Science, vol. 136, pp. 468–471.

GEORGE GAYLORD SIMPSON

Harvard University

Historical Science[1]

History, Science, and Historical Science

· The simplest definition of history is that it is change through time. It is, however, at once clear that the definition fails to make distinctions which are necessary if history is to be studied in a meaningful way. A chemical reaction involves change through time, but obviously it is not historical in the same sense as the first performance by Lavoisier of a certain chemical experiment. The latter was a nonrecurrent event, dependent on or caused by antecedent events in the life of Lavoisier and the lives of his predecessors, and itself causal of later activities by Lavoisier and his successors. The chemical reaction involved has no such causal relationship and has undergone no change before or after Lavoisier's experiment. It always has occurred and always will recur under the appropriate historical circumstances, but as a reaction in itself it has no history.

A similar contrast between the historical and the nonhistorical exists in geology and other sciences. The processes of weathering and erosion are unchanging and nonhistorical. The Grand Canyon or any gully is unique at any one time but is constantly changing to other unique, nonrecurrent configurations as time passes. Such changing, individual geological phenomena are historical, whereas the properties and processes producing the changes are not.

The unchanging properties of matter and energy and the likewise unchanging processes and principles arising therefrom are *immanent* in the material universe. They are nonhistorical, even though they occur and act in the course of history. The actual state of the universe or of any part of it at a given time, its configuration, is not immanent and is constantly changing. It is *contingent* in

---

[1] Parts of this essay have been developed from a talk on the explanation of unique events given in the Seminar on Methods in Philosophy and Science at the New School for Social Research on May 20, 1962. On that occasion I also profited from discussion and other talks pertinent to the present topic, especially by Dobzhansky, Nagel, and Pittendrigh.

Bernal's (1951) term, or *configurational*, as I prefer to say (Simpson, 1960). History may be defined as configurational change through time, i.e., a sequence of real, individual but interrelated events. These distinctions between the immanent and the configurational and between the nonhistorical and the historical are essential to clear analysis and comprehension of history and of science. They will be maintained, amplified, and exemplified in what follows.

Definitions of science have been proposed and debated in innumerable articles and books. Brief definitions are inevitably inadequate, but I shall here state the one I prefer: Science is an exploration of the material universe that seeks natural, orderly relationships among observed phenomena and that is self-testing. (For explanation and amplification see Simpson, 1962, 1963.) Apart from the points that science is concerned only with the material or natural and that it rests on observation, the definition involves three scientific activities: the description of phenomena, the seeking of theoretical, explanatory relationships among them, and some means for the establishment of confidence regarding observations and theories. Among other things, later sections of this essay will consider these three aspects of historical science.

Historical science may thus be defined as the determination of configurational sequences, their explanation, and the testing of such sequences and explanations. (It is already obvious and will become more so that none of the three phases is simple or thus sufficiently described.)

Geology is probably the most diverse of all the sciences, and its status as in part a historical science is correspondingly complex. For one thing, it deals with the immanent properties and processes of the physical earth and its constituents. This aspect of geology is basically nonhistorical. It can be viewed simply as a branch of physics (including mechanics) and chemistry, applying those sciences to a single (but how complex!) object: the earth. Geology also deals with the present configuration of the earth and all its parts, from core to atmosphere. This aspect of geology might be considered nonhistorical insofar as it is purely descriptive, but then it also fails to fulfill the whole definition of a science. As soon as theoretical, explanatory relationships are brought in, so necessarily are changes and sequences of configurations, which are historical. The fully scientific study of geological configurations is thus historical science. This is the *only* aspect of geology that is peculiar to this science, that is simply geology and not also something else. (Of course I do not mean that it can be studied without reference to other aspects of geology and to other sciences, both historical and nonhistorical.)

Paleontology is primarily a historical science, and it is simultaneously biological and geological. Its role as a part of historical biology is obvious. In this role, like all other aspects of biology, it involves all the immanent properties and processes of the physical sciences, but differs from them not only in being historical but also in that its configurational systems are incomparably more complex and have feedback and information storage and transmittal mechanisms unlike any found in the inorganic realm. Its involvement in geology and inclusion in that science as well as in biology are primarily due to the fact that the history of organisms runs parallel with, is environmentally contained in, and continuously interacts with the physical history of the earth. It is of less philosophical interest but of major operational importance that paleontology, when applicable, has the highest resolving power of any method yet discovered for determining the sequence of strictly geological events. (That radiometric methods may give equal or greater resolution is at present a hope and not a fact.)

Description and Generalization

In principle, the observational basis of any science is a straight description of what is there and what occurs, what Lloyd Morgan (1891) used to call "plain story." In a physical example, plain story might be the specifications of a pendulum and observations of its period. A geological plain story might describe a bed of arkose, its thickness, its attitude, and its stratigraphic and geographic position. An example of paleontological plain story would be the occurrence of a specimen of a certain species at a particular point in the bed of arkose. In general, the more extended plain stories of historical science would describe configurations and place them in time.

In fact, plain story in the strictest, most literal sense plays little part in science. Some degree of abstraction, generalization, and theorization usually enters in, even at the first observational level. The physicist has already abstracted a class of configurational systems called "pendulums" and assumes that only the length and period need be observed, regardless of other differences in individuals of the class, unless an observation happens to disagree with the assumption. Similarly, the geologist by no means describes all the characteristics of the individual bed of arkose and its parts but has already generalized a class "arkose" and adds other details, if any, only in terms of such variations within the class as are considered pertinent to his always limited purpose. The paleontologist has departed still further from true, strict plain story, for in recording a specimen as of a certain species he has not only generalized a particularly complex kind of class but has also reached a conclusion as to membership in that class that is not a matter of direct observation at all.

Every object and every event is unique if its configurational aspects are described in full. Yet, and despite the schoolteachers, it may be said that some things are more unique than others. This depends in the first place on the complexity of what is being described, for certainly the more complex it is the more ways there are in which it may differ from others of its general class. A bed of arkose is more complex than a pendulum, and an organism is to still greater degree more complex than a bed of arkose. The hierarchy of complexity and individual uniqueness from physics to geology to biology is characteristic of those sciences and essential to philosophical understanding of them. It bears on the degree and kind of generalization characteristic of and appropriate to the various sciences even at the primary observational level. The number of pertinent classes of observations distinguished in physics is much smaller than in geology, and much smaller in geology than in biology. For instance, in terms of taxonomically distinguished discrete objects, compare the numbers of species of particles and atoms in physics, of minerals and rocks in geology, and of organisms in biology. Systems and processes in these sciences have the same sequence as to number and complexity.

Another aspect of generalization and degree of uniqueness arises in comparison of nonhistorical and historical science and in the contrast between immanence and configuration. In the previous examples, the physicist was concerned with a nonhistorical and immanent phenomenon: gravitation. It was necessary to his purpose and inherent in his method to eliminate as far as possible and then to ignore any historical element and any configurational uniqueness in the particular, individual pendulum used in the experiment. He sought a changeless law that would apply to all pendulums and ultimately to all matter, regardless of time and place. The geologist and paleontologist were also interested in generalization of common properties and relationships between one occurrence of arkose and another, between one specimen and another of a fossil species, but their generalizations were of the configurational and not the immanent properties and were, or at least involved, historical and not only nonhistorical science. The arkose or the fossil had its particular as well as its general configurational properties, its significant balance of difference and resemblance, not only because of immanent properties of its constituents and immanent processes that had acted on it, but also because of its history, the configurational sequence by which these individual things arose. The latter aspect, not pertinent to the old pendulum experiment or to almost anything in the more sophisticated physics of the present day, is what primarily concerns geology and paleontology as historical sciences, or historical science in general.

Scientific Law

It has been mentioned that the purpose of the pendulum experiment was to formulate a law. The concept of scientific law and its relationship with historical and nonhistorical science are disputed questions requiring clarification. The term "law" has been so variously and loosely used in science that it is no longer clear unless given an explicit and restrictive definition. The college dictionary that I happen to have at hand (Barnhart, 1948) defines "law" in philosophical or scientific use as "a statement of a relation or sequence of phenomena invariable under the same conditions." This is satisfactory if it is made clear that a law applies to phenomena that are themselves variable: it is the *relationship* (or sequence, also a relationship) that is invariable. "Under the same conditions" must be taken to mean that other variables, if present, are in addition to and not inextricably involved with those specified in the law. Further, it is perhaps implicit but should be explicit that the relationship must be manifested or repeatable in an indefinitely recurrent way. A relationship that could or did occur only once would indeed be invariable, but surely would not be a law in any meaningful scientific sense. With these considerations, the definition might be rephrased thus: a scientific law is a recurrent, repeatable relationship between variables that is itself invariable to the extent that the factors affecting the relationship are explicit in the law.

The definition implies that a valid law includes all the factors that *necessarily* act in conjunction. The fact that air friction also significantly affects the acceleration of a body falling in the atmosphere does not invalidate the law of gravitational acceleration, but only shows that the body is separately acted on by some factor defined by another law. Friction and the factors of gravitational acceleration are independent. Both laws are valid, and they can be combined into a valid compound law. But if some factor *necessarily* involved in either one, such as force of gravitation for acceleration or area for friction, were omitted, that law would be invalidated.

Laws, as thus defined, are generalizations, but they are generalizations of a very special kind. They are complete abstractions from the individual case. They are not even concerned with what individual cases have in common, in the form of descriptive generalizations or definitions, such as that all pendulums are bodies movably suspended from a fixed point, all arkoses are sedimentary rocks containing feldspar, or all vertebrates are animals with jointed backbones. These and similar generalizations are obviously not laws by any usage. When we say, for instance, that arkose is a feldspathic sedimentary rock, we mean merely that we have agreed that if a rock happens to be sedimentary and within a certain range of texture and of composition including a feldspar, we will call it "arkose." We do not mean that the nature of the universe is such that there is an inherent relationship among sedimentary rocks and feldspars reducible to a constant. Laws are inherent, that is *immanent*, in the nature of things as abstracted entirely from contingent configurations, although always acting on those configurations.

Until recently the theoretical structure of the nonhistorical physical sciences consisted largely of a body of laws or supposed laws of this kind. The prestige of these sciences and their success in discovering such laws were such that it was commonly believed that the proper scientific goal of the historical sciences was also to discover laws. Supposed laws were proposed in all the historical sciences. By way of example in my own field, paleontology, I may mention

"Dollo's law" that evolution is irreversible, "Cope's law" that animals become larger in the course of evolution, or "Williston's law" that repetitive serial structures in animals evolve so as to become less numerous but more differentiated. The majority of such supposed laws are no more than descriptive generalizations. For example, animals do not invariably become larger in time. Cope's law merely generalizes the observation that this is a frequent tendency, without establishing any fixed relationship among the variables possibly involved in this process.

Even when a relationship seems established, so-called "historical laws" are almost always open to exceptions. For example, Rensch (1960), an evolutionist convinced of the validity of historical laws, considers "Allen's rule" a law: that when mammals adapt to colder climates their feet become shorter. But of the actual mammals studied by him, 36% were exceptions to the "law." Rensch explains this by supposing that "many special laws act together or interfere with one another. Thus 'exceptions' to the laws result." This is a hypothetical possibility, but to rely upon it is an act of faith. The "interfering" laws are unknown in this or similar examples. A second possibility is that the "laws," as stated, are invalid as laws because they have omitted factors necessarily and inherently involved. I believe this is true, not in the sense that we have only to complete the analysis and derive a complete and valid law, but in the sense that the omissions are such as to invalidate the very concept of historical law.

The search for historical laws is, I maintain, mistaken in principle. Laws apply, in the dictionary definition "under the same conditions," or in my amendment "to the extent that factors affecting the relationship are explicit in the law," or in common parlance "other things being equal." But in history, which is a sequence of real, individual events, other things never are equal. Historical events, whether in the history of the earth, the history of life, or recorded human history, are determined by the immanent characteristics of the universe acting on and within particular configurations, and never by either the immanent or the configurational alone. It is a law that states the relationship between the length of a pendulum—*any* pendulum—and its period. Such a law does not include the contingent circumstances, the configuration, necessary for the occurrence of a real event, say Galileo's observing the period of a particular pendulum. If laws thus exclude factors inextricably and significantly involved in real events, they cannot belong to historical science.

It is further true that historical events are unique, usually to a high degree, and hence cannot embody laws defined as recurrent, repeatable relationships. Apparent repetition of simple events may seem to belie this. A certain person's repeatedly picking up and dropping a certain stone may seem to be a recurrent event in all essentials, but there really is no applicable *historical* law. Abstraction of a law from such repeated events leads to a nonhistorical law of immanent relationships, perhaps in this case of gravity and acceleration or perhaps of neurophysiology, and not to a historical law of which this particular person, picking up a certain stone, at a stated moment, and dropping it a definite number of times would be a determinate instance. In less trivial and more complex events, it is evident that the extremely intricate configurations involved in and necessary, for example, as antecedents for the erosion of the Grand Canyon or the origin of *Homo sapiens* simply cannot recur and that there can be no laws of such one-of-a-kind events. (Please bear in mind that the true, immanent laws are equally necessary and involved in such events but that they remain nonhistorical; the laws would have acted differently and the historical event, the change of configuration, would have been different if the configuration had been different; this historical element is not included in the operative laws.)

It might be maintained that my definition of law is old-fashioned and is no longer accepted in the nonhistorical sciences either. Many laws of physics, considered nonhistorical, are now conceived as statistical in nature, involving not an invariable relationship but an average one. The old gas laws or the new laws of radioactive decay are examples. The gas laws used to assume an ideal gas. Now they are recognized as assuming that directions of molecular motion tend to cancel out if added together, and that velocities tend to vary about a mean under given conditions. This cannot be precisely true of a real gas at a given moment, but when very large numbers of molecules are involved over an appreciable period of time, the statistical result is so close to the state described by the gas laws that the difference does not matter. In this and similar ways the descent from the ideal to the real in physical science has been coped with, not so much by facing it as by finding devices for ignoring it.

The historical scientist here notes that a real gas in a real experiment has *historical* attributes that are *additional* to the laws affecting it. Every molecule of a real gas has its individual history. Its position, direction of motion, and velocity at a given moment (all parts of the total configuration) are the outcome of that history. It is, however, quite impractical and, for the purposes of physics, unnecessary to make an historical study of the gas. The gas laws apply well enough "other things being equal," which means here that the simple histories of the molecules tend, as observation shows, to produce a statistical result so nearly uniform that the historical, lawless element can be ignored for practical purposes.

The laws immanent in the material universe are not statistical in essence. They act invariably in variable historical circumstances. The pertinence of statistics to such laws as those of gases is that they provide a generalized description of usual historical circumstances in which those laws act, and not that they are inherent in the laws themselves. Use of statistical expressions, not as laws but as generalized descriptions, is common and helpful in all science and especially in historical science. For example, the statistical specifications of land forms or of grain size in sediments clearly are not laws but descriptions of configurations involved in and arising from history.

To speak of "laws of history" is either to misunderstand the nature of history or to use "laws" in an unacceptable sense, usually for generalized descriptions rather than formulations of immanent relationships.

Uniformitarianism

Uniformitarianism has long been considered a basic principle of historical science and a major contribution of geology to science and philosophy. In one form or another it does permeate geological and historical thought to such a point as often to be taken for granted. Among those who have recently given conscious attention to it, great confusion has arisen from conflicts and obscurities as to just what the concept is. To some, uniformitarianism (variously defined) is a law of history. Others, maintaining that it is not a law, have tended to deny its significance. Indeed, in any reasonable or usual formulation, it is not a law, but that does not deprive it of importance. It is commonly defined as the principle that the present is the key to the past. That definition is, however, so loose as to be virtually meaningless in application. A new, sharper, and clearer definition in modern terms is needed.

Uniformitarianism arose around the turn of the 18th to 19th centuries, and its original significance can be understood only in that context. (The historical background is well covered in Gillispie, 1951.) It was a reaction against the then prevailing school of catastrophism, which had two main tenets: (1) the general belief that God has intervened in history, which therefore has included both natural and supernatural (miraculous) events; and (2) the particular proposition that earth history consists in the main of a sequence of major catastrophes, usually considered as of divine origin in accordance with the first tenet. (For a historical review anachronistically sympathetic with these beliefs see Hooykaas, 1959.) Uniformitarianism, as then expressed, had various different aspects and did not always face these issues separately and clearly. On the whole, however, it embodied two propositions contradictory to catastrophism: (1) earth history (if not history in general) can be explained in terms of natural forces still observable as acting today; and (2) earth history has not been a series of universal or quasi-universal catastrophes but has in the main been a long, gradual development—what we would now call an evolution. (The term "evolution" was not then customarily used in this sense.) A classic example of the conflicting application of these principles is the catastrophist belief that valleys are clefts suddenly opened by a supernally ordered revolution as against the uniformitarian belief that they have been gradually formed by rivers that are still eroding the valley bottoms.

Both of the major points originally at issue are still being argued on the fringes of science or outside it. To most geologists, however, they no longer merit attention from anyone but a student of human history. It is a necessary condition and indeed part of the definition of science in the modern sense that only natural explanations of material phenomena are to be sought or can be considered scientifically tenable. It is interesting and significant that general acceptance of this principle (or limitation, if you like) came much later in the historical than in the nonhistorical sciences. In historical geology it was the most important outcome of the uniformitarian-catastrophist controversy. In historical biology it was the still later outcome of the Darwinian controversy and was hardly settled until our own day. (It is still far from settled among nonscientists.)

As to the second major point originally involved in uniformitarianism, there is no *a priori* or philosophical reason for ruling out a series of *natural* worldwide catastrophes as dominating earth history. However, this assumption is simply in such flat disagreement with everything we now know of geological history as to be completely incredible. The only issues still valid involve the way in which natural processes still observable have acted in the past and the sense in which the present is a key to the past. Uniformitarianism, or neo-uni-formitarianism, as applied to these issues has taken many forms, among them two extremes that are both demonstrably invalid. They happen to be rather amusingly illustrated in a recently published exchange of letters by Lippman (1962) and Farrand (1962).

Lippman, one of the neocatastrophists still vociferous on the fringes of geological science, attacks uniformitarianism on the assumption that its now "orthodox" form is absolute gradualism, i.e., the belief that geological processes have *always* acted gradually and that changes catastrophic in rate and extent have never occurred. Farrand, who would perhaps consent to being called an orthodox geologist, demonstrates that Lippman has set up a straw man. Catastrophes do now occur. Their occurrence in the past exemplifies rather than contradicts a principle of uniformity. It happens that there is no valid evidence that catastrophes of the kind and extent claimed by the original catastrophists and by Lippman have ever occurred or that they could provide explanations for some real phenomena, as claimed. This, however, is a different point. Farrand expresses a common, probably the usual modern understanding of uniformitarianism as follows: "The geologist's concept that processes that acted on the earth in the past are the *same processes* that are operating today, on the *same scale* and at approximately the *same rates*" (italics mine). But this principle also seems to be flatly contradicted by geological history. Some processes (those of vulcanism or glaciation, for example) have evidently acted in the past on scales and at rates that cannot by any stretch be called "the same" or even "approximately the same" as those of today. Some past processes (such as those of Alpine nappe formation) are apparently not acting today, at least not in the form in which they did act. There are innumerable exceptions that disprove the rule.

Then what uniformity principle, if any, is valid and important? The distinction between immanence and configuration (or contingency) clearly points to one: the postulate that immanent characteristics of the material universe have not changed in the course of time. By this postulate all the immanent characteristics exist today and so can, in principle, be observed or, more precisely, inferred as generalizations and laws from observations. It is in this sense that the present is the key to the past. Present immanent properties and relationships permit the interpretation and explanation of history precisely because they are *not* historical. They have remained unchanged, and it is the configurations that have changed. Past configurations were never quite the same as they are now and were often quite different. Within those different configurations, the immanent characteristics have worked at different scales and rates at different times, sometimes combining into complex processes different from those in action today. The uniformity of the immanent characteristics helps to explain the fact that history is not uniform. (It could even be said that uniformitarianism entails catastrophes, but the paradox would be misleading if taken out of context.) Only to the extent that past configurations resembled the present in essential features can past processes have worked in a similar way.

That immanent characteristics are unchanging may seem at first sight either a matter of definition or an obvious conclusion, but it is neither. Gravity would be immanent (an inherent characteristic of matter *now*) even if the law of gravity had changed, and it is impossible to prove that it has not changed. Uniformity, in this sense, is an unprovable postulate justified, or indeed required, on two grounds. First, nothing in our incomplete but extensive knowledge of history disagrees with it. Second, only with this postulate is a rational interpretation of history possible, and we are justified in seeking—as scientists we *must* seek—such a rational interpretation. It is on this basis that I have assumed on previous pages that the immanent is unchanging.

Explanation

Explanation is an answer to the question "Why?" But as Nagel (1961) has shown at length, this is an ambiguous question calling for fundamentally different *kinds* of answers in various contexts. One kind of answer specifies the inherent necessity of a proposition, and those are the answers embodied in laws. Some philosophers insist that this is the only legitimate form of explanation. Some (e.g. Hobson, 1923) even go so far as to maintain that since inherent necessity cannot be *proved*, there is no such thing as scientific explanation.

Nagel demonstrates that all this is in part a mere question of linguistic usage and to that extent neither important nor interesting. The only substantial question involved is whether explanation must be universal or may be contingent. Nagel further shows, with examples (ten of them in his Chapter 2), that contingent explanations are valid in any usual and proper sense of the word "explanation." Nagel does not put the matter in just this way and he makes other distinctions not pertinent in the present context, but in essence this distinction between universal and contingent explanation parallels that between, on one hand, immanence and nonhistorical science, which involves laws, and, on the other, configuration and historical science, which does not involve laws but which does also have explanations.

The question "Why?" can be broken down into three others, each evoking a different kind of explanation, as Pittendrigh (1958) and Mayr (1961), among others, have discussed. "How?" is the typical question of the nonhistorical sciences. It asks how things work: how streams erode valleys, how mountains are formed, how animals digest food—all in terms of the physical and chemical processes involved. The first step toward explanation of this kind is usually a generalized description, but answers that can be considered complete within this category are ultimately expressed in the form of laws embodying invariable relationships among variables. It is at this level that nonhistorical scientists not only start but usually also stop.

The historical scientists nevertheless go on to a second kind of explanation that is equally scientific and ask a second question, in the vernacular, "How come?" How does it happen that the Colorado River formed the Grand Canyon, that cordilleras arose along the edge of a continent, or that lions live on zebras? Again the usual approach is descriptive, the plain-story history of changes in configurations, whether individual, as for the Grand Canyon, or generalized to some degree, as for the concurrent evolution of lions and zebras. This is already a form of explanation, but full explanation at this more complex level is reached only by combination of the configurational changes with the immanent properties and processes present within them and involved in those changes. One does not adequately explain the Grand Canyon either by describing the structure of that area and its changes during the Cenozoic or by enumerating the physical and chemical laws involved in erosion, but by a combination of the two.

There are two other kinds of scientific explanation to be mentioned here for completeness, although they enter into geology only to a limited extent through paleontology and are more directly biological and psychological. Both are kinds of answers to the question "What for?" This question is inappropriate in the physical sciences or the physical ("How?") aspects of other sciences, historical or nonhistorical. "What does a stone fall for?" or "Why was the Grand Canyon formed?" (in the sense of "What is it now for?") are questions that make no sense to a modern scientist. Such questions were nevertheless asked by primitive scientists (notably Aristotle) and are still asked by some nonscientists and pseudoscientists. The rise of modern physical science required the rejection of this form of explanation, and physical scientists insisted that such questions simply *must not* be asked. In their own sphere they were right, but the questions are legitimate and necessary in the life sciences.

One kind of "What for?" question, for example, "What are birds' wings for?" calls for a teleonomic answer. That they are an adaptation to flying is a proper answer and partial explanation near the descriptive level. Fuller explanation is historical: through a sequence of configurations of animals and their environments wings became possible, had an advantageous function, and so evolved through natural selection. Such a history is possible only in systems with the elaborate feedback and information-storage mechanisms characteristic of organisms, and this kind of explanation is inapplicable to wholly inorganic systems (or other configurations). "What for?" may also be answered teleologically in terms of purpose, explaining a sequence of events as means to reach a goal. Despite Aristotle and the Neo-Thomists, this form of explanation is scientifically legitimate only if the goal is foreseen. It therefore is applicable only to the behavior of humans and, with increasing uncertainty, to some other animals.

The question "How come?" is peculiar to historical science and necessary in all its aspects. Answers to this question are *the* historical explanations. Nevertheless, the full explanation of history requires *also* the reductionist explanations (nonhistorical in themselves) elicited by "How?" Teleonomic explanations are also peculiar to historical science, but only to that part of it which deals with the history of organisms.

Predictive Testing and Predictability

All of science rests on postulates that are not provable in the strictest sense. The uniformity of the immanent, previously discussed, is only one such postulate, although perhaps the most important one for historical science. Indeed it may be said that not only the postulates but also the conclusions of science, including its laws and other theories, are not strictly provable. Proof in an absolute sense occurs only in mathematics or logic when a conclusion is demonstrated to be tautologically contained in axioms or premises. Since these disciplines are not directly concerned with the truth or probability of axioms or premises, and hence of conclusions drawn from them, their proofs are trivial for the philosophy of the natural sciences. In these sciences, the essential point is determination of the probability of the premises themselves, and mathematics and logic only provide methods for correctly arriving at the implications contained in those premises. Despite the vulgar conception of "proving a theory," which does sometimes creep into the scientific literature, careful usage never speaks of proof in this connection but only of establishment of degrees of confidence.

In the nonhistorical sciences the testing of a proposition, that is, the attempt to modify the degree of confidence in it, usually has one general form. A possible relationship between phenomena is formulated on the basis of prior observations. With that formulation as a premise, implications as to phenomena not yet observed are arrived at by logical deduction. In other words, a prediction is made from an hypothesis. An experiment is then devised in order to determine whether the predicted phenomena do in fact occur. The premise as to relationships, the hypothesis, often has characteristics of a law, although it may be expressed in other terms. As confidence increases (nothing contrary to prediction is observed) it becomes a theory, which is taken as simultaneously explaining past phenomena and predicting future ones.

Physical scientists (e.g. Conant, 1947) have often maintained or assumed that this is the paradigm of testing ("verification" or increase of confidence) for science in general. On this basis, some philosophers and logicians of science (notably Hempel and Oppenheim, 1953) have concluded that scientific explanation and prediction are inseparable. Explanation (in this sense) is a correlation of past and present; prediction is a correlation of present and future. The tense does not matter, and it is maintained that the logical characteristics of the two are the same. They are merely two statements of the same relationship. This conclusion is probably valid as applied to scientific laws, strictly defined, in nonhistorical aspects of science. In previous terms, it has broad—perhaps not completely general—validity for "How"? explanations. But we have seen that there are other kinds of scientific explanations and that some of them are more directly pertinent to historical science. It cannot be assumed and indeed will be found untrue that parity of explanation and prediction is valid in historical science.

Scriven (1959 and personal communication) has discussed this matter at length. One of his points (put in different words) is that explanation and prediction are not necessarily symmetrical, that in some instances a parity principle is clearly inapplicable to them. Part of the argument may be paraphrased as follows. If X is always preceded by A, A is a cause, hence at least a partial explanation, of X. But A may not always be followed by X. Therefore, although A explains X when X does occur, it is not possible to predict the occurrence of X from that of A. A simple geological example (not from Scriven) is that erosion causes valleys, but one cannot predict from the occurrence of erosion that a valley will be formed. In fact, quite the contrary may occur; erosion can also obliterate valleys.

The example also illustrates another point by Scriven (again in different terms). The failure of prediction is due to the fact that erosion (A) is only a partial cause of valleys (X). It is a (complex) immanent cause, and we have omitted the configurational cause. Erosion is always followed by a valley formation, A is followed by X, *if* it affects certain configurations. The total cause, as in all historical events, comprises both immanent and configurational elements. It further appears that prediction is possible in historical science, but only to a limited extent and under certain conditions. If the immanent causation is known and if the necessary similarities of configurational circumstances are known and are recurrent, prediction is possible.

The possibility of predicting the future from the past is nevertheless extremely limited in practice and incomplete even in principle. There seem to be four main reasons for these limitations. Mayr (1961) has discussed them in connection with historical aspects of biology, and with some modification his analysis can be extended to historical science in general.

(1) A necessary but insufficient cause may not be positively correlated with the usual outcome or event. This is related to the asymmetry of explanation and prediction already discussed, and it is also discussed in other words by Scriven (1959). Scriven's example is that paresis is caused by syphilis, but that most syphilitics do not develop paresis. A modification of Mayr's example is that mutation is a necessary cause for evolutionary change, but that such change rarely takes the direction of the most frequent mutations. A geological example might be that vulcanism is essential for the formation of basalt plateaus, but that such plateaus are not the usual result of vulcanism.

(2) The philosophical interest of the foregoing reason for historical unpredictability is reduced by the fact that the outcome might become predictable in principle if *all* the necessary causes were known. But as soon as we bring in configuration as one of the necessary causes, which must always be done in historical science, the situation may become extremely, often quite impossibly, complicated. Prediction is possible only to the extent that correlation can be established with pertinent, abstracted and generalized, recurrent elements in configurations. Considerations as to base level, slope, precipitation, and other configurational features may be generalized so as to permit prediction that *a* valley will be formed. It would be impossibly difficult to specify all the far more complex factors of configuration required to predict the exact form of a particular valley, an actual historical event. In such cases it may still be possible, as Scriven has pointed out in a different context, to recognize *a posteriori* the configurational details responsible for particular characteristics of the actual valley, even though these characteristics were not practically predictable. This reason for unpredictability of course becomes more important the more complex the system involved. As both Scriven and Mayr emphasize, it may become practically insurmountable in the extremely complex organic systems involved in evolution, and yet this does not make evolution inexplicable. Even in the comparatively extremely simple physical example of the gas laws, it is obviously

impossible in practice and probably also in principle (because of the limitations of simultaneous observation of position and motion) to determine the historical configurations of all the individual molecules, so that the *precise* outcome of a *particular* experiment is in fact unpredictable.

In this example the complications may be virtually eliminated and in historical science they may often be at least alleviated by putting specification of configurational causes on a statistical basis. This may, however, still further increase the asymmetry of explanation and prediction. For instance, in Scriven's previously cited example, as he points out, the only valid *statistical* prediction is that syphilis will not produce paresis; in other words, that a necessary cause of a particular result will *not* have that result. If, as a historical fact, a syphilitic does become paretic, the event was not predictable even in principle. The point is pertinent here because it demonstrates that a statistical approach does not eliminate the effect of configurational complication in making historical events unpredictable.

(3) As configurational systems become more complex they acquire characteristics absent in the simpler components of these systems and not evidently predictable from the latter. This is the often discussed phenomenon of emergence. The classical physical example is that the properties of water may be explicable but are not predictable by those of hydrogen and oxygen. Again the unpredictability increases with configurational complications. It is difficult to conceive prediction from component atoms to a mountain range, and to me, at least, prediction from atoms to, say, the fall of Rome, is completely inconceivable. It could be claimed that prediction of emergent phenomena would be possible if we really knew *all* about the atoms. This might just possibly, and only in principle, be true in nonhistorical science, as in the example of $2H + O \rightarrow H_2O$. It would, however, be true in historical science only if we knew all the immanent properties and *also* all the configurational histories of all the atoms, which is certainly impossible in practice and probably in principle. Whether or not the predictability of emergent phenomena is a philosophical possibility (and I am inclined to think it is not), that possibility would seem to have little heuristic and no pragmatic value.

(4) Scientific prediction depends on recurrence or repeatability. Prediction of unique events is impossible either in practice or in principle. Historical events are always unique in some degree, and they are therefore never precisely predictable. However, as previously noted, there are different degrees of uniqueness. Historical events may therefore be considered predictable in principle to the extent that their causes are similar. (This is a significant limitation only for configurational causes, since by the postulate of uniformity the immanent causes are not merely similar but identical.)

In practice, further severe limitations are imposed by the difficulties of determining what similarities of cause are pertinent to the events and of observing these causal factors. It must also again be emphasized that such prediction can only be general and not particular. In other words, prediction does not include any unique aspect of the event, and in historical science it is often the unique aspects that most require explanation. One might, for instance, be able to provide a predictive explanation of mountain formation (although in fact geologists have not yet achieved this) and also explanations of the particular features of say, the Alps (achieved in small part), but the latter explanations would not be predictive. (This is also an example of the fact that unpredictive *ad hoc* explanation may be easier to achieve than predictive general explanation.)

At this point, one might wish to raise the question of what is interesting or significant in a scientific investigation. In the physical study of gases or of sand grains, the individuality (uniqueness) of single molecules or grains, slight in any case, is generally beside the point. In dealing with historical events, such as the formation of a particular sandstone or mountain range, individuality often is just the point at issue. Here, more or less parenthetically, another aspect and another use of the statistical approach are pertinent. A statistical description of variation in sand grains or of elevations, slopes, etc. in a mountain range is a practical means of taking into account their individual contributions to the over-all individuality of the sandstone or the mountain range.

Two other aspects of explanation and prediction in historical science may be more briefly considered: the use of models, and prediction from trends and cycles. Past geological events cannot be repeated at will, and furthermore, prediction loses practical significance if, as is often the case in geology, its fulfillment would require some thousands or millions of years. This is the rationale for the experimental approach, using physical models to study the historical aspects of geology and, when possible, other historical sciences. The models abstract what are believed to be the essential general configurational similarities of historical events (folding and faulting, valley erosion, and the like) and scale these in space and time in such a way as to make them repeatable at will and at rates that permit observation. With such models predictive explanations can be made and tested. (The further problems of projecting from model to geological space and time need not be considered here.)

Finally, the most common form taken by attempts at actual historical prediction is the extrapolation of trends. In fact, this approach has no philosophical and little pragmatic validity. Its philosophical justification would require that contingent causes be unchanging or change always in the same ways, which observation shows to be certainly false. Its degree of pragmatic justification depends on the fact that trends and cycles do exist and (by definition) continue over considerable periods of time. Therefore, at randomly distributed times, established trends and cycles are more likely to continue than not. Predictions through the extrapolation of trends are useful mostly for short ranges of time; for larger ranges their likelihood decreases until the appropriate statistical prediction becomes not continuation but termination or change of trend or cycle within some specified time. The period of likely continuation or justifiable extrapolation is, furthermore, greatly reduced by the fact that a trend or cycle must *already* have gone on for a considerable time in order to be recognized as actually existent. Present knowledge of geological and biological (evolutionary) history suggests that all known trends and cycles have in fact ended or changed except those which are now still within the span of likelihood that is statistically indicated by the trends and cycles of the past. Moreover, many supposed examples, such as regular cycles of mountain building or trends for increase in size of machairodont sabers, now seem to have been mistaken. Many real trends and cycles also turn out to be neither so uniform nor so long continued as was formerly supposed, often under the influence of invalid historical "laws" such as that of orthogenesis or of the pulse of the earth. It is improbable that prediction about a total historical situation on this basis alone is ever justified, even when prediction from causal properties and configurations is possible within limits.

Strategy in Historical Science

The sequence hypothesis-prediction-experiment is not the only strategy of explanation and testing in nonhistorical physical science. It is, however, so often appropriate and useful there that philosophers who base their concepts of science on physical science, as most of them do, tend to consider it ideal if not obligatory. (On this point of view see, as a single example among many, Braithwaite, 1953.) This is an example of the existing hegemony of the physical sciences, which is not logically justifiable but has been fostered by human historical and pragmatic factors. It has been shown that this strategy is also possible in historical science, but that it here plays a smaller and less exclusive role. It must be supplemented and frequently supplanted by other strategies. These are in part implicit in what has already been said, but further notice of some of the more important ones remains as the final aim of this essay. One purpose is to demonstrate more fully and distinctly that nonpredictive explanation and testing are in fact possible in historical geology and other historical sciences.

The primary data of the historical scientist consist of partial descriptions of configurations near the level of plain story. If the configurations are sequential and connected, that is, if the later historically arose from the earlier, the antecedent can be taken as including, at least in part, the configurational requirements and causes for the consequent. Even in such simple circumstances, a direct causal connection can often be assumed on the basis of principles already developed or on the basis of known parallels. For instance, partial configurational causation is clearly involved in the sequence *Hyracotheriun* (Eohippus)–*Orohippus* or sand-sandstone. The latter example adds an important point: the earlier configuration of a stratum now sandstone is not actually observed but is inferred from the latter. The examples illustrate two kinds of explanatory sequences available to the historical scientist. In one we have dated documents contemporaneous with the events and so directly historical in nature and sequence. In the other we have a pseudohistorical sequence such as that of presently existing sands and sandstones. Their resemblances and differences are such that we can be confident that they share some elements of historical change, but that one has undergone more change than the other. In this case it is easy to see that the sandstone belongs to a later period in the pseudohistorical sequence. One therefore infers for it a historically antecedent sand and can proceed to determine what characteristics are inherited from that sand and the nature of the subsequent changes.

The use of pseudohistorical sequences is another way in which the present is a key to the past, but it does not involve another principle of uniformity. The addition to the element of uniformity of immanent characteristics is simply a descriptive resemblance or generalization of configuration applicable to the particular case as a matter of observation. In practice, an historical interpretation commonly involves both historical and pseudohistorical sequences. For example, study of the stratigraphy of a given region simultaneously concerns the directly historical sequence of strata and the history of each stratum from deposition (or before) to its present condition as inferred on the basis of appropriate pseudohistorical sequences.

A second form of strategy has a certain analogy with the use of multiple experiments with controlled variables. The method is to compare different sequences, either historical or pseudohistorical, that resemble each other in some pertinent way. Resemblances in the antecedent configurations may be taken to include causes of the consequent resemblances. It is not, however, legitimate to assume that they are all necessary causes or that they include sufficient causes. Even more important at times is the converse principle that factors that differ among the antecedents are not causes of resemblances among the consequents. By elimination when many sequences are compared, this may warrant the conclusion that residual antecedent resemblances are necessary causes. There is here applicable a principle of scientific testing in general: absolute proof of a hypothesis or other form of inference is impossible, but disproof is possible. Confidence increases with the number of opportunities for disproof that have not in fact revealed discrepancies. In this application, confidence that residual resemblances are causal increases with the number of different sequences involved in the comparison. This form of strategy is applicable to most geological sequences, few of which are unique in *all* respects. Obvious and important examples include the formation of geosynclines and

their subsequent folding, or many such recurrent phenomena as the stratigraphic consequences of advancing and retreating seas.

An interesting special case arises when there is more resemblance among
consequent than among antecedent configurations: the phenomenon of convergence. This has received much more attention in the study of organic
evolution than elsewhere, but nonorganic examples also occur. If I am correctly informed, the origin of various granites from quite different antecedents
is a striking example. Another fair example might be the formation of more
or less similar land forms by different processes: for example, the formation of
mountains by folding, faulting, or by erosion of a plateau; or the development
of plains and terraces by erosion or deposition. Doubtless most geologists can
find still other examples in their specialities. The special strategic interest of
convergence is that its elimination of noncausal factors often gives confidence
in identification of causes and increases knowledge of them. In organic evolution it has greatly increased understanding of the nature and limits of adaptation by natural selection. In the example of the granites it shows that an essential
antecedent is not some one kind of lithology but atomic composition, and it
pinpoints the search for the processes bringing about this particular kind of
configuration of the atoms.

It has been previously pointed out that the explanation of an historical event
involves both configuration and immanence, even though the latter is not
historical in nature. Historical science therefore requires knowledge of the
pertinent immanent factors, and its strategy includes distinguishing the two
and studying their interactions. Nonhistorical science, by its primary concern
with the immanent, is the principal source of the historian's necessary knowledge
of immanent factors and his principal means of distinguishing these from configurational relationships. A typical approach is to vary configurations in
experiments and to determine what relationships are constant throughout the
configurational variations. To a historical geologist, the function of a physical
geologist is to isolate and characterize the immanent properties of the earth
and its parts in that and other ways. The historical geologist is then interested
not in what holds true regardless of configuration, but in how configuration
modifies the action of the identified immanent properties and forces. In this
respect, the nonhistorical scientist is more interested in similarities and the
historical scientist in differences.

Here the historical scientist has two main strategies, both already mentioned.
They may be used separately or together. One proceeds by controlled experimentation, in geology usually with scaled-down models although to a limited
extent experimentation with natural geological phenomena is also possible.
(The opportunities for experimentation are greater in some other historical
sciences.) The other might be viewed as complementary to the previously
discussed study of similarities in multiple sequences. In this strategy, attention

is focused on consequent differences, the causes of which are sought among the observable or inferable differences of antecedent configurations. Although the explanation is rarely so simple or so easy to identify, a sufficiently illustrative example would be the presence in one valley and absence in another of a waterfall caused by a fault, of a ledge of hard rock above shale, or of some other readily observable local configuration.

Points always at issue in historical science are the consistency of proposed immanent laws and properties with known historical events and the sufficiency and necessity of such causation acting within known configurations. Probably the strongest argument of the catastrophists was that known features of the earth were inconsistent with their formation by known natural forces within the earth's span of existence, which many of them took to be about 6000 years. The fault of course was not with their logic but with one of their premises. The same argument, with the same fallacy, was brought up against Darwin when it was claimed that his theory was inadequate to account for the origin of present organic diversity in the earth's span, then estimated by the most eminent physicists as a few million years at most. Darwin stuck to his guns and insisted, correctly, that the calculation of the age of the earth must be wrong. Historical science has an essential role, both philosophical and practical, in providing such cross checks (mostly nonpredictive and nonexperimental), both with its own theories and with those of other sciences as part of the self-testing of science in general. A current geological example, perhaps all the more instructive because it has not yet reached a conclusion, is the controversy over continental drift and the adequacy of physical forces to bring it about if indeed it did occur. (Incidentally the original motive for writing Simpson, 1944, was to test the consistency and explanatory power of various neontological theories of evolution by comparison with the historical record.)

The testing of hypothetical generalizations or proposed explanations against a historical record has some of the aspects of predictive testing. Here, however, one does not say, "If so and so holds good, such and such will occur," but, "If so and so has held good, such and such must have occurred." (Again I think that the difference in tense is logically significant and that a parity principle is not applicable.) In my own field one of the most conspicuous examples has been the theory of orthogenesis, which in the most common of its many forms maintains that once an evolutionary trend begins it is inherently forced to continue to the physically possible limit regardless of other circumstances. This view plainly has consequences that should be reflected in the fossil record. As a matter of observation, the theory is inconsistent with that record. A more strictly geological example is the "pulse of the earth" theory, that worldwide mountain-making has occurred at regularly cyclic intervals, which also turns out to be inconsistent with the available historical data (Gilluly, 1949, among others).

The study of human history is potentially included in historical science by our definition. One of its differences from other branches of historical science is that it deals with configurational sequences and causal complexes so exceedingly intricate that their scientific analysis has not yet been conspicuously successful. (Toynbee's (1946) correlation of similar sequences would seem to be a promising application of a general historical strategy, but I understand that the results have not been universally acclaimed by his colleagues.) A second important difference is that so much of this brief history has been directly observed, although with varying degrees of accuracy and acuity and only in its very latest parts by anyone whose approach can reasonably be called scientific. Direct observation of historical events is also possible in geology and other historical sciences, and it is another of their important strategies. Meticulous observation of the history of a volcano (Parícutin) from birth to maturity is an outstanding example. More modestly, anyone who watches a flash flood in a southwestern arroyo or, for that matter, sees a stone roll down a hillside is observing an historical event.

In geology, however, and in all historical science except that of human history, the strategic value of observing actual events is more indirect than direct. The processes observed are, as a rule, only those that act rapidly. The time involved is infinitesimal in comparison with the time span of nonhuman history, which is on the order of $n10^9$ years for both historical geology and historical biology. Currently practicable resolution within that span varies enormously but is commonly no better, and in some instances far worse, than $n10^6$. The observed events are also both local and trivial in the great majority of instances. They are in fact insignificant in themselves, but they are extremely significant as samples or paradigms, being sequences seen in action and with all their elements and surrounding circumstances observable. They thus serve in a special and particularly valuable way both as historical (and not pseudohistorical) data for the strategies of comparison of multiple sequences and as natural experiments for the strategies of experimentation, including on some but not all occasions that of prediction. (This, incidentally, is still a third way in which the present is a key to the past, but again it involves no additional uniformity principle.)

Direct observation of historical events is also involved in a different way in still another of the historical strategies, that of testing explanatory theories against a record. For example, such observations are one of the best means of estimating rates of processes under natural conditions and so of judging whether they could in fact have caused changes indicated by the record in the time involved. Or the historical importance of observed short-range processes can be tested against the long-range record for necessity, or sufficiency, or both. An interesting paleontological example concerns the claims of some Neo-Lamarckians who agree that although the inheritance of acquired characters is too slow to be directly observed, it has been an (or *the*) effective long-range process of evolution. The fossil record in itself cannot offer clear disproof, but it strips the argument of all conviction by showing that actually observed short-range processes excluded by this hypothesis are both necessary and sufficient to account for known history.

Conclusion

The most frequent operations in historical science are not based on the observation of causal sequences—events—but on the observation of results. From those results an attempt is made to infer previous causes. This is true even when a historical sequence, for example one of strata, is observed. Such a sequence is directly historical only in the sense that the strata were deposited in a time sequence that is directly available to us. The actual events, deposition of each stratum, are not observable. In such situations, and in this sense, the present is not merely a key to the past—it is all we have in the way of data. Prediction is the inference of results from causes. Historical science largely involves the opposite: inferring causes (of course including causal configurations) from results.

The reverse of prediction has been called, perhaps sometimes facetiously, postdiction. In momentary return to the parity of explanation and prediction, it may be noted that if A is the necessary and sufficient cause of X and X is the necessary and sole result of A, then the prediction of X from A and the postdiction of A from X are merely different statements of the same relationship. They are logically identical. It has already been demonstrated and sufficiently emphasized that the conditions for this identity frequently do not hold in practice and sometimes not even in principle for historical science. Here, then, postdiction takes on a broader and more distinct meaning and is not merely a restatement of a predictive relationship. With considerable oversimplification it might be said that historical science is mainly postdictive, and nonhistorical science mainly predictive.

Postdiction also involves the self-testing essential to a true science, as has also been exemplified—although not, by far, fully expounded. Perhaps its simplest and yet most conclusive test is the confrontation of theoretical explanation with historical evidence. A crucial historical fact or event may be deduced from a theory, and search may subsequently produce evidence for or against its actual prior occurrence. This has been called "prediction," for example, by Rensch (1960), sometimes with the implication that historical science is true science because its philosophical basis does not really differ from that of nonhistorical physics. The premise that the philosophy of science is necessarily nonhistorical is of course wrong, but the argument is fallacious in any case. What is actually predicted is not the antecedent occurrence but the subsequent discovery; the antecedent is postdicted. Beyond this, perhaps quibbling, point, the antecedent occurrence is not always a *necessary* consequence of any fact, principle, hypothesis, theory, law, or postulate advanced before the postdiction was made. The point is sufficiently illustrated on the pragmatic level by the sometimes spectacular failure to predict discoveries even when there is a sound basis for such prediction. An evolutionary example is the failure to predict discovery of a "missing link," now known (*Australopithecus*), that was upright and tool-making but had the physiognomy and cranial capacity of an ape. Fortunately such examples do not invalidate the effectiveness of postdiction in the sense of inferring the past from the present with accompanying testing by historical methods. In fact the discovery of *Australopithecus* was an example of such testing, for without any predictive element it confirmed (i.e. strengthened confidence in) certain prior theories as to human origins and relationships and permitted their refinement.

Another oversimplified and yet generally significant distinction is that historical science is primarily concerned with configuration, and nonhistorical science with immanence. Parallel, not identical, with this is a certain tendency for the former to concentrate on the real and the individual, for the latter to focus on the ideal and the generalized, or for both to operate with different degrees of abstraction. We have seen, however, that interpretation and explanation in historical science *include* immanence and, along with it, *all* the facts, principles, laws, and so on, of nonhistorical science. To these, historical science adds its own configurational and other aspects. When it is most characteristically itself, it is compositionist rather than reductionist, examining the involvement of primary materials and forces in systems of increasing complexity and integration.

Historical science, thus characterized, cuts across the traditional lines between the various sciences: physics, chemistry, astronomy, geology, biology, anthropology, psychology, sociology, and the rest. Each of these has both historical and nonhistorical aspects, although the proportions of the two differ greatly. Among the sciences named, the historical element plays the smallest role in physics, where it is frequently ignored, and the greatest in sociology, where the existence of nonhistorical aspects is sometimes denied—one of the reasons that sociology has not always been ranked as a science. It is not a coincidence that there is a correlation with complexity and levels of integration, physics being the simplest and sociology the most complex science in this partial list. Unfortunately philosophers of science have tended to concentrate on one end of this spectrum, and that the simplest, so much as to give a distorted, and in some instances quite false, idea of the philosophy of science as a whole.

Geology exhibits as even a balance of historical and nonhistorical elements as any of the sciences, and here the relationships of the two may be particularly clear. It is in a strategic position to illuminate scientific philosophy—an opportunity not yet sufficiently exploited.

Addendum

The preceding essay was read in manuscript and constructively criticized by a number of geologists, mostly authors of other chapters in this work. The following additional comments bear on points brought up by them.

A few critics objected to the term "immanent" on the grounds that it is unfamiliar and is liable to confusion with "imminent," a word different in origin and meaning. The most nearly acceptable substitute proposed was "inherent," which does not seem to me equally precise or strictly appropriate in the intended sense. Since "immanent" is here clearly defined and consistently used, I cannot believe that it will prove misleading. It did not, in fact, mislead the readers who nevertheless criticized it.

Another critical suggestion was that under some special circumstances extrapolation from historical trends may make unique events predictable. This is, I think, possible to a limited extent and for relatively short-range prediction on a strictly probabilistic basis, as is, indeed, pointed out in the preceding essay. The example given by the commentator also illustrates the limitations: that the exhaustion of the preponderant part of the fossil fuels within the next few centuries is predictable. In fact, contingent circumstances have changed so radically and unpredictably over recent years that the term of this prediction has had to be greatly changed and has evidently become looser and less reliable than was earlier believed. Even though some confidence may yet be felt in the eventual outcome, such a historical prediction is on a different level from one based on causal analysis apart from or in addition to trends.

Along similar lines, it was also remarked that prediction from cycles may be extremely reliable when the phenomena are definitely known to be cyclical, with planetary motions as one example. That is, of course, true for the given example and for others in which such current configurational changes as occur have come to be almost entirely governed by cyclical immanent processes. The prediction is then based on the latter, alone, and a truly historical element is limited. If a nonrecurrent historical change should occur, for example if the mass of any planet were significantly altered, the predictions would prove false. To the extent that prediction is possible in such examples, it depends on knowledge of immanent causes and on strictly recurrent configurations, as specified above. Moreover, as this critic agrees in the main, similarly predictable cycles may be discounted so far as geology is concerned.

Finally, radioactive decay of an isotope is cited as an example of a precisely predictable noncyclical phenomenon. I consider radioactive decay to be analogous to the gas laws or to a chemical reaction; in each case the prediction of actual historical events is not precise in principle, but the historical circumstances may be statistically so uniform that changes in them can often be ignored in practice. Then the laws or the generalized descriptions expressed in the appropriate equations hold good just to the extent that the historical element can safely be ignored, and their predictions are not historical in principle.

REFERENCES CITED

BARNHART, C. L., ed., 1948, The American college dictionary: New York and London, Harper, 1432 pp.

BERNAL, J. D., 1951, The physical basis of life: London, Routledge and Kegan Paul, 80 pp.

BRAITHWAITE, R. B., 1953, Scientific explanation: New York, Cambridge Univ. Press, 375 pp.

CONANT, J. B., 1947, On understanding science: New Haven, Yale Univ. Press, 145 pp.

FARRAND, W. R., 1962, Frozen mammoths: Science, vol. 137, pp. 450–452. [See also Lippman, 1962.]

GILLISPIE, C. C., 1951, Genesis and geology; a study in the relations of scientific thought, natural theology, and social opinion in Great Britain, 1790–1850: Cambridge, Mass., Harvard Univ. Press, 315 pp.

GILLULY, J., 1949, Distribution of mountain building in geologic time: Geol. Soc. Am., B., vol. 60, pp. 561–590.

HEMPEL, C. G., and OPPENHEIM, P., 1953, The logic of explanation, in Readings in the philosophy of science, H. Feigl and M. Brodbeck, eds.: New York, Appleton-Century-Crofts, pp. 319–352.

HOBSON, E. W., 1923, The domain of natural science; The Gifford Lectures delivered in the Univ. of Aberdeen in 1921 and 1922: New York, Macmillan, 510 pp.

HOOYKAAS, R., 1959, Natural law and divine miracle; a historical-critical study of the principle of uniformity in geology, biology, and theology: Leiden, E. J. Brill, 237 pp.

LIPPMAN, H. E., 1962, Frozen mammoths: Science, vol. 137, pp. 449–450. [See also Farrand, 1962.]

MAYR, E., 1961, Cause and effect in biology; kinds of causes, predictability, and teleology are viewed by a practicing biologist: Science, vol. 134, pp. 1501–1506.

MORGAN, C. L., 1890–91, Animal life and intelligence: London, E. Arnold, 512 pp.

NAGEL, E., 1961, The structure of science; problems in the logic of scientific explanation: New York, Harcourt, Brace, and World, 618 pp.

PITTENDRIGH, C. S., 1958, Adaptation, natural selection, and behavior, in Behavior and evolution, A. Roe and G. G. Simpson, eds.: New Haven, Yale Univ. Press, 557 pp.

RENSCH, B., 1960, The laws of evolution, in Evolution after Darwin, S. Tax, ed., vol. 1: Chicago, Univ. Chicago Press, pp. 95–116.

SCRIVEN, M., 1959, Explanation and prediction in evolutionary theory; satisfactory explanation of the past is possible even when prediction of the future is impossible: Science, vol. 130, pp. 477–482.

SIMPSON, G. G., 1944, Tempo and mode in evolution: New York, Columbia Univ. Press, 237 pp.

———, 1960, The history of life, in Evolution after Darwin, S. Tax, ed., vol. 1: Chicago, Univ. of Chicago Press, pp. 117–180.

———, 1962, Notes on the nature of science by a biologist, in Notes on the nature of science: New York, Harcourt, Brace, and World, pp. 7–12.

———, 1963, Biology and the nature of science: Science, vol. 139, pp. 81–88.

TOYNBEE, A., 1946–47, A study of history: London, Oxford Univ. Press, 617 pp.

DAVID B. KITTS

University of Oklahoma

The Theory of Geology[1]

Geologists have, throughout the history of their discipline, asked questions about the nature of geology and its relationship to the other natural sciences. Self-consciousness has been increasing among geologists during the past decade as it has been increasing among all scientists. In print the most obvious sign of an inclination toward self-examination is to be found in discussions of the ideal geologic curriculum in colleges and universities. Many of the questions raised in these discussions may be interpreted as questions about the theoretical structure of the science.

Geologic Generalizations

In the discussion that follows, "geologic term" will be understood to mean a term which fulfills a particular function in geology and is not a term necessary for meaningful discourse outside geology. Geologic terms may have been invented for the specific role which they fill, for example, "syncline"; or they may be terms of the common language whose meaning has been expanded, or more often restricted, to fill a particular technical role, for example, "sand." A general statement which employs geologic terms in the above sense will be called a "geologic generalization."

In a recently published paper (Kitts, 1963) I expressed the opinion that geologic explanations are justified in terms of generalizations which may be compared to the laws of the other natural sciences. Most geologists have been reluctant to attach the label "law" to any of the statements which they employ. A few geologists, for example Bucher (1933), have used the term freely. It is

[1] I should like to express my gratitude to the members of the advanced seminar in the history of science at the University of Oklahoma for their critical reading of the manuscript. Carolyn Wares has given valuable assistance in the preparation of the manuscript. Certain alterations in the last section of the paper have been made at the suggestion of Dr. M. King Hubbert.

not my intention to discuss the question of which statements should or should not be called laws. This question has been discussed at some length by most philosophers of science. For excellent recent discussions of the concept of a scientific law, I refer the reader to Nagel (1961), Braithwaite (1953), and Hempel and Oppenheim (1948). Although I shall have occasion to mention current opinion on the kinds of statements which are to be called laws, my main purpose here is to examine that great variety of general statements, whatever we choose to call them, which serve as a part of the logical justification for various kinds of geologic explanations.

Traditionally, scientific explanation has been regarded as a deductive operation. A generalization which functions in a deductive argument must be of strictly universal form, that is, it must admit of no exceptions whatever. Consequently, many writers have restricted the term "natural law" to statements of strictly universal form. One can cite examples of geologic generalizations which are universal. For example, the statement, "If the supply of new sand is less than that moved over the crest . . . the windward slope will be degraded as the leeward slope grows, and thus the dune will migrate with the wind by transfer of sand from one slope to the other" (Dunbar and Rodgers, 1957, p. 20) is in form, though perhaps not in principle, universal.

Generalizations employing terms denoting probability or possibility, however, far outnumber generalizations of universal form in the geologic literature. A striking feature of geologic discourse is the frequency with which such words and phrases as "probably," "frequently," and "tends to," occur in generalizations.

Explanations which contain these nonuniversal general statements are not deductive, but rather inductive in form. As Hempel (1958, p. 40) has put it, "This kind of argument, therefore, is inductive rather than strictly deductive in character: it calls for the acceptance of E [a sentence stating whatever is being explained] on the basis of other statements which constitute only partial, if strongly supporting, grounds for it." Few geologists would disagree that the generalizations which they employ seldom provide more than "partial, if strongly supporting, grounds" for their conclusions.

It is customary to call general statements which admit of some exceptions "statistical" or "probabilistic." According to Bunge (1961, p. 267) statistical lawlike statements are ". . . propositions denoting regularities in the large or in the long run. They contain logical constructs belonging to mathematical statistics and characterizing central or overall trends ('average,' 'dispersion,' 'correlation,' and the like)." The generalization which states the rate of decay of carbon fourteen is statistical in this sense.

General statements which contain terms denoting probability or possibility but which are characterized by no precise formulation of statistical constructs in numerical terms are better labeled "probabilistic" than "statistical." The geologic literature abounds in statements of this sort. For example: "Wind-driven sand, like snow, tends to settle in drifts in the wind shadow of topographic obstructions." (Dunbar and Rodgers, 1957, p. 19)

Statistical inference is playing an increasingly important role in geologic investigation and one cannot help being impressed by the frequency with which statistical constructs appear in geologic literature. In much of this literature, however, the precise statistical terminology employed may obscure the loosely probabilistic character of the generalizations containing it. In the following quotation the antecedent portions of the generalization are framed with statistical precision but the operators, for example "most" and "many," lack such precision.

> Dune sands *tend to be* better sorted than river sands and a plot of standard deviation (sorting) against mean grain-size indicates three fields, one for river sands, one for dune sands, and a third field of overlap. This figure points out that *many* river sands can be distinguished from dune sands and vice versa on the basis of their textural parameters but that a wide field of overlap exists. In practice this field of overlap is not necessarily a serious matter, since *most* coastal, barrier bar, and lake dune sands have a standard deviation of less than 0.40, and *many* desert and inland dune sands do not exceed 0.50, whereas *most* river sands have a standard deviation in excess of 0.50. (Friedman, 1961, p. 524, italics mine)

Scriven (1959) has recently suggested that the generalizations in terms of which explanations of individual events are justified are usually neither universal nor statistical, nor even probabilistic, but rather belong to another category of statements which he calls "normic statements." Scriven's concept of the normic statement throws particular light on the problem of geologic generalizations and explanations. He states (p. 464), "I suggest there is a category of general statements, a hybrid with some universal features and some statistical features, from which alone can be selected the role-justifying grounds for good explanations of individual events," and (p. 466),

> The statistical statement is less informative than the normic statement in a very important way, although an exact statistical statement may be informative in a way a normic statement is not. The statistical statement does not say anything about the things to which it refers except that some do and some do not fall into a certain category. The normic statement says that *everything* falls into a certain category *except* those to which *certain special conditions* apply. And although the normic statement itself does not explicitly list what count as exceptional conditions, it employs a vocabulary which reminds us of our knowledge of this, our trained judgment of exceptions.

and (p. 466)

> Now if the exceptions were few in number and readily described, one could convert a normic statement into an exact generalization by listing

them. Normic statements are useful where the system of exceptions, although perfectly comprehensible in the sense that one can learn how to judge their relevance, is exceedingly complex. We see immediately the analogy with—in fact, the normic character of—physical laws. The physicist's *training* makes him aware of the system of exceptions and inaccuracies, which, if simpler, could be put explicitly in the statement of scope.

and finally (p. 467)

> ... statistical statements are too weak—they abandon the hold on the individual case. The normic statement tells one what had to happen in *this* case, unless certain exceptional circumstances obtained; and the historical judgment is made (and open to verification) that these circumstances did not obtain.

Let us consider again the generalization from Dunbar and Rodgers (1957, p. 19) concerning the accumulation of wind driven sand. "Wind-driven sand, like snow, tends to settle in drifts in the wind-shadow of topographic obstructions." Offhand one would be inclined to regard this statement as probabilistic because of the distinct probabilistic, or even statistical, connotation of the phrase "tends to." But was it the intention of the authors to assert that if certain specified conditions are realized then *in a majority of cases* certain other specified conditions will follow, in which case the generalization must indeed be regarded as probabilistic; or was it their intention to assert that if certain specified conditions are realized then certain other specified conditions will *always* follow *except* where certain special conditions apply, in which case the generalization may be regarded as normic? I do not know what the intentions of the authors were, but in the absence of this knowledge it seems to me fully as plausible to regard the statement as normic as to regard it as probabilistic. The question of meaning raised in connection with this generalization can be raised in connection with a great number of seemingly probabilistic geologic generalizations, and, for that matter, about a great number of seemingly universal statements.

Most geologic generalizations, whatever their explicit form, could be regarded as normic statements, and the sense in which we actually understand them is better conveyed by the term "normic" than by the terms "universal," "statistical," or "probabilistic." One thing is certain and that is the geologist will not "abandon the hold on the individual case" by allowing statistical statements to assume too important a role in his procedures, for, as I have suggested earlier, it is the individual case which is his primary concern.

The normic character of some generalizations is made explicit. Whenever the terms "normally" or "ordinarily" are encountered in a generalization it can usually be assumed that the statement is normic. The following statement is explicitly normic. "Carbonaceous material is a residue that remains after various more or less mobile compounds, produced during the decomposition of organic matter in an oxygen-deficient environment, have moved away. Methane gas, for example, evolves and escapes under ordinary conditions." (Weller, 1960, p. 152)

Scriven holds out the hope at least that normic statements can be converted into universal statements. Von Engeln's (1942, p. 457) statement of the "law of adjusted cross sections" represents an attempt to list "exceptional circumstances" which, if they should apply, invalidate the generalization.

> Given that the surfaces of the joining glaciers are at the same level, that the width of the main valley is not abruptly increased below the junction point, and that the rate of motion of the main glacier is not greater below than above the junction—and all these conditions are met in numerous instances—it follows that there must be an abrupt increase in depth of the main valley to accommodate the volume of the combined ice streams at the place where they join.

It is clear that geologists tolerate a good deal more imprecision in their generalizations than is technically necessary. Let us turn once again to the generalization from Dunbar and Rodgers (1957, p. 19) on the accumulation of wind-driven sand. It might be possible to specify the circumstances under which wind-driven sand would *always* accumulate in the wind-shadow of topographic obstructions. To accomplish this it would be necessary to specify restricted ranges for the pertinent initial and boundary conditions such as the velocity of the wind, the character and quantity of the sand, the form of the obstruction, etc. The framing of universal statements is not, however, the primary goal of the geologist. The primary goal is to frame *general* statements, universal or not, on the basis of which explanations can be justified. The introduction of specific initial and boundary conditions may permit the formulation of strictly universal statements, but these statements will be of no use whatsoever unless these specific conditions can be independently determined. Very often it is not possible to determine these conditions, and generalizations are intentionally left in a loosely formulated state. This does not preclude the possibility of taking certain specific conditions into account when they can be independently inferred.

The view, not uncommon among geologists, that geology is as much an "art" as a science, may stem from the fact that the system of exceptions associated with geologic generalizations is usually so complex that "judgment" of their relevance may play an important role in investigation—more important a role than in the natural sciences in which the system of exceptions seems simpler.

The employment of many seemingly statistical and probabilistic generalizations imparts to geology an aspect of "indeterminacy." It would be very misleading to equate, as some geologists have done, this geologic indeterminacy with the indeterminacy principle of modern physics. In modern quantum-statistical mechanics indeterminacy is an integral part of theory. It is *not* assumed that uncertainty can be removed by a more complete and detailed specification of a particular set of variables. In geology, it seems to me, the opposite assumption is usually made. Uncertainty is regarded as a feature to be tolerated until more complete knowledge of variables allows its replacement with certainty or, to put it another way, until probabilistic and normic statements can be replaced by universal statements. Geologists are fundamentally deterministic in their approach to scientific investigation. Indeterminacy, in the sense that it is understood in physics, may enter into geology in those cases where the principles of statistical mechanics enter directly into a geologic inference.

One final point should be made in connection with probability. Logicians have called attention to the fact that there are two senses in which the term "probability" may be used in connection with scientific hypotheses. In the first sense it may be asserted that a particular hypothesis is probable or more probable than some other hypothesis; for example, "It is probable that glauconite marl represents the normal primary occurrence and that greensand is a concentrate brought together like any other kind of sand during transportation on the sea floor" (Dunbar and Rodgers, 1957, p. 184). In the second sense a probability is assigned to an event within a hypothesis, for example, "Almost all moving masses that begin as landslides in subaqueous situations become mud flows." (Weller, 1960, p. 158). Probabilistic terms are so frequently and loosely employed by geologists that it is often difficult to determine in which of the two senses a particular probabilistic term is to be understood.

Whether or not a geologic generalization is of universal form is certainly not the only question which need concern us. A statement may be of strictly universal form but be restricted in scope. The scope of a statement corresponds to the class of objects or events to which the statement applies. Every statement is to some degree restricted in scope. Certain kinds of restrictions of scope can seriously detract from the usefulness of a general statement which is intended to have explanatory power. Among the most serious of these restrictions is that imposed by reference to particular objects, or to finite classes of objects, in particular spatio-temporal regions.

Generalizations which contain references to particular objects, or which contain terms whose definition requires reference to particular objects are rare in geology, as they are in other sciences. Generalizations in which reference is made to a particular finite class of objects falling into a definite spatio-temporal region are quite common and could conceivably cause some difficulty. In the statement, "Major streams of the northern Appalachian region rise in the Allegheny Plateau and flow southeastward to the Atlantic directly across the

northeast-southwest grain of rocks and structures ranging in age from Precambrian to Tertiary" (Mackin, 1938, p. 27), for example, it is clear that the
scope is restricted to a finite class of objects. Obviously the statement has no
explanatory power. We should not be justified in explaining the fact that a
particular major stream of the northern Appalachian region flowed southeastward by reference to this statement, because, as Nagel (1961, p. 63) puts it, "if
a statement asserts in effect no more than what is asserted by the evidence for
it, we are being slightly absurd when we employ the statement for explaining or
predicting anything included in this evidence." No geologist would attempt to
explain anything at all by reference to this statement, nor did Mackin intend
that they should. The statement was obviously framed not to provide a means
of explanation and prediction, but rather to convey, as economically as possible,
information about some particular objects in a particular region. The statement
could have been formulated as a conjunction of singular statements without
change of meaning. Many general statements in geology whose scope is explicitly restricted are of this type.

As Nagel (1961, p. 63) has pointed out, a general statement which refers
to a group of objects or events which is presumably finite may be assigned an
explanatory role if the evidence for the statement is not assumed to exhaust
the scope of predication of the statement. The evidence cited to support the
statement, "As the velocity of a loaded stream decreases, both its competence
and its capacity are reduced and it becomes *overloaded*," (Dunbar and Rodgers,
1957, p. 9), for example, would consist of a finite number of observations, and
yet it is clearly not the intention of the authors to assert that this set of observations exhausts the scope of the statement.

A problem about the intention of the framer of a general statement might
arise. This problem is particularly likely to come up in connection with general
statements concerning the association of past events where the number of
instances cited in support of the statement is small. Do the instances cited to
support the following generalization exhaust its scope of predication or not?
"Fold mountains have their origin in the filling of a geosyncline chiefly with
shallow water sediments, conglomerates, sandstone, shales, and occasional
limestones." (von Engeln and Caster, 1952, p. 234) The class of fold mountains
contains a finite number of individuals. The question of scope cannot be answered by an analysis of the statement, nor can it be answered by examining
the evidence for the statement. The answer lies in a determination of the
intention of the authors. Is it their intention merely to convey information
about a finite number of instances, or do they intend to assert that fold mountains, past, present and future, have their origin in the filling of geosynclines?
If the latter is the case, then the intention is to assign an explanatory, and
possibly even a predictive, role to the statement. I cite this example to illustrate

the importance of intention. I have no doubt that the authors meant to go beyond a mere historical report.

It might be argued that all general geologic statements are restricted in scope, because they contain—implicitly or explicitly—the individual name, "the planet earth." Nagel (1961) regards Kepler's laws of planetary motion as lawlike even though they contain individual names because, as he puts it (p. 59), "The planets and their orbits are not required to be located in a fixed volume of space or a given interval of time." I think that it is true of geologic generalizations that the objects covered are not required to be associated with "the planet earth." The generalization will hold wherever certain, to be sure very specific, conditions obtain. In other words, it would be possible, in principle at least, to express every term, including "the planet earth," in universal terms and so eliminate essential reference to any particular object. The fact is, of course, that no one worries about essential reference to the earth, and need not worry so long as we practice our profession on earth.

A serious problem concerns suspected but unstated restriction of the temporal scope of geologic statements. Because this problem stands at the very core of any consideration of the uniformitarian principle, I shall discuss it in a separate section of this paper.

The Theory of Geology

Is there any justification whatever for speaking about a "theory" of geology? The answer to this question obviously hinges on another, namely, "What do we mean by theory?" In an attempt to answer the latter question I shall quote three philosophers of science on the subject.

Hempel (1958, p. 41) has this to say.

> For a fuller discussion of this point, it will be helpful to refer to the familiar distinction between two levels of scientific systematization: the level of *empirical generalization*, and the level of *theory formation*. The early stages in the development of a scientific discipline usually belong to the former level, which is characterized by the search for laws (of universal or statistical form) which establish connections among the directly observable aspects of the subject matter under study. The more advanced stages belong to the second level, where research is aimed at comprehensive laws, in terms of hypothetical entities, which will account for the uniformities established on the first level.

Nagel (1961, p. 83) recognizes the usefulness of a distinction between "theoretical laws" and what he calls "experimental laws," but calls attention to the difficulties which may arise in the attempt to label a particular law as one or the other. He points out, however, that,

> Perhaps the most striking single feature setting off experimental laws from
> theories is that each "descriptive" (i.e. nonlogical) constant term in the
> former, but in general not each such term in the latter, is associated with at
> least one overt procedure for predicating the term of some observationally
> identifiable trait when certain specified circumstances are realized. The
> procedure associated with a term in an experimental law thus fixes a definite,
> even if only partial, meaning for the term. In consequence, an experimental
> law, unlike a theoretical statement, invariably possesses a determinate
> empirical content which in principle can always be controlled by observa-
> tional evidence obtained by those procedures.

And finally Carnap (1956, p. 38), emphasizing the linguistic consequences
of the distinction made by Nagel and Hempel, states:

> In discussions on the methodology of science, it is customary and useful
> to divide the language of science into two parts, the observation language
> and the theoretical language. The observation language uses terms desig-
> nating observable properties and relations for the description of observable
> things or events. The theoretical language, on the other hand, contains
> terms which may refer to unobservable events, unobservable aspects or
> features of events, e.g., to microparticles like electrons or atoms, to the
> electromagnetic field or the gravitational field in physics, to drives and
> potentials of various kinds in psychology, etc.

We may now proceed to examine geology with these "theoretical" characteristics in mind. The claim has been repeatedly made that geology was in the
past, and to some extent remains today, "descriptive." For example, Leet and
Judson (1954, p. ii) state, "Originally geology was essentially descriptive, a
branch of natural history. But by the middle of the 20th century, it had developed into a full-fledged physical science making liberal use of chemistry,
physics and mathematics and in turn contributing to their growth." Just what
is meant by "descriptive" in this sort of statement? It certainly cannot be taken
to mean that geology is today, or has been at any time during the last two
hundred years, wholly, or even largely, concerned with the mere reporting of
observations. The very fact that during this period geologists have remained
historical in their point of view belies any such contention. The formulation
of historical statements requires inferential procedures that clearly go beyond
a mere "description."

The feature that has apparently been recognized by those who characterize
geology as descriptive, and indeed the feature which we can all recognize, is
that most geologic terms are either framed in the observation language or can
be completely eliminated from any geologically significant statement in favor

of terms that are so framed. This is simply to say that most geologic terms are not theoretical. Even Steno's four great "axioms" may be regarded as "observational" rather than "theoretical."

The abundance of historical terms in geology may give rise to some confusion when an attempt is made to distinguish between observation terms and theoretical terms. Historical terms involve some kind of historical inference to a past event or condition and consequently require for their definition reference to things which have not been observed by us. Consider, for example, the term "normal fault" which has been defined as a fault "in which the hanging wall has apparently gone down relative to the footwall" (Billings, 1954, p. 143). The label "theoretical" would probably be denied this term by most philosophers of science because the past event can be described in the observation language and could consequently, in *principle* at least, be observed.

The question then arises, are there *any* geologic terms which clearly qualify as theoretical? This is a difficult question because, as many authors have pointed out, the distinction between theoretical terms and observation terms is far from clear. There are certainly no geologic terms so abstract as the higher-level theoretical constructs of quantum mechanics, for example. On the other hand there are a number of geologic terms which almost certainly qualify as, what might be called, "lower-level theoretical terms," that is terms of relatively limited extension. "Geosyncline," it seems to me, is such a term. According to Kay (1951, p. 4) a geosyncline may be defined as "a surface of regional extent subsiding through a long time while contained sedimentary and volcanic rocks are accumulating; great thickness of these rocks is almost invariably the evidence of the subsidence, but not a necessary requisite. Geosynclines are prevalently linear, but nonlinear depressions can have properties that are essentially geosynclinal."

Another candidate for the title "theoretical term" is "graded stream." According to Mackin (1948, p. 471),

> A graded stream is one in which, over a period of years, slope is delicately adjusted to provide, with available discharge and with prevailing channel characteristics, just the velocity required for the transportation of the load supplied from the drainage basin. The graded stream is a system in equilibrium; its diagnostic characteristic is that any change in any of the controlling factors will cause a displacement of the equilibrium in a direction that will absorb the effect of the change.

If I am correct in regarding these terms as theoretical, we might expect that some difficulties would arise if an attempt were made to define these expressions in terms of observables. I do not, however, feel inclined or qualified to go into the problem of "rules of correspondence" at this point.

What is the function of theoretical terms in a scientific system? The answer to this question was given, I think, in the passage from Hempel (1958, p. 41) quoted earlier, and in the words of Nagel (1961, pp. 88–89) when he says,

An experimental law is, without exception, formulated in a single statement; a theory is, almost without exception, a system of several related statements. But this obvious difference is only an indication of something more impressive and significant: the greater generality of theories and their relatively more inclusive explanatory power.

The general statements which contain the terms "geosyncline" and "graded stream" have, relative to other geologic statements, great generality and quite clearly fulfill the function which theoretical terms are designed to fill, that is, they establish some considerable "explanatory and predictive order among the bewildering complex 'data' of our experience, the phenomena that can be directly observed by us." (Hempel, 1958, p. 41)

One of the most striking features of scientific systems with a highly developed theoretical structure is the degree to which it is possible to make logical connections between the various general statements contained in the system. A given general statement may, in combination with other general statements or even with singular statements, serve as the basis for the deductive derivation of other general statements, or itself be derivable from other generalizations in the same way. It is this feature which provides empirical systems with their systemicity. The importance of system is indicated by Braithwaite (1953, pp. 301–302), who holds that a hypothesis is to be considered "lawlike" only on the condition that it "either occurs in an established scientific deductive system as a higher-level hypothesis containing theoretical concepts or that it occurs in an established scientific deductive system as a deduction from higher-level hypotheses which are supported by empirical evidence which is not direct evidence for itself."

As Braithwaite suggests, in the case of a generalization (G) which is deductively related to other generalizations, it is possible to distinguish between indirect and direct supporting evidence for it. Any empirical evidence which supports a generalization which is deductively related to G will count as indirect evidence in support of G. Nagel (1961, p. 66) emphasizes the importance of indirect evidence in the statement, "Indeed, there is often a strong disinclination to call a universal conditional L a 'law of nature,' despite the fact that it satisfies the various conditions already discussed, if the only available evidence for L is direct evidence."

How much systematization is there in the body of geologic knowledge? If we consider geologic generalizations, that is, general statements containing only special geologic terms, we are immediately struck with how little systematization obtains. There is some, of course, and it is usually provided in terms of such unifying concepts as "graded stream" and "geosyncline." This low-degree systematization is not surprising, for, as every elementary geology text insists, geology is not a discipline unto itself. We have only to introduce into our system the generalizations and laws of physical-chemical theory and the logical connections within the branches and between the branches of geology become more impressive. It may still be a matter of contention among geologists as to whether every geologic generalization has been, or in principle could be, incorporated into a theoretical system in terms of physical-chemical laws. If a geologic generalization is truly independent, however, no matter how useful it may be, its status will suffer because no indirect evidence can be presented to support it, and we are likely to speak of it as "merely" an empirical generalization.

The question is not whether geology is chemistry and physics, but whether or not geologists will utilize physical-chemical theory with all its admitted imperfections and all its immense power. The question has been answered. Almost all geologists proceed as if every geologic statement either has now, or eventually will have, its roots in physical-chemical theory. Geologic theory is modified to accommodate physical-chemical theory and never conversely. Furthermore, this confidence in physics and chemistry is not a unique feature of twentieth-century geology, for Hutton (1795, pp. 31–32) said:

> It must be evident, that nothing but the most general acquaintance with the laws of acting substances, and with those of bodies changing by the powers of nature, can enable us to set about this undertaking with any reasonable prospect of success; and here the science of Chemistry must be brought particularly to our aid; for this science, having for its object the changes produced upon the sensible qualities, as they are called, of bodies, by its means we may be enabled to judge of that which is possible according to the laws of nature, and of that which, in like manner, we must consider as impossible.

Certainly no consistent, economical, complete deductive system of geology exists, but I think that we can detect a suggestion of such a system. In this system the higher-level universals, or postulates, which serve as the basis for the deductive derivation of other generalizations and of singular statements of the system are exactly those universals which serve this purpose in physics and chemistry. The theory of geology is, according to this view, the theory of physics and chemistry. The geologist, however, unlike the chemist and the physicist, regards this theory as an instrument of historical inference.

The generalizations containing the theoretical terms "geosyncline" and "graded stream" are not regarded as "fundamental laws of nature" nor as postulates of a theory of geology. Geologists are committed to the view that generalizations containing these terms can be derived from higher-level generalizations which belong to physics. Thus Leopold and Langbein (1962, p. A 11) state with reference to the graded-stream state, "A contribution made by the entropy concept is that the 'equilibrium profile' of the graded river is the profile of maximum probability and the one in which entropy is equally distributed, constituting a kind of isentropic curve."

The activity of attempting to relate geologic generalizations to physical-chemical theory is not a game played by geologists for its own sake, nor is it played solely for the sake of increasing our confidence in these generalizations by providing indirect supporting evidence for them. It is the hope of those engaged in this activity, which I am tempted to call "theoretical geology," that putting a geologic generalization into a theoretical setting will allow a more precise and rigorous formulation of it, and thus may increase its utility. This consideration is undoubtedly behind Leopold and Langbein's statement (1962, p. A 1), "The present paper is an attempt to apply another law of physics to the subject for the purpose of obtaining some additional insight into energy distributions and their relation to changes of land forms in space and time."

A major objection to the view that geology is "descriptive" and thus in some sense not "mature" is that the scope of geologic knowledge and theory is in no sense now, nor has it ever been, exhausted by what can be framed in special geologic terms and in terms of the common language alone. The laws which provide for much of the higher-level systematization in geology are perhaps not immediately associated with a theory of geology because they are laws without particular geologic reference which are ordinarily recognized as belonging to the theory of chemistry and physics. To consider the science of geology as composed of just those statements containing particular geologic references amounts to a wholly artificial decapitation of a rather highly organized theoretical structure. An arbitrary distinction among physical, chemical, and geologic terms is not significant here. What is significant is the role played by laws and terms, no matter what their origin or what we may choose to call them, in the theory of geology. Modern geology assumes *all* of contemporary physical-chemical theory and presents on the basis of this assumption a high degree of logical integration.

It has been suggested, for example by Leet and Judson (1954, p. ii) in the statement quoted above, that geology not only draws upon physical-chemical theory but may contribute to this theory. In some sense, at least, this is true since geologic problems may serve to stimulate investigations which are primarily physical or chemical in nature, particularly if the problems arise in such fields as geochemistry, geophysics, and crystallography in which the borderline between geology and the rest of physical science is difficult to draw. Traditionally, however, geologists have not tampered with nongeologic theory in any very direct way. The physical-chemical theory of their time is a standard which tends to be accepted by each generation of geologists.

The Origin of Geologic Generalizations

It has often been said that geology is "inductive." It may be that, in some cases at least, the application of this label is meant to convey the fact that the explanations proposed by geologists are probabilistic rather than deductive. Usually, however, I think that the term "inductive" when applied to geology is meant to convey that the generalizations of geology are to be regarded as inductive generalizations. If we agree that most geologic generalizations are not theoretical, then this latter view of the inductive nature of geology is entirely plausible since, as Nagel (1961, p. 85) has pointed out, "An immediate corollary to the difference between experimental laws and theories just discussed is that while the former could, in principle, be proposed and asserted as inductive generalizations based on relations found to hold in observed data, this can never be the case for the latter." The problem of the process by which theoretical laws are formulated is far beyond the scope of this paper.

Although the usual procedure in geology is to explain a generalization which has been formulated inductively in terms of higher-level generalizations, using the laws of chemistry and physics, it is possible to start with these higher-level generalizations and deduce from them generalizations of geologic significance and utility. We thus speak of the deduction of the mineralogical phase rule from the phase rule of Gibbs (see, for example, Turner, 1948, p. 45). It is my belief that the most dramatic advances in geologic theory are to be expected from this deductive method.

The Uniformitarian Principle

There is widespread agreement among geologists that some special principle of uniformity is a fundamental ingredient of all geologic inference. Longwell and Flint (1955, p. 385) go so far as to say that, "The whole mental process involved in this reconstruction of an ancient history is based on that cornerstone of geologic philosophy, the principle of uniformitarianism, probably the greatest single contribution geologists have made to scientific thought." Despite this general agreement about the importance of the principle, geologists hold widely divergent views as to its meaning. So divergent are these views, in fact, that one is led to conclude that there has been little or no resolution of the problems which gave rise to the famous controversies between the "uniformitarians" and the "catastrophists" in the nineteenth century. Though the problems have not been solved, the controversy has subsided. A number of accounts of the history of the uniformitarian principle are available, including an excellent recent one by Hooykaas (1959).

There are two principal problems concerning the concept of uniformity. The first problem concerns the grounds upon which the assertion of uniformity rests. The second problem concerns the precise nature of the restriction which it imposes.

As to the grounds upon which the assertion of uniformity rests, it would be difficult, if not impossible, to contend that any meaningful empirical support can be presented for the view that "geologic process" in the past was in any way like this process in the present, simply because statements about process must be tested in terms of statements about particulars and no observation of past particulars can be made. We do, of course, formulate statements about particular past conditions. These statements are not supported by direct observations, however, but rather are supported by inferences in which some assumption of uniformity is implicit. *In terms of the way a geologist operates, there is no past until after the assumption of uniformity has been made.* To make statements about the past without some initial assumption of uniformity amounts, in effect, to allowing any statement at all to be made about the past. Geologists, as I have suggested earlier, are primarily concerned with deriving and testing singular statements about the past. The uniformitarian principle represents, among other things, a restriction placed upon the statements that may be admitted to a geologic argument, initially at the level of primary historical inference. Once the assumption of uniformity has been made for the purposes of primary historical inference, then it may be possible to "demonstrate" some uniformity or, for that matter, depending upon how strictly the principle is applied in the first place, some lack of uniformity. The essential point is that the assumption of uniformity must precede the demonstration of uniformity and not vice versa. In principle, at least, it would be possible to make at the outset some assumptions about particular conditions at some time in the past and on the basis of these assumptions "test" whether some law held at that time. Geologists have chosen to do the opposite, however, by making some assumptions about the uniformity of the relationships expressed in a law and on this basis to derive and test some singular statements about the past.

The view that the uniformity of "nature" or of "geologic process" represents an *assumption* that is made in order to allow geologists to proceed with the business of historical inference is a very old one. In Hutton (1788, p. 301–302), for example, we find this view expressed in the statement, "We have been representing the system of this earth as proceeding with a certain regularity, which is not perhaps in nature, but which is necessary for our clear conception of the system of nature." And Lyell (in a letter to Whewell, 1837, from "Life, Letters and Journals," 1881, Vol. II, p. 3) expresses a similar view when he states,

> The former intensity of the same or other terrestrial forces may be true; I never denied its possibility; but it is conjectural. I complained that in at-tempting to explain geological phenomena, the bias has always been on the

wrong side; there has always been a disposition to reason *a priori* on the extraordinary violence and suddenness of changes, both in the inorganic crust of the earth, and in organic types, instead of attempting strenuously to frame theories in accordance with the ordinary operations of nature.

The uniformitarian principle is not usually formulated as an *assumption* by contemporary geologists.

If the uniformitarian principle is to be regarded as a methodological device rather than an empirical generalization, a reasonable step toward a solution of the problems surrounding the principle would be an attempt to explicate it. "What statements in the theory of geology shall be regarded as untimebound"? is a question which might be asked in connection with such an attempt.

It is plausible to regard every singular descriptive statement in geology as timebound, to some degree at least, simply because a principal aim of geologic endeavor is to "bind" singular descriptive statements temporally, which is another way of saying that a principal aim of geologic endeavor is to produce historical chronicle. Singular descriptive statements may apply to different times and different places, but it cannot be assumed that they apply to all times and to all places, and consequently their uniformity cannot be assumed for the purposes of inference.

There are few geologists who would disagree with this view regarding singular descriptive statements, and for this reason I may be accused of propounding the obvious. Before the accusation is made, however, let us consider a passage from Read (1957, p. 26).

> This difficulty confronting static metamorphism has been tackled by Daly, who meets it by relaxing the rigidity of the doctrine of uniformitarianism. He admits that, compared with its proposed potency in the Pre-Cambrian times, load metamorphism must have been of relatively little importance in later geological eras. To account for this, he assumes that the earth's thermal gradient was steeper during the formation of the Pre-Cambrian so that regional metamorphism under a moderate cover was possible. He considers that this speculation concerning a hotter surface to the earth is 'no more dangerous than the fashionable explanation of all, or nearly all, regional metamorphism by orogenic movements.' I agree that. . . [although] uniformitarianism suits the events of the 500 million years of geological history as recorded in the Cambrian and later fossiliferous rocks, it may quite likely not be so valid for the 2,000 million years of Pre-Cambrian time.

To suggest that the thermal gradient of the earth was steeper during the Precambrian than it is today is to make an assertion about particular conditions during the past. This assertion is perhaps not so soundly based as many others, but it has resulted from the kind of retrodictive inference that geologists frequently perform. To claim that this statement requires a relaxation of the doctrine of uniformitarianism is, in principle, equivalent to claiming that an assertion that the topography of Oklahoma during Permian time was different from what it is today requires a similar relaxation.

The statements that the geologist wishes to regard as untimebound are of general form. This is revealed by the fact that he speaks of uniformity of "cause" or "process" or "principle" or "law," concepts which are expressed in general statements. The whole problem of the strictness with which the uniformitarian assumption is to be applied revolves ultimately around the question of *which* of the many statements of general form in the theory of geology are to be regarded as being without temporal restriction.

Geologists usually speak of the problem of uniformitarianism as though it were a problem of whether or not the relationships expressed in scientific laws could be regarded as constant throughout geologic time. Is this really the problem? Are geologists bothered, for example, by the question of whether or not the relationship expressed in the equation $F = G \cdot m_1 m_2 / d^2$ can be regarded as independent of time? They may occasionally speculate about the "uniformity of nature," but such speculations do not enter into the conduct of geologic investigation in any significant way. Here again it is to the authority of physical-chemical theory that appeal is made. If an expression is untimebound in this theory, it is untimebound in the theory of geology, particularly if the expression is regarded as a "fundamental law." Furthermore, if a law should be formulated in which the expressed relationship were a function of the passage of historic time, and if this law should come to be regarded as a valid part of some physical or chemical theory, there would probably be no reluctance on the part of geologists to accept the law nor would the acceptance signal an abandonment of the uniformitarian principle. The view that it is "law" which is to be regarded as uniform has been suggested many times before, for example in the following statement from Moore (1958, p. 2): "As foundation, we accept the conclusion that nature's laws are unchanging."

Not only is the most general form of a fundamental law regarded as untimebound but so are substitution instances and other logical consequences of such a law. We should agree, for example, that at any time and place where two spherical masses of one pound each and of uniform density are held with their centers one foot apart, the force of attraction between them will be 3.18×10^{-11} pounds weight. We do not conclude from this, however, that the attraction between *any* two objects at *any time* is 3.18×10^{-11} pounds weight, for to do so would necessitate the assumption of the temporal uniformity of certain particular conditions. This particular attractive force is to be inferred only where the specified antecedent conditions actually obtain. That these particular conditions, or for that matter any particular conditions, did in fact obtain at a particular time and place is a matter for independent verification. The law does not "change," but different substitution instances of the law are applicable to different times and places. The immediate problem which the geologist faces is not one of uniformity, but one of determining which, if any, of the infinite number of substitution instances of a general law is applicable in a particular case.

Let us consider a geologic statement in which doubt about temporal extension is expressed. "Probably only time and the progress of future studies can tell whether we cling too tenaciously to the uniformitarian principle in our unwillingness to accept fully the rapid glacial fluctuations as evidenced by radiocarbon dating." (Horberg, 1955, p. 285) The author has suggested, has he not, that there was available a generalization concerning the rate of glacial fluctuation, perhaps supported by observations of extant glaciers, whose validity had become doubtful because of our greater confidence in another generalization. Isn't there something suspicious about a statement which is supposed to have some degree of temporal extension and which contains a reference to a particular rate or even to a limited range of rates? There are many physical laws in the form of equations which allow the calculation of a particular rate when particular values are substituted for variables. The unsubstituted form of a physical equation, however, contains no reference to a particular rate. Rate of glacial fluctuation does not remain constant throughout time any more than the force of attraction between objects remains constant throughout time. Rate of glacial advance and retreat is dependent upon a number of variables, among which are the topography, the thickness of the ice, and the temperature of the atmosphere. Unless specific values can be substituted for each of these variables a law of glacial movement cannot be meaningfully applied at all, and could certainly not be called upon to serve as the basis for the assertion that the rate of glacial movement had some uniformity in geologic time. Horberg's problem did not involve a question of the "uniformity of nature" but rather it involved a question of whether or not he was in a position to determine particular values for each of the variables upon which rate of glacial movement might be presumed to be dependent. No explication of the concept of "the uniformity of nature" nor "universal causation" could have served as a basis for the solution of this problem.

Another problem presents itself at this point. Is there a law of glacial movement which has been formulated with sufficient precision to allow us to say what the pertinent variables are, let alone determine specific values for them? The answer would have to be that there is not. What is available is an imprecisely formulated generalization, probably normic in form, which may serve as the basis for a variety of inferences but cannot serve as a basis for a calculation of the rate of glacial advance and retreat during a particular interval of time. The temporal universality of imprecisely formulated probabilistic and normic generalizations will always be suspect simply because it is characteristic of such statements that they contain what must be regarded as hidden references to particulars. We are able to increase our confidence in the temporal universality of a generalization by formulating it with greater precision. It must be borne in mind, however, that progress in geology has depended upon the willingness of geologists to assume the temporal uniformity of a great variety of imprecisely formulated generalizations.

There is a long-standing philosophical problem concerning the uniformity of nature. It has been discussed at great length in the past and it will be discussed in the future. This problem is everybody's problem, not a special problem for geologists. The special problem for geologists concerns first the availability of appropriate laws and second the applicability of laws to particular situations. In an attempt to solve the problem, many geologists are engaged in work that is directed toward the goal of increasing the precision with which geologic generalizations are formulated. They proceed by observing in the field, experimenting in the laboratory and, increasingly, by paper and pencil operations within a theoretical framework. The latter procedure may turn out to be the most satisfying of all because never are we so confident in the precision of a law as when it has been made a part of some theory.

The precise formulation of geologic generalizations cannot be expected to lead to an immediate solution of all the problems facing the contemporary geologist. The principal use to which geologic generalizations are put is as a basis for explanatory inferences which allow the derivation and testing of singular statements about the past. A generalization cannot be used in this way unless specific values can be substituted for most of the variables contained in it. A specific value which is substituted for a variable in a generalization employed in a retrodictive inference must have been determined on the basis of another retrodictive inference which is itself dependent upon some generalization. The necessary interdependence of the bewildering variety of geologic retrodictive inferences upon one another seems, at times, to result in a piling of uncertainty upon uncertainty. Remarkably, however, confidence in geologic statements about the past as reliable descriptions of particular conditions, in particular places, at particular times, is high. The basis of this confidence is that not only are retrodictive inferences to a large extent dependent upon one another, but that they serve as the only means of verification of one another. Each statement about the past is tested against other statements about the past. Laboriously we build the chronicle, selecting, eliminating, and modifying as we proceed, bringing to bear, in addition to an immensely complicated inferential apparatus, our trained judgment.

REFERENCES CITED

BILLINGS, M. P., 1954, Structural geology: New York, Prentice-Hall, 514 pp.

BRAITHWAITE, R. B., 1953, Scientific explanation: New York, Cambridge Univ. Press, 375 pp.

BUCHER, W. H., 1933, The deformation of the earth's crust; an inductive approach to the problems of diastrophism: Princeton, Princeton Univ. Press, 518 pp.

BUNGE, M., 1961, Kinds and criteria of scientific laws: Phil. Sci., vol. 28, pp. 260–281.

CARNAP, R., 1956, The methodological character of theoretical concepts, p. 38–76 *in* H. Feigl and M. Scriven, eds., Minnesota Studies in the Philosophy of Science, vol. 1. The foundations of science and the concepts of psychology and psychoanalysis: Minneapolis, Univ. Minnesota Press, 346 pp.

DUNBAR, C. O., and RODGERS, J., 1957, Principles of stratigraphy: New York, John Wiley, 356 pp.

FRIEDMAN, G. M., 1961, Distinction between dune, beach, and river sands from their textural characteristics: J. Sediment. Petrology, vol. 31, pp. 514–529.

HEMPEL, C. G., 1958, The theoretician's dilemma; a study in the logic of theory construction, pp. 37–98 *in* H. Feigl, M. Scriven, and G. Maxwell, eds., Minnesota Studies in the Philosophy of Science, vol. 2. Concepts, theories, and the mind-body problem: Minneapolis, Univ. Minnesota Press, 553 pp.

———— and OPPENHEIM, P., 1948, Studies in the logic of explanation: Phil. Sci., vol. 15, pp. 135–175.

HOOYKAAS, R., 1959, Natural law and divine miracle: Leiden, E. J. Brill, 237 pp.

HORBERG, L., 1955, Radiocarbon dates and Pleistocene chronological problems in the Mississippi Valley region: J. Geol., vol. 63, pp. 278–286.

HUTTON, JAMES, 1788, Theory of the earth: Roy. Soc. Edinburgh, Tr., vol. 1, pp. 209–304.

————, 1795, Theory of the earth with proofs and illustrations, vol. I: Edinburgh, Cadell, Junior and Davies, 620 pp.

KAY, M., 1951, North American geosynclines: Geol. Soc. Am., Mem. 48, 143 pp.

KITTS, D. B., 1963, Historical explanation in geology: J. Geol., vol. 71, pp. 297–313.

LEET, L. D., and JUDSON, S., 1954, Physical geology: New York, Prentice-Hall, 466 pp.

LEOPOLD, L. B., and LANGBEIN, W. B., 1962, The concept of entropy in landscape evolution: U. S. Geol. Survey, Prof. Paper 500-A, pp. A1–A20.

LONGWELL, C. R., and FLINT, R. F., 1955, Introduction to physical geology: New York, John Wiley, 432 pp.

LYELL, CHARLES, 1881, Life, letters and journals of Sir Charles Lyell *Bart*, Mrs. Lyell, ed.: London, John Murray, 489 pp.

MACKIN, J. H., 1938, The origin of Appalachian drainage—a reply: Am. J. Sci., vol. 236, pp. 27–53.

————, 1948, Concept of the graded river: Geol. Soc. Am., B., vol. 59, pp. 463–512.

MOORE, R. C., 1958, Introduction to historical geology, 2nd ed.: New York, McGraw-Hill, 656 pp.

NAGEL, E., 1961, The structure of science: New York and Burlingame; Harcourt, Brace, and World, 618 pp.

READ, H. H., 1957, The granite controversy: New York, Interscience publishers, 430 pp.

SCRIVEN, M., 1959, Truisms as the grounds for historical explanations, pp. 443–475 *in* P. Gardiner, ed., Theories of history: Glencoe, Illinois, The Free Press, 549 pp.

TURNER, F. J., 1948, Mineralogical and structural evolution of the metamorphic rocks: Geol. Soc. Am., Mem. 30, 342 pp.

VON ENGELN, O. D., 1942, Geomorphology: New York, Macmillan, 655 pp.

————, and CASTER, K. E., 1952, Geology: New York, McGraw-Hill, 730 pp.

WELLER, J. M., 1960, Stratigraphic principles and practice: New York, Harper, 725 pp.

V. E. McKELVEY

U. S. Geological Survey

Geology As the Study of Complex Natural Experiments[1]

Geology offers almost unique opportunity to observe the results of processes that not only involve interplay of more variables and larger masses than can be handled in the laboratory, but that also extend over much greater periods of time and hence reveal the effects of reactions too slow to observe under ordinary conditions. Other natural sciences, of course, offer similar opportunities to observe the interplay of many variables on a grand scale, but none save astronomy observes the complete record and results of "natural experiments" that have required millions or billions of years to complete.

Because it observes the results of complex natural experiments conducted on a large scale in both time and space, geology is an exploratory science that provides opportunity to observe phenomena and processes not predictable on the basis of knowledge and theory acquired and developed through the laboratory sciences alone. In the past, geology has therefore guided the concepts and set limits to the scope of the laboratory sciences, and it will continue to do so in the future. Beyond this, geology provides means of solving a wide variety of problems too complex to be attacked by artificial experiments.

Like artificial experiments, the experiments of nature are of little value unless their results are carefully observed and viewed through the frame of searching question and imaginative hypothesis. However, approached in this manner, they have led to the discovery of new phenomena and to the formulation of principles that might not have been developed otherwise. A few examples will illustrate this point.

---

[1] In recent years, I have discussed the significance of geology as an exploratory and problem-solving science with a number of friends whose ideas I am sure are reflected in this essay. I wish especially to acknowledge stimulating discussions on the subject with J. R. Balsley, W. H. Bradley, R. M. Garrels, R. A. Gulbrandsen, and H. L. James, and to thank for similar stimulation as well as specific suggestions on this manuscript C. A. Anderson, Michael Fleischer, E. D. Jackson and E. M. Shoemaker.

Discovery of the Nonpredictable

Observations of natural phenomena lie at the root of all science, and most of these phenomena were at some stage not predictable on the basis of accumulated human knowledge and theory. Perhaps more than other realms accessible to human observation, the earth has been the source of the discovery of phenomena that have stimulated scientific inquiry or posed challenging problems which led eventually to the principles forming the web of physical science. Thus observations of minerals posed many of the problems that stimulated the growth of chemistry, crystal chemistry, crystallography, and optics; observations of the properties of uranium minerals and compounds formed the base of both radiochemistry and nuclear physics; and the discovery of the natural phenomena of fluorescence, luminescence, and magnetism played similar roles in other branches of physics. At the time these various phenomena were observed they could not have been predicted from available knowledge and theory, and indeed many of them would be unpredictable even today if they were not known to exist in nature.

There would not be much point here in calling attention to the study of the earth, its processes, and history as a source of discovery of phenomena stimulating general science, if this form of contribution were a thing of the past. The fact is, however, that geology is still playing an important role as an exploratory science and has abundant opportunity to do so in the future. Some of these discoveries may come in the form of single observations—for example, T. F. W. Barth's and E. Posnjak's discovery of the inverse structure of the spinels, which contributed significantly to the theory and development of semiconductors; and K. J. Murata's discovery that the fluorescence of natural halite and calcite, previously ascribed to the presence of manganese, actually occurs only when two activating elements, lead and manganese, are present, a phenomenon that led to the synthesis of many new fluorescent compounds. Some of the most significant discoveries, however, are likely to be of complex phenomena, including those of a secular nature, whose recognition depends on the collection and synthesis of many and perhaps diverse data. The concepts of biologic evolution, folded geosynclines, and periodic reversal in polarity of the earth's field are examples of secular processes discovered through the synthesis and analysis of many diverse geologic observations.

The process of piecing together and analyzing isolated geologic observations is notoriously difficult and slow, not only because of the number and diversity of the phenomena involved but also because of their scale. Thousands of square miles may have to be mapped, scores of stratigraphic sections measured and correlated, volumes of data accumulated on rock properties, and many hypotheses tested and discarded before even a valid empirical relation among such data can be formulated.

The fable of the blind men and the elephant—the incorrect conclusions reached by observers whose vision is limited compared to the breadth and complexity of the problem—has sometimes been cited to ridicule the stumbling operation of inductive reasoning. This tale, however, carries a meaning of far deeper significance than is generally recognized in the telling, namely, that it is only by patient exploration that an elephant—or a folded geosyncline—can be discovered. Once the existence of an elephant has been established, many of its other characteristics can be deduced, but accumulated scientific theory is not yet and may never be adequate to predict its existence in the first place.

What are some of the areas in which geologic elephants are likely to be discovered in the future? Because I am talking about phenomena that are not predictable, I can hardly be expected to be very specific, but a few examples of some of the poorly explored areas that may yield the unexpected are in order. Surely the subject of crustal structure and composition is one such promising field; the relation between local structure, thickness, and composition of rocks of the upper crust, and similar properties in the lower crust and upper mantle are as yet poorly known and can be expected to yield relationships not imagined now. In stratigraphy and paleontology, data adequate to permit a comprehensive view of the paleogeographic, paleoclimatic, paleoecologic, and paleotectonic records are just now being synthesized, and their analysis very likely will disclose relations not now anticipated: between rate and direction of biologic evolution and environmental controls, between geologic history and secular changes (perhaps related to unidirectional or evolutionary changes in the composition of the ocean and the atmosphere) in the composition of sedimentary rocks, and between tectonic history and climatic changes. Data on the abundance of the elements, especially the minor ones, and on the mass of major rock units in the earth's crust are as yet so sparse and poorly integrated that we can still expect surprises on the subject of the composition of the earth's crust and its major components. Generally speaking, the data being accumulated on rock structure—the wavelength and amplitude of folds; the distribution, orientation, and frequency of fractures, the magnitude of the displacements along them, and the orientation of minerals within them—have not been synthesized and analyzed with respect to such factors as areal magnitude, thickness, and composition of the deformed units, depth of burial or load, and duration of the deforming forces. Finally, integration of knowledge in all these areas will be necessary to test such concepts as continental drift and an expanding or shrinking earth. No doubt other elephants will be discovered in the process.

Use of Natural Experiments in Solving Complex Problems

In using nature's completed experiments to solve problems involving such a large number of variables, large mass, or long period of time that they cannot be attacked satisfactorily in the laboratory, we begin with the problem or question and observe results of experiments already performed. What minerals will precipitate from a complex silicate melt, given time for slow reactions to reach equilibrium? Igneous differentiates and their ores will yield the answer in a detail unobtainable otherwise. Can specific minerals ordinarily formed at high temperatures form at low temperatures, given time? Their presence or absence as authigenic minerals in sedimentary rocks may suggest the answer (and incidentally Charles Milton's work on authigenic minerals formed in saline deposits has shown that the list not only includes such well-known forms as feldspar but also many other high-temperature forms, such as riebeckite and leucosphenite). What diadochous substitutions, including doubly compensated ones, can occur in a given compound? Analysis of mineral specimens from a variety of geologic environments is likely to yield a more comprehensive answer than artificial experiments do. What are the relative solubilities of refractory minerals in dilute aqueous solutions? Their behavior during weathering will give valuable qualitative data, and if analyzed with regard to the characteristics of soil solutions, runoff, and mean annual temperature, it may be possible to obtain more quantitative answers. To what extent will brittle minerals deform plastically, and under what physical conditions? Natural experiments provide a parameter—time—that cannot be evaluated in the laboratory.

The usefulness of natural experiments in problem solving depends, of course, on the degree to which the conditions of the experiment can be established, and this may require use of both field and laboratory data. For example, the relative conditions under which syngenetic minerals are deposited from seawater can be established from lithofacies analysis of beds known from geologic evidence to have been synchronously deposited. If physical and chemical data are available for a few of the minerals, however, the conditions under which the others have been deposited may be interpolated. Using this approach, H. L. James demonstrated from stratigraphic analysis that iron sulfides, iron silicates, iron carbonate, and the iron oxides, hematite and (most surprising, for it is ordinarily thought of as a high-temperature mineral) magnetite, are synchronously deposited in a regular lateral sequence reflecting progressive change in redox potential and pH. And R. P. Sheldon, my co-worker in the study of the phosphorite family of sediments, defined rather closely, from lithofacies analysis and existing physical and chemical data, the physical and chemical conditions in the Phosphoria sea, in which black shale, phosphorite, chert, carbonates, redbeds and salines were deposited in a laterally changing environment ranging from the deeper part of the shelf to coastal lagoons.

The work of E. M. Shoemaker and others on meteorite craters illustrates the deliberate use of geology in solving problems of multidisciplinary interest. Measurements of the depth and radius of craters formed artificially by chemical and nuclear explosives and the radius of mixing due to shock show a consistent relation to yield, and similar features in meteorite craters appear to obey the same scaling laws. The dimensions and other features of natural meteorite craters are equivalent to those of craters formed by the impact of explosions in the range of tens or even hundreds of megatons. Study of their structure and other features, therefore, yields data valuable in predicting the effects of nuclear explosives that are more powerful than those tested artificially in the past, as well as the effects of nuclear explosions in rock types, such as granite and limestone, in which nuclear devices have not yet been tested. Artificial tests thus far have been limited to a few rock types, and provide little basis for predicting the effects of natural structures, such as joints, on crater shape. A natural experiment, Meteor Crater, Arizona, already completed in jointed limestone, however, shows that joints do influence crater shape, for the outline of Meteor Crater is nearly square and the diagonals of the square correspond to the direction of the two principal joint systems. It is interesting to note also that the discoveries of the high-pressure silica polymorphs, coesite and stishovite, by E. C. T. Chao and co-workers, in impactites associated with meteorite craters demonstrated for the first time that these high-pressure phase changes could be produced by shock pressure of extremely short duration.

The power of laboratory experiments stems in large part not only from the fact that they can be closely controlled, but also that they can be repeated to isolate and measure the effect of a single variable. This advantage is not wholly lost in natural experiments, however, for similar experiments may have taken place under differing circumstances that bring to light the effects of various factors. For example, according to E. D. Jackson (personal communication, 1963), the composition of the original magmatic liquid in the Precambrian Stillwater complex of Montana and the still liquid lava lake at Kilauea Iki, Hawaii, is essentially the same, so that differences in their crystallization history and products can be related to their size and position in the crust.

Summary

Geology, like other sciences, has many economic or practical objectives that in themselves more than justify its pursuit and support. The knowledge and principles it develops enable us to use more fully the land, water, mineral, and energy resources of our physical environment—and if it yielded no other dividends it would, for these reasons alone, deserve high emphasis among scientific endeavors in the modern world. The opportunities it provides, however, for observing the results of natural experiments make it important also as one of the prime exploratory and analytical fields of general science, capable not only of uncovering challenging problems but also of solving many difficult and complex ones that are beyond the reach of artificial experiments.

REFERENCES CITED

BARTH, T. F. W., and POSNJAK, E., 1931, The spinel structure: an example of variate atom equipoints: J. Washington Acad. Sci., vol. 21, pp. 255–258.

CHAO, E. C. T., FAHEY, J. J., and LITTLER, J., 1962, Stishovite, SiO_2, a very high pressure new mineral from Meteor Crater, Arizona: J. Geophys. Res., vol. 67, pp. 419–421.

———, SHOEMAKER, E. M., and MADSEN, B. M., 1960, First natural occurrence of coesite: Science, vol. 132, pp. 220–222.

JAMES, H. L., 1954, Sedimentary facies of iron-formation: Econ. Geol., vol. 49, pp. 235–293.

MILTON, CHARLES, 1957, Authigenic minerals of the Green River formation of the Uinta Basin, Utah: Intermountain Assoc. Petroleum Geol., 8th Ann. Field Conf., pp. 136–143.

MURATA, K. J., and SMITH, R. L., 1946, Manganese and lead as coactivators of red fluorescence in halite: Am. Mineralogist, vol. 31, pp. 527–538.

SHELDON, R. P., in press, Physical stratigraphy and mineral resources of Permian rocks in western Wyoming: U. S. Geol. Survey, Prof. Paper 313-B.

SHOEMAKER, E. M., 1960, Brecciation and mixing of rock by strong shock: U. S. Geol. Survey, Prof. Paper 400-B, pp. 423–425.

———, 1960, Penetration mechanics of high velocity meteorites illustrated by Meteor Crater, Arizona: Internat. Geol. Cong., 21st, Copenhagen, 1960, pt. 18, sec. 18, Pr., pp. 418–434.

A. O. WOODFORD

Pomona College

Correlation by Fossils

The presence of successive and dissimilar fossil faunas in the stratified rocks of northwestern Europe was demonstrated by William Smith and his contemporaries as early as 1815. Some forty-five years later, Darwin convinced the scientific community that evolution of stratigraphically lower faunas into higher ones is more probable than alternating creations and extinctions. Soon after the "Origin of Species" appeared, however, Thomas Henry Huxley (1862, 1870) challenged the assumption, already well established in his time, that two widely separated sedimentary rock masses containing closely similar faunas or floras must have been deposited at the same time. He asked for a sharp distinction between *homotaxis* (identical or similar successions of faunas or floras) and the kind of correlation that implies *synchronism* (identical age for each correlated faunal or floral pair). Huxley (1862, p. xlvi) asserted that "a Devonian fauna and flora in the British Islands may have been contemporaneous with Silurian life in North America, and with a Carboniferous fauna and flora in Africa."

I have no intention of championing this heresy, but I do intend to follow Huxley's logic, working from homotaxis to possible time correlation, without making the assumption that homotaxis necessarily implies synchronism.

Guide Fossils

Correlation by fossils involves two problems. First we must determine the changes in the successive fossil faunas at one locality; and second, we must learn how to use the faunal changes in making correlations from one local column to another, carefully distinguishing between time and facies correlations. Even while working on a single column it is desirable to keep two objectives in mind. Paleontologically, we use our collections of fossil faunas— relatively small and probably biased samples of the original, much larger, biological populations—as bases for unscrambling the ecological facies and evolutionary sequences of the animals. Stratigraphically, we subdivide the

75

column by use of differences between the species at different levels. Note that the evolutionary and the stratigraphic values of species require emphasis on exactly opposite aspects of the observations. For evolution we emphasize similarities between the species at successive levels, and for correlation we emphasize differences.

Subdivision of the column depends on how fossiliferous the rocks are and how clearly the succession is exposed. If the local succession is well exposed and the faunas are rich, we must choose between two possible methods of work: (1) statistical study of a large collection of each fauna (or a large sample of the ammonites or brachiopods or other selected group), a procedure that in the past has usually seemed excessively time-consuming, or (2) use of selected guide species (or genera), the customary procedure. With computers at hand to make the calculations, statistical methods are coming into vogue, but for any general discussion it is still necessary to stick to guide fossils.

The ideal set of guides would belong to a group that evolved rapidly, occurs abundantly in all kinds of stratified rocks, and is worldwide in distribution. The fossils that approach this ideal most closely appear to be the Ordovician-Silurian graptolites, the Upper Paleozoic fusuline foraminifera, the Upper Paleozoic goniatitic ammonoids, the ammonites of the three Mesozoic systems, and a few Cretaceous and Tertiary planktonic foraminifera, and still smaller nannoplankton. The ammonites appear to be the best of the lot. Among the Mesozoic systems, the Jurassic includes, in northwestern Europe, the most usefully fossiliferous sequence, with excellent preservation and the most favorable set of well-studied exposures. Almost every aspect of stratigraphic subdivision by the use of guide fossils can be illustrated from the Jurassic System, in Europe and elsewhere.

Lower and Middle Jurassic Zones of Northwestern Europe

Subdivision of Jurassic. The Jurassic has been divided and subdivided into stages, substages, zones, and subzones. We shall take the stratigraphic zone as our starting point. It is true that zones were not the first divisions of the Jurassic to be invented. Historically, several of William Smith's formations—Lias, Blue Marl, Under Oolyte, Great Oolyte, Forest Marble, Cornbrash Limestone, Kelloways Stone, Clunch Clay, Coral Rag, Oak Tree Clay, Portland Rock, and Purbeck Stone—were put together to form the Jurassic System. Then Alcide d'Orbigny (1842–1851; summary, pp. 600–623) reversed the process and divided most of the Jurassic into 10 paleontologically defined stages, using ammonites primarily. Finally, the stages were subdivided into zones by d'Orbigny and others, notably A. Oppel of Germany (1856–58). Current usage for the Lower and Middle Jurassic is shown in Table 1 on pp. 78–79.

Zones.[1] A zone is made up of the stratified rocks deposited with a particular assemblage of fossils. This definition is vague and very nearly begs the vital time question, but it has nevertheless proved fairly easy to use. We shall come back later to the possible time significance of a zone.

The implications of the zonal concept are grasped most readily in connection with an idealized example. First, we study in detail a sequence of beds at one location, *A*. We study and name the fossils contained therein, emphasizing the ammonites in the Jurassic. Almost always the ammonite succession is discontinuous; the section yields several distinct successive faunas. We choose one species in each fauna as a special guide or index and use its name to label the fauna. The limits of the faunal ranges do not necessarily coincide with rock boundaries.

We repeat the process at a second exposure, *B*. The rock succession is different, but the faunal succession at *B* has elements in common with that at *A*. In particular, some of the faunal zones established at *A* can be recognized at *B*, even though others cannot. The reverse may also be true. In this manner we compare faunal successions in ever widening geographical extent. We find that some of our faunas at *A* can be identified over distances of hundreds of miles while others are very local. By compilation of successive faunas of suitably wide extent we can construct a table of standard zones for a particular area, such as northwestern Europe. The names of the standard zones are derived from faunal index species, used to designate stratigraphical sets of beds, not paleontological entities. A particular zone is referred to as the "Zone of *Parkinsonia parkinsoni*" or merely "Parkinsoni Zone" (No. 30 in Table 1).

Now, returning to our starting point *A*, we see that some of our original local zones at that place have become standard zones. Others, that proved to be more or less local in extent, are usually attached to one or another of the standard zones, as subzones. Moreover, we may find that not all of the standard zones are represented at *A*. That is, the section at *A* is not paleontologically complete; it contains paleontological lacunas. Finally, of the nonfossiliferous beds between zones we can say nothing.

Note that (a) for the recognition of a zone, we need both rock and fossils; (b) a zone is characterized by an *assemblage* of species (especially that at the type locality), and the zone index species may be rare or even missing from any one place or even from a region; (c) it is a matter of convenience, based usually on geographical extent, as to which units we call zones and which subzones; (d) the existence of a standard zone table implies widespread homotaxis; and (e) such homotaxis may prove to be explainable only in terms of synchronism (time correlation), making the standard zonal table also a table of

---

[1] The first six paragraphs of this discussion of the zone are modified from a statement furnished by Dr. J. H. Callomon of University College, London.

TABLE 1

<small>Correlation Table for Marine Lower and Middle Jurassic,†</small>

Stage		Zone	1 England	2 Eastern France	3 South-western Germany	4 North-western Germany
Middle Jurassic	U	41. *Quenstedtoceras lamberti*	z	z	z	z
	U	40. *Peltoceras athleta*	z	z	z	z
Callovian	M	39. *Erymnoceras coronatum*	z	z	z	z
	M	38. *Kosmoceras jason*	z		?	z
	L	37. *Sigaloceras calloviense*	z	z	z	z
	L	36. *Macrocephalites macrocephalus*	z	z	z	z
	U	35. *Clydoniceras discus*	z	z		z
	U	34. *Oppelia aspidoides*	z	?	?	?
Bathonian	M	33. *Tulites subcontractus*	z	z	z	
	M	32. *Gracilisphinctes progracilis*	z			
	L	31. *Zigzagiceras zigzag*	z	z	z	z
	U	30. *Parkinsonia parkinsoni*	z	z	z	z
	U	29. *Garantiana garantiana*	z	z	z	z
	U	28. *Strenoceras subfurcatum*	z	z	z	z
	M	27. *Stephanoceras humphriesianum*	z	z	z	z
Bajocian	M	26. *Otoites sauzei*	z	z	z	z
	M	25. *Sonninia sowerbyi*	z	z	z	z
	L	24. *Graphoceras concavum*	z	z	z	z
	L	23. *Ludwigia murchisonae*	z	z	z	z
	L	22. *Tmetoceras scissum*	z		z	z
	L	21. *Leioceras opalinum*	z	z	z	z
Lower Jurassic (Lias)	U	20. *Dumortieria levesquei*	z	z	z	z
	U	19. *Grammoceras thouarsense*	z	z	z	?
Toarcian	U	18. *Haugia variabilis*	z	z	z	z
	L	17. *Hildoceras bifrons*	z	z	z	z
	L	16. *Harpoceras falcifer*	z	z	z	z
	L	15. *Dactylioceras tenuicostatum*	z	z	z	z
	U	14. *Pleuroceras spinatum*	z	z	z	z
	U	13. *Amaltheus margaritatus*	z	z	z	z
Pliensbachian	L	12. *Prodactylioceras davoei*	z	z	z	z
	L	11. *Tragophylloceras ibex*	z	z	z	z
	L	10. *Uptonia jamesoni*	z	z	z	z
	U	9. *Echioceras raricostatum*	z	z	z	z
	U	8. *Oxynoticeras oxynotum*	z	z	z	z
	U	7. *Asteroceras obtusum*	z	z	z	z
Sinemurian		6. *Caenisites turneri*	z	z	z	z
	L	5. *Arnioceras semicostatum*	z	z	z	z
	L	4. *Arietites bucklandi*	z	z	z	z
		3. *Schlotheimia angulata*	z	z	z	z
Hettangian		2. *Alsatites liasicus*	z	z	z	z
		1. *Psiloceras planorbis*	z	z	z	z

† Compiled from W. J. Arkell's Jurassic Geology of the World, with modifications from Dean, Donovan, and Howarth (1961), J. H. Callomon (1955, 1961), and H. K. Erben (1956). U = Upper. M = Middle. L = Lower. S = stage present. z = zone present. x = fauna

5 Jura Mts.	6 Cau-casus	7 Arabia	8 Cutch, India	9 Eastern Greenland	10 Western Canada	11 Wyoming	12 Eastern Mexico	13 Andes	
z	ss		z			z			41
z			z				z		40
ss	ss	z	?					S	39
ss	ss		z		ss	+	x		38
z	z		?	z	ss	+			37
z	z		z	z		+			36
z		ss?	ss	1					35
z				1					34
z	S	ss		1					33
?				1					32
z		?		1	?	?	z		31
z	z								30
z		ss		ss?					29
z	z								28
z	z				z			z	27
z	z	ss			z	ss	S	?	26
z	?				z			z	25
z	?								24
z	z								23
z					z			z	22
z	z								21
?									20
z		ss?		ss	ss			ss	19
*	S								18
*				z					17
*								ss	16
*		ss			ss				15
z								ss	14
z									13
?	S			z	S			z	12
z								z	11
z				z			z	z	10
z							z		9
z							?	ss	8
z	S?				?		?		7
?								?	6
z					z		z	?	5
z					z		z	z	4
z					z			?	3
z	S?								2
z					z		z	z	1

bridging Middle and Lower Callovian. ? = zone perhaps present. 1 = 6 local Bathonian zones. + = 5 local zones. ss = substage present. ss? = substage perhaps present. * = perhaps all zones; condensed.

TABLE 2

DISTRIBUTION OF AMMONITE SPECIMENS IN BETHEL BRICK QUARRY AT

Zone	29–30 transition	29 (*G. garantiana*), 13 meters							
Bed number	1	2	3–4	7	8	15	16–17	19	21
Parkinsonia acris and *P. raricostata*	6								
Garantiana (Subgarantiana) depressa	2								
Garantiana (Subgarantiana) tetragona	1	6	4		3	6	1		
Garantiana (Subgarantiana) suevica			1ª		1				
Garantiana (Subgarantiana) alticosta						1			
Garantiana (Subgarantiana) subgaranti									
Garantiana (Subgarantiana) wetzeli									
Garantiana (Subgarantiana) trauthi									
Garantiana (Subgarantiana) pompeckji									
Garantiana (Subgarantiana) coronata									
Garantiana (Subgarantiana) cyclogaster									
Garantiana (Subgarantiana) subangulata									
Garantiana (Garantiana) garantiana									1
Garantiana (Garantiana) dubia									
Garantiana (Garantiana) baculata									
Garantiana (Garantiana) althoffi									
Garantiana (Garantiana) filicosta									
Garantiana (Pseudogarantiana) minima									
Garantiana (Pseudogarantiana) dichotoma									
Perisphinctids	1	1					1	1	1
Bigotites sp. indet.								2	
Garantiana (Orthogarantiana) inflata									
Garantiana (Orthogarantiana) schroederi									
Garantiana (Orthogarantiana) densicostata									
Strenoceras subfurcatum									
Strenoceras bajocensis									
Strenoceras latidorsatum									
Strenoceras robustum									
Strenoceras rotundum									

time correlation, with each zone made up of the rocks deposited during the time when the group of zonal guide fossils was living.

Historically, Oppel set up the first table of standard Jurassic zones for northwestern Europe in 1856. This event was fortunately located, for the unusually complete and extensively fossiliferous European sequence gives geographic zone ranges of the order of 1000 miles, and the experience of the hundred years after Oppel has shown that this is a suitable extent for a zone.

	28–29 transition, 12 meters													28 (*S. subfurcatum*), 4 meters	
22	23	24	25	26	27	27A*	28	29–32	34	35	36	41	42	Upper	Lower
	1						1								
1															
			1			4	2					1			
	2α	1					6		4						
							3								
							2	1							
							1								
	1					1α				1					
				1											
											1				
												1			
					1	1					1				
	1					4					1				
														4	4
														3	1
														2	
	1														
	1				2	8									
												2		2	
														15	
														5	
															11
														2?	4
															1
															2
														2	

* Specimens from nodules, not all from one horizon.
αcf.

Some peculiarities of actual faunas are shown in Table 2, representing the ammonites of a sequence of Upper Bajocian units in the clays and shales of a brick quarry near Bielefeld in northwestern Germany. The Garantiana Zone (No. 29 of Table 1) and the Subfurcatum Zone (No. 28) are present and in addition, there are the 28–29 and 29–30 transitional units. Here the paleontological units are also lithologic units. The 29–30 transitional beds, at the top of the section, are blue-black micaceous shales. Zone 29 is made up of 13 meters of more calcareous shales with few fossils, though some ammonites are present, as shown in the table, and a reptile skeleton was found at the base of the zone. The 28–29 transition beds, which are 12 meters thick, are somewhat micaceous marly clays. Fossils are moderately numerous. Zone 28, that of *Strenoceras subfurcatum*, is four meters thick and is distinguished by its fauna. Paleontologically, the transition beds between zone 30, that of *Parkinsonia parkinsoni*, and zone 29, that of *Garantiana garantiana*, are characterized by the occurrence together of *Parkinsonia* and *Garantiana*. Zone 29, at this locality, yielded but a single example of the index species, *Garantiana garantiana*, and is characterized by perisphinctids. The 28–29 transition beds have the distinction of being the only ones containing *Pseudogarantiana*. In zone 28 the zone species *Strenoceras subfurcatum* is common; in this section, the genus *Strenoceras* is limited to this zone.

At Bielefeld, paleontological subdivision goes beyond the standard zones in two ways. (a) Two extra units are present, both well marked paleontologically, and these units contain faunas which are transitional from one standard zone to the next. Such transitional units are unusual in the Jurassic of northwestern Europe. (b) The Subfurcatum Zone is divided into two subzones. Subzones are more numerous in some other parts of the northwest European Jurassic. The 20 zones of the Lower Jurassic (Lias) include 50 subzones, most of which have been recognized in most parts of the province (Dean and others, 1961).

Kosmoceras in the Callovian at Peterborough. For details concerning species and specimens we turn to a part of the Callovian, here considered the uppermost stage of the Middle Jurassic, following the practice of Arkell (1956) and the German geologists. Some of the commonest Callovian ammonites exhibit nearly continuous transitions from one species to another, and some of the vaguely delimited species are used as guide or even index fossils. With the aid of these guides, exceptionally satisfactory homotaxial parallels have been demonstrated, notably between the sections in the Oxford (Clunch) Clay at Peterborough and Kidlington, England.

The Peterborough section was examined by Roland Brinkmann of Germany (1929) in a statistical study that involved 3035 specimens which he assigned to the genus *Kosmoceras*. Brinkmann also identified the few other ammonites he found, as well as the numerous pelecypods, belemnites, and other invertebrates that he collected. He mentioned the fine fish specimens found in the quarries by others, as well as the skeletons of large plesiosaurs that are exhibited in the British Museum.

The Oxford Clay near Peterborough is flat-lying and at least 98 ft thick. It is mostly a dark gray, poorly laminated bituminous rock. The 1300 cm (42 ft) of clay in the lower part of the formation, which was studied statistically by Brinkmann (compare Table 3), is exposed in the lower parts of the walls of three quarries of the London Brick Company. One of the quarries is two miles south of Peterborough; the others are close together, three or four miles southeast of the city. The clay contains numerous white layers called plasters, usually only a few millimeters thick, rarely several centimeters, which separate the dark-colored rock into bands. The plasters are made up of collapsed ammonite shells, mostly in separated fragments. Local lithologic correlation, from one part of a pit to another part, or between pits, is made possible by the plasters and by three much thicker reference beds: (1) a concretionary layer 56–78 cm above Brinkmann's zero horizon (perhaps 176–198 cm above the Kellaways Rock that underlies the clay), (2) a very dark, thick-bedded clay at 560–680 cm above the zero level, and (3) a green clay at 1130–1160 cm. The thicknesses of the plasters and other reference beds and the intervals between them are uniform throughout the Peterborough quarries.

Brinkmann recognized 14 *Kosmoceras* species at Peterborough in the 1300 cm of clay to which the statistical study was restricted (Fig. 1). He concluded that each of the four columns of species in Fig. 1 represents an evolutionary lineage that should be recognized as a subgenus of *Kosmoceras*. Each subgenus is designated by one of the many names previously coined by S. S. Buckman: *Zugo-kosmokeras* (column 1), *Kosmoceras* s. s. (column 2), *Gulielmiceras* [*Anakosmokeras*] (column 3), and *Spinikosmokeras* (column 4). Other workers, notably Callomon (1955), separate the part of the first column below the 135.5-cm horizon (*K. jason* and lower) as the subgenus *Gulielmites* (another of Buckman's names).

The shells of the last two columns are similar to those of the first two, horizon by horizon, except for smaller size and the possession of prongs called *lappets* on either side of the aperture (the back lappet of a pair being hidden by the front one in a side view). At almost every horizon a form figured in column 3 corresponds to one of similar sculpture in column 1 that is twice as big and lacks lappets. The same relation holds somewhat less clearly between columns 2 and 4. Brinkmann (1929, pp. 212–213) concluded that the dimorphism is *not* sexual and that the unlappeted lineages were derived from *Sigaloceras* (Table 4) slightly before the beginning of Oxford Clay deposition. Now J. H. Callomon (letter, February 10, 1963) doubts the distinctness of the four lineages and considers the *Kosmoceras* sequence at Peterborough a single lineage, with sexual dimorphism. Brinkmann's collections actually were not large enough to demonstrate bimodal distributions.

Whatever the number of lineages, Brinkmann's statistics are useful, in part because of the numerical predominance of *Zugokosmokeras* (column 1 of Fig. 1), with 1802 specimens, 703 complete, over *Kosmoceras* s.s. (column 2), with 67 specimens, 50 complete. The statistics are consistent with an explanation in terms of persistent evolutionary changes, if there are lacunas in the fossil record at some of the plasters. Brinkmann grouped measurements and ratios

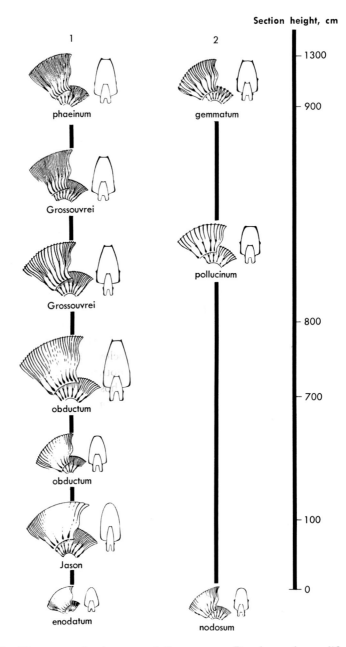

Fig. 1. Lineages and subgenera of *Kosmoceras* at Peterborough, modified slightly from Brinkmann (1929, Tafel V). 1, *Zugokosmokeras* and (*jason* and lower) *Gulielmites;* 2, *Kosmoceras* s.s. Sizes greatly reduced.

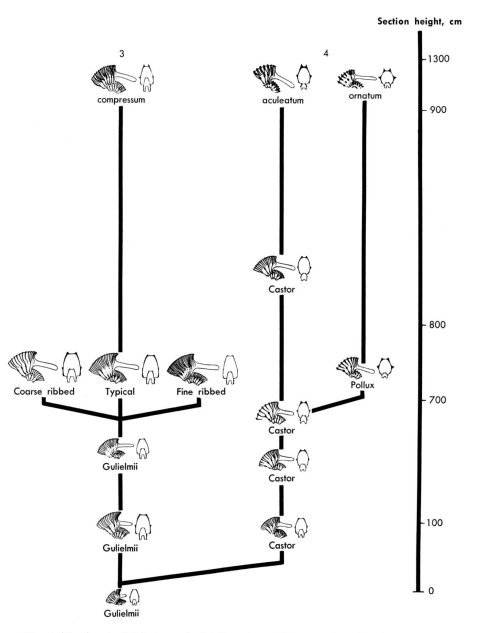

Fig. 1 (*Cont.*). 3, *Gulielmiceras;* 4, *Spinikosmokeras*. Sizes greatly reduced.

by lineages and horizons, the 1300 cm of clay being divided into 48 strata groups. The measurements for one lineage in one strata group tended toward normal distribution. Two of the many sets of data are selected for presentation here. The first set is shown as Table 3, representing the variations in diameter among the 703 complete specimens, most of them flattened to thin discs, that were assigned to the *Gulielmites-Zugokosmokeras* lineage (column 1 of Fig. 1). Note the rapid increase in size up to the 135-cm plaster, the sharp drop there, and the slow and interrupted increase thereafter, with the maximum mean diameter 146.6 ± 2.0 mm for the 31 specimens from 793 cm (individuals up to almost 170 mm). Standard deviations of the differences between adjacent means have been added to the table, together with t-values (difference between adjacent means divided by the standard deviation of the difference). All t-values greater than 3—for the differences 1, 3, 4, 6, 10, and 27—are strongly indicative of dissimilar populations. Difference 10, at the 135.5-cm horizon, is between the highest Jason Zone strata group and the lowest Coronatum Zone strata group. These two zones are the two parts of the Middle Callovian (compare Table 4). Most other pertinent statistical measures for all lineages also show breaks at this horizon.

The second set of Brinkmann statistics pertains to the ratio between the numbers of outer ribs and peripheral spines in the *Spinikosmokeras* sequence of Fig. 2. In this sequence, note the change from the approximately 1/1 ratio between outer ribs and spines in Fig. 2(c) to the approximately 2/1 ratio in Fig. 2(d). The statistics (Fig. 3a) show that this change is largely concentrated between 1093 and 1094 cm (1093.5 cm of Fig. 3a), at a horizon which is now about to be established as the Athleta-Coronatum zonal contact (J. H. Callomon, letter of February 10, 1963; see also Table 4). The regression lines on the two sides

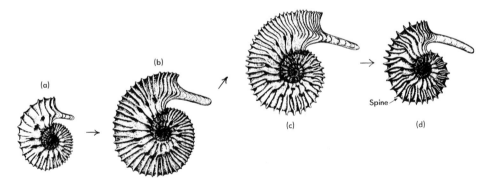

Fig. 2. A *Spinikosmokeras* succession at Peterborough, after Brinkmann (1929, Tafel III). (a) *K.* (*S.*) *castor anterior*, from 312 cm; (b) *K.* (*S.*) *castor castor*, from 670 cm; (c) *K.* (*S.*) *aculeatum anterior*, from 988 cm; (d) *K.* (*S.*) *aculeatum aculeatum*, from 1277 cm. Approx. $\times \frac{1}{2}$ natural size.

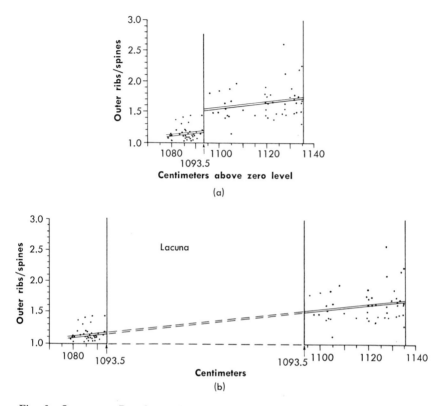

Fig. 3. Lacuna at Peterborough, shown by *Spinikosmokeras* statistics and regression lines. After Brinkmann (1929, Abb. 20). (a) plotted by strata-groups; (b) expanded to evaluate lacuna.

of the 1093.5-cm plaster actually have the same slope. This slope represents a rate of change that Brinkmann attempted to use in estimating the relative length of time represented by the lacuna. By assuming that (1) the rib-spine ratio changed at a uniform rate, (2) the clay between the plasters accumulated at a uniform rate, and (3) each plaster represents a time of nondeposition of clay, he was enabled to draw a second diagram with a gap at 1093.5 cm, wide enough to produce a single straight rib-spine regression line (Fig. 3b), in which the new abscissas became measures of time and from which the relative lengths of the two periods of clay deposition and the intervening lacuna could be determined. The result is dependent on the slopes of the two partial regression lines of Fig. 3(a), which are not very precise because of the scatter of the rib-spine ratios. Despite this and the other uncertainties, Brinkmann's data show clearly enough that some plasters, both interzonal and intrazonal, are horizons of exceptionally large changes in the statistical properties of the ammonites

TABLE 3

END-DIAMETERS OF ZUGOKOSMOKERAS (AND GULIELMITES) FROM

Strata-group, cm	Number of specimens	Mean and its Stand. Dev., mm	For the differences: Number	Stand. Dev.	t
7–20	12	61.6 ± 1.5			
			1	2.12	10.00
21–25	12	82.8 ± 1.5			
			2	2.42	0.91
26–28	23	85.0 ± 1.9			
			3	2.10	3.24
29–39	32	78.2 ± 0.9			
			4	1.66	4.04
40–45	16	84.9 ± 1.4			
			5	3.67	0.98
46–50	9	88.5 ± 3.4			
			6	5.03	3.44
56–78	19	105.8 ± 3.7			
			7	4.84	0.72
79–90	8	109.3 ± 3.1			
			8	3.80	1.42
91–120	15	114.7 ± 2.2			
			9	3.72	1.16
121–135	9	119.0 ± 3.0			
			10	3.72	6.29
136–160	9	95.6 ± 2.2			
			11	3.25	0.22
161–200	11	96.3 ± 2.4			
			12	3.76	0.40
201–240	5	94.8 ± 2.9			
			13	3.58	0.31
241–260	12	93.7 ± 2.1			
			14	3.83	0.52
261–300	7	95.7 ± 3.2			
			15	5.12	2.05
301–320	5	85.2 ± 4.0			
			16	4.47	1.30
321–340	14	91.0 ± 2.0			
			17	4.20	1.64
341–360	7	97.9 ± 3.7			
			18	4.25	0.99
361–380	7	93.7 ± 2.1			
			19	3.50	2.37
381–440	6	102.0 ± 2.8			
			20	4.18	0.53
441–460	12	99.8 ± 3.1			
			21	5.46	2.45
461–500	6	113.2 ± 4.5			
			22	5.76	0.40
501–520	19	110.9 ± 3.6			
			23	4.11	2.21

* Not a plaster; no data; ammonites not classified because of lack of time.

† First 3 columns from Brinkmann, 1929, p. 103. Plasters (and strata-groups whose fossils were not studied) shown by horizontal lines. Stand. Dev. = Standard Deviation. For t see text.

Strata-group, cm	Number of specimens	Mean and its Stand. Dev., mm	For the differences: Number	Stand. Dev.	t
521–530	20	101.8 ± 2.0			
			24	3.20	1.34
531–539	13	106.1 ± 2.5			
			25	3.14	2.13
540	38	112.8 ± 1.9			
			26	3.14	0.03
541–559	10	112.7 ± 2.5			
			27	2.92	5.24
560	27	128.0 ± 1.5			
			28	3.80	0.34
561–680	15	126.7 ± 3.5			
			29	4.14	0.89
681–690	13	130.4 ± 2.2			
			30	4.91	2.59
691–759	13	117.7 ± 4.4			
			31	5.50	2.47
760–780	16	131.3 ± 3.3			
?			32	5.58	2.29
781–792	8	144.1 ± 4.5			
			33	4.93	0.51
793	31	146.6 ± 2.0			
			34	10.05	1.73
794–854	6	129.2 ± 10.3			
			35	10.05	0.01
855	23	129.1 ± 2.0			
			36	3.69	1.17
856–864	21	124.8 ± 3.1			
			37	3.98	0.58
865	33	127.1 ± 2.5			
			38	9.53	1.45
866–880	7	140.9 ± 9.2			
			39	11.19	0.76
881–894	7	132.4 ± 6.4			
			40	7.39	2.07
895	9	117.1 ± 3.7			
			41	4.76	1.43
896–920	15	123.9 ± 3.0			
*			42	3.84	2.79
961–980	11	113.2 ± 2.4			
			43	3.61	1.16
981–990	12	109.0 ± 2.7			
*			44	3.48	1.72
1080–1093	22	115.0 ± 2.2			
			45	4.56	1.47
1094–1120	14	121.7 ± 4.0			
			46	4.94	0.18
1121–1135	21	120.8 ± 2.9			
*			47	4.32	0.60
1270–1310	23	123.4 ± 3.2			

and hence may well represent relatively long periods of nondeposition of clay, during which the ammonites changed at their usual rates.

At Peterborough there is no sign of erosion, just deposition and nondeposition. The plasters are uninterrupted sheets, even though just beneath some of them the clay was reworked by pre-plaster burrowing animals.

Correlations in the Oxford Clay (Callovian) between Peterborough and Kidlington. The qualitative and quantitative changes of the lower strata groups at Peterborough are closely paralleled at Kidlington near Oxford, 70 miles southwest of Peterborough. The 0–135 cm portion of the Oxford Clay at Peterborough is the Jason Zone, the lower part of the Middle Callovian. It can be correlated with 450–500 cm of Oxford Clay that in 1948–51 was temporarily exposed at Kidlington. At that place, Callomon (1955) collected 165 measurable specimens of the *Gulielmites* and *Gulielmiceras* subgenera of *Kosmoceras*. Brinkmann had 1086 *Kosmoceras* specimens (349 measurable) collected from the 0–135 cm clay at Peterborough, and all but seven were assigned to the same two subgenera. The *Kosmoceras* (*Gulielmites* and *Gulielmiceras*) diameters at Peterborough and Kidlington are similar at corresponding horizons.

The most exact Peterborough-Kidlington correlation is for the faunal break which occurs at the 51.5-cm plaster in the Peterborough quarries and probably at the plaster 173 cm above the zero level at Kidlington, although the clay just below the Kidlington plaster lacks ammonites. Shell sizes for both *Gulielmites* and *Gulielmiceras* are markedly greater above this horizon. Other characteristics change too, especially for *Gulielmites*, so that Callomon described the new species *Kosmoceras* (*Gulielmites*) *medea* (*endodatum*, Fig. 1) to include the *Gulielmites* shells below this horizon (boundary of Jason/Medea subzones, Table 4). There are eight plasters in the Jason Zone at Peterborough and six at Kidlington. Although the plasters in the Peterborough quarries extend for miles, the Jason/Medea plaster correlation is the only one that can be made between Peterborough and Kidlington with any confidence. The plasters mark times when clay was not being deposited, although ammonite shells were accumulating, and the area must have been covered by clear sea water. The failure of most plaster correlations between Peterborough and Kidlington may mean that most plasters were relatively local; perhaps they were formed on that side of a large delta which for a time was not receiving muddy water.

In the Oxford-Peterborough belt of Kellaways Rock and Oxford Clay, the Upper Callovian Athleta and Lamberti zones are not subdivided, but each Middle or Lower Callovian zone is divided into two or more subzones (Table 4). The subzones have been recognized in some but not all British Callovian sections. The *Erymnoceras coronatum* Zone, i.e., the upper part of the Middle Callovian, has as its index species a heavy-ribbed ammonite 16–20 in. in diameter that is common in Britain; the zone can also be recognized by the *Kos-*

TABLE 4

CALLOVIAN ZONES AND SUBZONES IN BRITAIN, AFTER CALLOMON (1955)

	Zone	Subzone
Upper Callovian	*Quenstedtoceras lamberti*	
	Peltoceras athleta	
Middle Callovian	*Erymnoceras coronatum*	*Kosmoceras (Zugokosmokeras) grossouvrei* *Kosmoceras (Zugokosmokeras) obductum*
	Kosmoceras (Gulielmites) jason	*Kosmoceras (Gulielmites) jason* *Kosmoceras (Gulielmites) medea*
Lower Callovian	*Sigaloceras calloviense*	*Sigaloceras planicerclum* *Sigaloceras calloviense* *Proplanulites koenigi*
	Macrocephalites (Macrocephalites) macrocephalus	*Macrocephalites (Kamptokephalites) kamptus* *Macrocephalites (Macrocephalites) macrocephalus*

moceras guides to the two subzones. At Peterborough, the Coronatum Zone is divided into the Obductum Subzone, from 135.5 to about 854 cm, and the Grossouvrei Subzone, from about 854 cm to 1093.5 cm. The *Kosmoceras* guides to the subzones have been found at Christian Malford in the Oxford Clay belt 35 miles southwest of Oxford, and *K. grossouvrei* (Table 4), at least, is present at Weymouth on the south coast (Arkell, 1947, p. 29). The Jason Zone at Peterborough is divided into the Medea Subzone, 0–51.5 cm, and the Jason Subzone, 51.5–135.5 cm.

Brinkmann and Callomon emphasized different aspects of the *Kosmoceras* evidence. Brinkmann mentioned species and zones, but for him the *Gulielmites-Zugokosmokeras* lineage was one unit, in which variations in size, form, and sculpture were treated statistically. Statistical breaks at plasters were interpreted as proofs of lacunas in the record of a continuously evolving population or sequence of populations. Callomon gave statistics but used them to define species, zones, and subzones. Callomon's correlations between Peterborough and Kidlington were correlations of the Medea and Jason subzones, in the course of which it was shown that the *Kosmoceras* shells went through similar changes in adult size at the two localities.

Callovian in Germany, France, and Switzerland. The Callovian is well represented throughout the Northwest European Province. In the Schwabian and Fran-

conian Alb of southwestern Germany all six zones are probably present, although the Calloviense Zone (No. 37 in Table 1) is poorly represented and
probably incomplete. The Middle and Lower Callovian has the thin "Macro-
cephalenband" at the base, but mostly consists of the clay called *Ornatenton*,
which is 10 meters thick and richly fossiliferous, with abundant *Kosmoceras*.
The sequence of *Kosmoceras* species is confusing and unexplained (Arkell, 1956,
p. 118). The Upper Callovian, fully exposed during the building of the Auto-
bahn in 1937 (R. and E. Model, 1938), is a three-meter clay crowded with
ammonites, many of which are pyritized or phosphatized. Large specimens
of the knobby *Peltoceras athleta* occur near the base, and specimens of the sharp-
keeled, streamlined *Quenstedtoceras lamberti* occur at higher levels. An overlying
half-meter of nodular clay contains more or less crushed pyritized or phosphatized specimens of both *Q. lamberti* and the Lower Oxfordian (lowest Upper
Jurassic) guides, forming one of the "condensed" zones that are common in
the continental Jurassic and may be the result of erosion and redeposition of at
least part of the ammonites.

In the Jura tableland, including the region in eastern France around Besançon and Belfort north of the Jura Mountains and also extending into Switzerland beyond Basel to the Herznach iron mine, all six Callovian zones are
present (Theobald, 1957), although not all are known throughout the area.
The best faunas are found in 10.5-ft deposits of iron ore and associated strata
in the Herznach iron mine (Callomon, 1955, p. 250). Here the Lower Callovian
is present, but the Jason Zone kosmocerids are lacking, and the next fossiliferous
horizons are the well-marked Coronatum and Athleta zones. The successive
faunas are sharply contrasted instead of including closely related kosmocerids
as at Peterborough. At Besançon, a newly exposed Coronatum-Athleta-
Lamberti sequence (Rangheard and Theobald, 1961) includes a Coronatum
Zone with *Erymnoceras coronatum* and abundant *Hecticoceras* of Middle Callovian
species, but no *Kosmoceras*.

In general, on the European continent the distribution of *Kosmoceras* is very
spotty, but the Callovian zones can be correlated with those in England by
the use of kosmocerids and other guide ammonites. Callovian lacunas are
present on the continent, as in England, and some of these, at several levels,
coincide with slight erosional unconformities and concentrations of battered,
pyritized, or phosphatized ammonites.

At lower horizons, in the Bajocian, one or two slight angular unconformities
occur, in England and in Normandy. In Wiltshire, S. S. Buckman (1901)
demonstrated extensive overlap and a discordance of 7 feet per mile.

European Lower and Middle Jurassic zones. The Lower and Middle Jurassic
zones of the Northwest European Province are all of the same general type as
those described for the Callovian. All 41 zones are present in England (column 1
of Table 1). Almost all are present in France, especially on the east side of the

Paris Basin and in the Jura tableland (column 2 of Table 1), and in the cuestas of the Schwabian and Franconian Alb of southwestern Germany (column 3). Almost all the zones are probably present in the thick strata of the northwest German basin between the North Sea and the Harz Mountains (column 4) and in the folded Jura of the Franco-Swiss border (column 5).

Facies zones. The Lower and Middle Jurassic zones of northwestern Europe have long been considered time-stratigraphic units. Before we accept this important inference, we should survey all the other possibilities. Under the general assumption of organic evolution, there are two other possibilities or possible complications: (1) local evolution, with lag elsewhere as a result of poor communications, and (2) migration of relatively long-lived facies faunas. We shall consider facies faunas first, illustrating them with the present-day marine facies found off north-south coasts, with special attention to foraminiferal facies off California because the foraminiferal species living there are also found fossil in nearby Pleistocene and Pliocene strata.

The present-day shallow-water marine faunal temperature and depth facies have been thoroughly studied along several north-south trending coasts, including the Pacific Coast of North America (for the mollusks, see Burch, 1945–46; Keen, 1958). On the Pacific Coast, breaks between well-defined molluscan provinces occur at the tip of the Lower California Peninsula, at Point Conception, California, and elsewhere.

Local and regional differences in the Pleistocene and Pliocene molluscan and foraminiferal faunas can be established by comparisons with living species. One kind of facies succession in the rocks is clearly the result of temperature change. Examples are successions of alternately warm and cold Pleistocene molluscan faunas at many places along the east and west coasts of North America. No doubt these faunas moved south during glacial epochs and north during interglacial periods. Practically all the species are living somewhere along these coasts today: the cold-water species live in the north and the warm-water species in the south. But the same species also have a tendency to move down into deeper colder water somewhat south of their inshore, shallow-water range. There can be no doubt that these molluscan species, still living today, are facies fossils in their Pleistocene occurrences, rather than guides to some particular parts of Pleistocene time, but there may be some uncertainty as to whether, at any particular latitude, the facies succession is due to climatic change or to change in the depth of the water in which the Pleistocene animals lived (Woodring and others, 1946). In either case, the Pleistocene facies successions at different localities can be no more than homotaxial and cannot be used as evidence of synchronism.

In other facies successions, change of depth seems to have been the variable factor. Examples are found in southern California in two small basins, each some 25 × 60 miles in horizontal dimensions, where the sediments and faunas have been studied in connection with oil field exploitation. In the Los Angeles and Ventura basins, the presumably Pliocene strata are 10,000 to 15,000 ft thick and are made up of alternating beds of sandstone and shale, with minor marginal conglomerate. In both basins, foraminiferal (foram) species are locally satisfactory guide fossils. The zones occur in the same order in the two basins, are of comparable thickness, and conform to the structures in the basins, notably to the folds and faults determined from the sandstone layers that are the reservoir rocks in the numerous oil fields. But the same foram assemblages found in the basin strata also occur living on the floor of the nearby Pacific Ocean, with well-marked depth-of-water ranges. In a way, the order offshore is the same as in the rocks. The shallowest foram fauna of the oil-well sequence is also found on the sea floor in shallow water, and the oil-field zones follow in order down the slope of the sea floor, until the deepest oil-well foram assemblage is found living on the continental slope of the present ocean at depths greater than 6000 ft (Natland, 1933, 1957; Bandy, 1953). Almost all the foram species found in the wells or in Pliocene outcrops are also living offshore today. The very few extinct species are almost all in the lowest zone in the rocks. All the zones in the rocks, including the lowest one, must be primarily *depth zones*, distinguished by the faunal facies of a particular depth, namely the depth of water at the time of deposition of the strata involved. Apparently the lowest strata, those containing several extinct foram species, were deposited in water more than 6000 ft deep, and all the higher strata were deposited in shallower and shallower water as the basins filled. The deep-water marine basins appear to have been steep sided, with very narrow marginal selvages. These selvages have been involved in deformation and erosion, so that horizons are hard to trace, but on the east side of the Los Angeles Basin lateral transitions from deep to shallow facies are probably preserved.

In the two southern California basins, the homotaxis of foram zones does not necessarily involve synchronism. We do not know whether any particular facies zone was deposited at the same time in both basins, although the identical extinct species in the lowest zone of the Pliocene rocks have been considered sufficient to justify time correlation for this zone.

The weakness of the depth-zone forams as guides to relative age has been demonstrated by comparisons with the faunas in the Neogene of the Great Valley of California, 200–300 miles to the north. The strata called Pliocene in the Valley contain assemblages of shallow-water foraminifera, all assignable to living species, and are underlain by strata called Miocene. The deeper foraminiferal facies zones are missing. It is impossible by the use of foraminifera alone to develop parallelism between subdivisions of the Pliocene strata of the Great Valley and the zones set up for the southern California basins.

Facies fossils are harder to recognize in the older rocks. The stratigrapher feels his way, working back from the present. Facies that merely indicate depth differences can usually be avoided by looking for forms whose structures (or relationships to living forms of known behavior) suggest the swimming or floating mode of life. The very fact of wide geographic distribution, essential for a guide fossil, is suggestive of mobility unlikely in organisms narrowly restricted in habitat.

In evaluating an extinct kind of guide, such as the ammonites, one must rely in part on lithofacies and the nonammonitic biofacies. Ammonites are especially abundant in clays. In the British Callovian they are common in the Oxford and other clays but are not found in the interbedded sandstone, the Kellaways Rock. The ammonites of the Oxford Clay are associated with numerous pelecypods, including oysters. Oysters are commonly shallow-water forms. In general, ammonites have been found associated with all marine biofacies except reef corals. They have not been found in brackish, lagoonal, estuarine, or freshwater associations.

Westermann (1954) recognized at least two alternating ammonite facies (stephanoid and sonniniid) in the Middle Bajocian calcareous-sandy clays of the northwest German trough at Alfeld east of Bielefeld, close to the Harz horst. The stephanoid facies occurs three times, the sonniniid twice, but the whole sequence can probably be divided satisfactorily between the *Stephanoceras humphriesianum* Zone (No. 27 in Table 1) and the *Otoites sauzei* Zone (No. 26), since both index fossils are members of the stephanoid group.

On a larger scale, there are two European ammonite facies of provincial scope, which may be temperature or depth facies. The ammonites of the whole northwest European platform, including those in the Oxford Clay and also those in the northwest German trough, may represent a cooler or shallower facies than that of the Mediterranean Tethys, the home of the smooth, globose genera called *Lytoceras* and *Phylloceras*, which are almost absent from the platform.

Gayle Scott (1940) attempted to establish five Mesozoic depth zones, which he lettered from A to E. The deepest zone (E) was the Tethyan zone of *Lytoceras* and *Phylloceras*. The four shallower zones were all illustrated by Texas Cretaceous faunas, the shallowest (A) without ammonites. The ammonites of depth(?) zone D are smoothly rounded shells, found in marls and marly limestones. In the supposed depth zone C, the ammonites are quadrate and highly sculptured; they occur in marls and clays as well as in chalk and dense limestone. The slender sharp-keeled ammonites of depth(?) zone B (15–20 fathoms?) are found in sandy limestones and sandy shales.

Stratigraphic paleontologists have a built-in bias against facies interpretations of their stock in trade, the guide fossils, and Scott's suggestions were not spontaneously accepted. In this case, caution seems to have been justified, as ammonites of the supposed depth zone D have been found in a Fort Worth quarry associated with sea weeds and with genera of foraminifera that today live attached to plants in shallow water (Claude Albritton, personal communication).

Comparison of European ammonite and California foram zones. The northwestern European Jurassic ammonite zones resemble the foram facies zones of the southern California Pliocene in one way. Both have been found invariably in the same order. But the Pliocene forams were sedentary bottom animals with living relatives confined to depth zones. The ammonites were probably active swimming animals similar to the living *Nautilus*. Not only did the ammonites probably get around easily but their empty shells may occasionally have been spread rather widely by currents, just as a few nautilid shells have been carried hundreds of miles to Japan, far northeast of the haunts of the living animals. Finally, the unfailing ammonite homotaxis in the large European Jurassic area contrasts with the failure of Pliocene foram homotaxis between the southern California basins and the Great Valley of central California.

Possible faunal lag in the European Jurassic. In the northwest European Lower and Middle Jurassic there is little or no evidence for local lag in faunal change at a specific horizon, or series of horizons, as a result of temporary barriers or the time required for migration. The practically complete homotaxis throughout the province, zone by zone, combined with the Peterborough evidence for an evolutionary sequence, is explainable by the easy migration of rapidly evolving animals and probably in no other way. If this explanation is the correct one, the homotaxis implies time correlations.

Before accepting this conclusion of synchronism for each zone throughout the province, we should try to discover the implication for travel times expressed in years. Since the time of deposition for the whole Jurassic System was probably of the order of 45 million years (compare Holmes, 1960; Kulp, 1961) and the system is divided into upwards of 60 zones (41 for the Middle and Lower Jurassic, 20 or more for the Upper), the average zone accumulated in about 750,000 years. Modern marine clams and snails have spread through scores or even hundreds of miles of shallow water in a few decades (Elton, 1958). If the ammonites got around as quickly as the clams and snails do now, which seems likely, the spread of a new European zonal fauna must have been geologically instantaneous. The conclusion follows that the Lower and Middle Jurassic zones really are temporal units throughout the Northwest European Province.

Extent and meaning of lacunas in the northwest European Lower and Middle Jurassic. If the northwest European Lower and Middle Jurassic zones are time-stratigraphic units within the province, what are the extent and meaning of the frequently sharp zonal boundaries? Brinkmann and Callomon showed that in Britain the Coronatum-Jason boundary of the Middle Callovian marks a lacuna in the paleontological record. Apparently this boundary also coincides with a paleontological lacuna at many places in the continental portion of the

TABLE 5

LOWER JURASSIC CORRELATIONS: NORTHWEST EUROPE-MEXICO (ERBEN, 1956)

Stage	Northwest European zone (Table 1)	East-central Mexico ammonite "faunizones"
Pliensbachian	10. *Uptonia jamesoni*	*Uptonia* sp.
Sinemurian	9. *Echioceras raricostatum*	{*Microderoceras bispinatum altespinatum* {*Echioceras burckhardti* {*Pleurechioceras? james-danae* {*Pleurechioceras subdeciduum*
	8. *Oxynoticeras oxynotum*	? ?
	7. *Asteroceras obtusum*	*Vermiceras bavaricum mexicanum** *Oxynoticeras* sp.†
	6. *Caenisites turneri*	? ?
	5. *Arnioceras semicostatum*	{*Euagassiceras subsauzeanum* {*Arnioceras geometricoides*
	4. *Arietites bucklandi* (*Coroniceras* subzones)	*Coroniceras pseudolyra*

* Doubtful correlation.
† Perhaps equal to European zone 8.

province, with at least local disconformity and the reworking of ammonites. However that may be, the kosmocerids must have lived right through the time of restricted deposition, in some part or parts of the region. Northwestern Europe was their homeland, and they were never abundant elsewhere. At other zone boundaries exotic guide fossils appear, perhaps as immigrants from Tethys (compare Spath, 1933, p. 427) and disappear, perhaps becoming extinct without issue.

Worldwide significance of northwest European Jurassic zones. No northwest European Lower or Middle Jurassic zone is worldwide in extent. Nevertheless, many of the zones have been recognized at one or more places outside the province (compare Table 1), through the presence of the index species of the zone, other guide species, or closely related species. Take, for example, the Lower Jurassic correlations between Europe and eastern Mexico (Table 5). Note that zones 4, 5, 9, and 10 of the European sequence are confidently correlated with local Mexican zones ("faunizones") although no index (zone name) species, and almost no ammonite species, is common to the two regions. Some Mexican species, however, are very similar to guides for the European zones; examples are *Echioceras densicosta* of Mexico, with about 25 costae on the last whorl, compared to 18 for the index species of the *Echioceras raricostatum*

Zone, and *Coroniceras pseudolyra* of Mexico, similar to *Coroniceras lyra* of the *Arietites bucklandi* Zone. There are difficulties at the horizons of zones 6, 7, and 8 (Table 1). Nothing like zone 6 has been recognized in Mexico. The author of Table 5 (Erben, 1956) seriously considered correlating zone 8 (*Oxynoticeras oxynotum*) of northwestern Europe with the *Oxynoticeras* sp. Zone of Mexico, but finally chose the zone 7 (*Asteroceras-Vermiceras*) correlation, shown in Table 5. This drops *Oxynoticeras* two notches. The correlation of Table 5 or any other possible set of matches leaves two zones in each region unmatched in the other.

Actually, the matching of zones between eastern Mexico and northwestern Europe is exceptionally close. In general, intercontinental correlation, zone by zone, is not practical. For most horizons, larger and more generalized units —substages—must be used.

Lower and Middle Jurassic Stages and Substages

Standard stages and substages of northwestern Europe. The zones of Table 1 are grouped into stages. Although stages were established before zones, a *stage* is most precisely defined in terms of the zones that make it up in its type area, which for the Lower and Middle Jurassic is northwestern Europe. Since the stages are based on zones, they too are defined on a paleontological basis. Stages have boundaries that may cross formation boundaries obliquely, even in the type areas; stages may be represented by different lithologic facies in different areas; stages can be identified in isolated distant places—all because they are based on assemblages of guide fossils. In 1956, just before his death, the British stratigrapher W. J. Arkell (1956, p. 9) wrote of the Jurassic stages[2]: "As units of the single world scale of classification, stages must be based on zones . . . They are essentially groupings of zones, but they transcend zones both vertically and horizontally." Vertically, a sequence of zones makes one stage. Horizontally, the characteristic zone assemblages of fossils may disappear, but the stage may still be recognizable and still divisible. For distant correlations, therefore, both stages and substages are needed. A *substage* is a major subdivision of a stage, defined in terms of the zones that make it up in

---

[2] The Middle Jurassic stages were based fairly closely on William Smith's formations. The Callovian Stage was named from Smith's Kelloways Stone, by Latinization; it also includes most of the overlying Oxford Clay. The Bathonian Stage includes Smith's Great Oolyte, or Bath Freestone, named after Bath, England, and also the Forest Marble and Clay. The Bajocian is Smith's Under Oolyte, but the type locality is across the Channel at Bayeux, Normandy. The four Lower Jurassic stages were all carved out of Smith's Lias clay, shale, and limestone, but the type localities are in France and Germany. Unlike the zones, the stages have remained practically unchanged since 1864.

the type area. Each Middle Jurassic stage is divided into upper, middle, and lower substages. The three higher Lias stages—Toarcian, Pliensbachian, and Sinemurian—have upper and lower substages; the Hettangian is not divided.

Recognition of Callovian and other stages outside Europe. Sample Middle and Lower Jurassic sections in Asia and America are shown in Table 1, columns 6–13. The Callovian is the only stage represented in all 8 columns. The three lowest stages are found together in two and probably in three of the 8 columns, and in these two or three they are rather fully represented. The Caucasus Mountains (column 6) and the central and southern Andes (column 13) have exceptionally complete sections. Note particularly the number of European zones that have been identified in the Andes, two-thirds of the way around the globe.

The Callovian Stage, at the top of the Middle Jurassic, is both widespread and varied. Several Callovian zones are recognizable outside western Europe, notably in the Caucasus and in Cutch, India (Table 1). Cutch, at the northeastern edge of the Arabian Sea, has perhaps the most fossiliferous and paleontologically complex sequence of the lower part of the Callovian in the world. Close correlation with Europe is difficult because the Cutch faunas are composed largely of Oriental elements. *Kosmoceras* is unknown there.

In western North America the Lower Callovian substage has been reported in several areas. In the Wyoming-Montana area five regional zones have been distinguished (Imlay, 1953). In this same region a zone with *Quenstedtoceras* may be approximately equivalent to the *Quenstedtoceras lamberti* Zone of Europe, the highest Callovian zone in the type section (Table 4).

In the southern hemisphere some of the most characteristic European Callovian genera do not exist, but the Callovian Stage can be recognized "by the general grade of evolution of the ammonite fauna as a whole and by a chain of overlapping correlations carried link by link round the world" (Arkell, 1956, p. 12).

Time correlation from stage and substage homotaxis. In the statement just quoted, Arkell assumed (1) that the presence of the same guide ammonites at two localities provides sufficient evidence for synchronism, and (2) that local "overlaps" of provincial ammonite taxa are almost equally good evidence for synchronism. Similar assumptions are made by most, but not all, stratigraphic paleontologists. We must now consider whether the assumptions are justified.

Possibilities other than synchronism are hard to formulate in a general and exhaustive way, especially because the data vary from horizon to horizon. With respect to the ammonite guides of the Lower and Middle Jurassic stages and substages, we shall assume that local facies variations have been accounted for at the zone level. Facies of provincial scope do not provide homotaxial problems. The possibilities for significant error at the substage level appear to be two: (1) difference in the time range of the substage guides in two or more districts or provinces, as by survival in a distant province after extinction in the homeland, or vice versa, and (2) misinterpretation of differences in details or rate of evolution in two provinces separated by a barrier. The questions at issue are the probability and magnitude of these sources of error. Every case must be treated on its own merits, although the cumulative effect of evidence for synchronism at horizon after horizon would be to establish a presumption favorable to synchronism for other cases.

We shall take the Toarcian Stage of the Lower Jurassic as an example. Typical Toarcian faunas can be followed around the world in the northern hemisphere, from western Europe to the Donetz Basin of southern Russia, the Caucasus, Persia, Baluchistan, Indonesia, Indochina, Korea, Japan, Alaska, a Canadian Arctic island, eastern Greenland, and back to northwestern Europe (Arkell, 1956). Everywhere European guide genera are found and in many places European guide species. *Grammoceras thouarsense* is a guide fossil for a zone in the midst of the stage in the type section at Thouars, France. The same species is found in the same homotaxial position in the Toarcian of the Caucasus. Other west European guides also occur in the Caucasus, in about the standard order, although the thick section has structural complexities and definitive studies have not yet been made. In Japan the Toarcian zones are almost the same as in western Europe, with typical European genera but peculiar Japanese zone species. In eastern Greenland the Upper Toarcian and a Lower Toarcian zone (No. 17) can be distinguished, both with guide species similar to those in Europe (Callomon, 1961). The Toarcian localities range in latitude from the equator (Indonesia) nearly to the North Pole (the Arctic island). The facies range from platform to thick geosynclinal with interbedded volcanics (Caucasus). In Japan some 1500 feet of Toarcian sand-stone and shale are known, and in the Caucasus 15,000 to 20,000 feet of sand-stone and shale, interbedded with freshwater strata containing coal.

Let us imagine that the two successive Toarcian faunas that can be generally recognized (Lower and Upper) originated in northwestern Europe and migrated eastward, and only eastward, around the world, evolving slowly as they migrated, and that after circumnavigation the lower fauna had evolved into the upper. By the time the migrants reached Japan new species might well have developed. To this extent the hypothesis fits the evidence. But evidence for eastward migration ends with Japan. The Japanese species did not get to Alaska or Greenland. The somewhat scanty evidence suggests a different hypothesis, namely, migration both east and west from an evolutionary center that may have included both Tethys and the European platform, with development of local species in distant, more or less isolated areas, such as Japan, but with communication sufficiently complete and rapid to permit the earlier Toarcian fauna to be everywhere overwhelmed by the second soon after the second had become well characterized anywhere. This hypothesis explains the similar succession of Toarcian genera all around the world, in Japan as well as in Europe. That is to say, the evidence favors interpretation of the Toarcian homotaxis in Europe, Japan, etc., as evidence for the time correlation of the highly varied enclosing strata, substage by substage, or even in some places zone by zone.

The Toarcian is a specially instructive stage, for one must work around the world with some care in order to find at all localities the same typical European Lower Toarcian genera. A more southern course from Europe to the Indian Ocean yields a somewhat different set of results for the Lower Toarcian. This route goes from the northwestern European Platform to Portugal and then jumps to Arabia, East Africa, and Madagascar, where, on the south side of Tethys, the peculiar *Bouleiceras* fauna, unlike anything in northwestern Europe, characterizes a province called Ethiopian by Arkell (1956, p. 614). In Portugal, *Bouleiceras* itself occurs in the same beds with northwestern European guides; this is the "overlap." The Ethiopian Lower Toarcian fauna has Oriental affinities that perhaps make possible correlations with Baluchistan and eastern Asia, but this correlation is not so well established as those on the northern route. One cannot assert positively that the Lower Toarcian of Arabia is the time equivalent of the Lower Toarcian of northwestern Europe, but one can say that this time correlation is more likely than any other.

Upper Jurassic Provincialism

Ammonite provincialism increases in the Upper Jurassic. Correlations in the lowest Upper Jurassic stage, the Oxfordian, are achieved in the same way as for the Callovian (Arkell, 1956, p. 12). Worldwide correlations are also possible for the lower part of the next higher stage, the Kimeridgian. In the remainder of the Upper Jurassic, however, three European provinces are only too well defined: northwestern European, Tethyan, and Russian-Arctic, or Boreal. The uppermost Jurassic faunas which are most satisfactory for worldwide homotaxis and time correlation are those of the Tithonian Stage of western Tethys (Gignoux, 1955, p. 354), with type localities in or near the French Alps. For these uppermost Jurassic levels, northwestern Europe cannot furnish a standard for the world.

The Russian-Arctic faunas may reflect a cold-water facies, although some of the genera are known from widely separated parts of the great Pacific region. In some parts of this region ammonites are rare or absent and uppermost Jurassic-lowest Cretaceous correlations are made by using species of the oyster-like genus *Aucella* (also called *Buchia*). The shells of several species of *Aucella* are abundant in European Russia and California and are known in Mexico and New Zealand.

The Upper Jurassic faunas of the Northwest European Province may represent the alternation of cold-water and warm-water conditions. Northern ammonite genera appear in the Mediterranean at the base of the Oxfordian, and Upper Oxfordian coral reefs are present as far north as central England.

Once the provinces become sharply defined, correlation between them becomes difficult but not impossible. Worldwide Upper Jurassic correlations may yet be achieved, but the present situation still makes impressive, by contrast, the well-established correlations of the Lower Jurassic and part of the Middle Jurassic.

Top and Bottom of Jurassic

Boundaries in type section. In southern England, the marine Jurassic formations, with guide ammonites, form a natural unit, bounded above and below by beds transitional to nonmarine formations. The uppermost English Jurassic unit, the brackish and freshwater Purbeckian, without ammonites, is overlain by the continental Wealden beds of the Weald anticline, south of London, which are called Cretaceous. The basal transition beds, called the Rhaetic (or Rhaetian), are made up largely of shale and limestone containing pectens and other shallow marine mollusks, but also include the Rhaetic bone bed with its abundant remains of fish, amphibians, and reptiles. The Rhaetic has its type area in southern Germany and northern Tyrol; there, in the northeastern Alps, it contains a few ammonites of Triassic aspect that justify its incorporation in that system. In both England and Germany the Rhaetic is overlain conformably by the *Psiloceras planorbis* Zone, zone 1 of the Jurassic.

Extent of Planorbis Zone. The lowest Jurassic is recognizable as the Planorbis Zone throughout the northwest European platform area, and in England and France, it is divisible into two subzones. The Planorbis Zone has also been recognized in Sicily, western British Columbia (West Canada in Table 1), and Peru. Beds containing species of the guide genus *Psiloceras*, and hence probably at the approximate Planorbis Zone horizon, are also known in western Nevada, New Zealand, New Caledonia, and (from boulders) on Timor. In central Europe and Nevada, Planorbis strata overlie beds with characteristic uppermost Triassic ammonites.

Precision of the base of the Jurassic. The base of the Planorbis Zone, lowest in the Jurassic, seems to be a fair example of a fossil-determined Mesozoic horizon that is recognizable in several continents. We shall make estimates of the probable precision of this horizon, in years and in percent of its age. We take the probable average span of a Jurassic zone as 750,000 years, as developed on a previous page. Judging by the ranges found for the zone guides on the European platform, the Jurassic guide species did not last longer than the time represented by a European zone. If the Planorbis Zone took twice the average time for its deposition, that is, about 1.5 million years, the age of the base of the Jurassic, where the Planorbis Zone is present, probably does not vary by more than this length of time. Since 180 million years is a reasonable guess for the radiometric age of the base of the Jurassic (Holmes, 1960; Kulp, 1961), the base of the Planorbis Zone, wherever it is present, can be correlated, even from continent to continent, with a probable precision of one percent or better, even though this estimate is obviously not based on standard statistical procedures.

Triassic and Cretaceous Homotaxis and Correlations

The Triassic and Cretaceous systems have been zoned, and the zones have been grouped into stages in about the same manner as was done for the Jurassic. Ammonites are the principal marine guide fossils. Homotaxis, supplemented by overlapping correlations, is worldwide for large parts of each system. The marine Cretaceous is considerably more widespread than the Jurassic, the marine Triassic considerably less. The type area for the Triassic is in the eastern Alps, where 6 stages have been established (Brinkmann, 1954, p. 175). The type sections for the 12 Cretaceous stages now commonly recognized are mostly in France, although some are just outside that country (Gignoux, 1955, pp. 392, 398; see also "Danian," below, under Cenozoic). In many regions the Upper Cretaceous contains few ammonites. Echinoids, forams, pelecypods, and gastropods must then take the ammonites' place, especially for local correlations. Study of the ammonite (and planktonic foraminiferal) faunas indicates that correlations to the substage level are generally justified, as in the Jurassic.

Conclusions Concerning Mesozoic Stages

As a summary of our consideration of Mesozoic stages and their ammonite faunas, the following statements may be made.

1. Mesozoic stages are groupings of the rock sheets called zones, based on ammonite assemblages.

2. Although zones are more or less local, Mesozoic stages and even substages are mostly worldwide, made so by step-by-step correlations of geographically changing ammonite assemblages.

3. Mesozoic stages and substages are time-stratigraphic units: each stage or substage is composed of strata that accumulated at about the same time in all the places where the stage or substage has been properly identified.

This statement is vitally important, but it contains two ambiguous phrases, "about the same time" and "properly identified," which need to be reemphasized. The second is easier to handle. A proper identification should involve the use of ammonites, whose stratigraphic range should be connected with the ranges of the guide ammonites in the pertinent European stages by methods indicated on previous pages. "About the same time" expresses confidence that there is little time overlap of the stages (or substages). For example, we think that practically all the marine Sinemurian of all regions was deposited before the accumulation of any ammonite-bearing strata anywhere that have been assigned to the Pliensbachian. The degree of our confidence and the reasons for it have been stated in such paragraphs as those on the European-Mexican Lower Jurassic homotaxis (compare Table 5).

Paleozoic Guide Fossils and Correlations

For the Paleozoic, no single group of animals has provided an adequate set of guide fossils. Goniatitic ammonoids are useful in the Upper Paleozoic, but they are less numerous and less widely distributed than their Mesozoic relatives. Goniatite zones have about the same significance as Mesozoic stages. Zones almost equally valuable may be established by using other organisms. Trilobites are outstanding for the Cambrian, graptolites for the geosynclinal facies of the Ordovician and Silurian, and fusuline forams in the Pennsylvanian and Permian. In the highly fossiliferous and widespread limestones and shales of the broad continental platforms, the most useful guide fossils, especially for relatively short-distance correlations, are brachiopods.

Paleozoic subsystems and stages. Each Paleozoic system below the Carboniferous is divided into thirds, and these subsystems have worldwide correlative significance. Below the Devonian, stages or other worldwide units smaller than subsystems seem to be in uncertain status, at least temporarily. Recently, Bell (1960) and Berry (1961) have emphasized the difficulties of interprovincial stage correlations in the Cambrian and Ordovician. In the marine Devonian, useful stages have been established, with type areas in Belgium or the Rhineland. Gignoux (1955, p. 120) gave the following stages, from the base up: Gedinnian and Coblencian in the Lower Devonian, Eifelian and Givetian in the Middle Devonian, Frasnian and Famennian in the Upper Devonian. Brinkmann (1954) gave a somewhat different list, with 9 stages. The Carboniferous is divided into Lower (also called Dinantian or Mississippian, although these two terms are not synonymous; compare Brinkmann, 1954, opposite p. 106) and Upper (Pennsylvanian or Coal Measures). The Upper Carboniferous is divided into three stages designated, in ascending order,

Namurian, Westphalian, and Stephanian, with the most satisfactory type sections (probably even for the Stephanian) in Belgium, west central Germany, and central Russia because of the presence of marine bands there. Each stage has characteristic goniatites and the upper two have guide fusulines (Brinkmann, 1954, opposite p. 106). For the Permian, Brinkmann (1954, opposite p. 132) gave a composite set of five Old World stages, with guide ammonoids and fusulines. From the base up, with the West Texas equivalent in parentheses, Brinkmann's stages are Sakmara (Wolfcamp), Artinsk (Leonard), Sosio (Word), Basleo (Capitan), and Chideru (Ochoa). A composite set of stages is unsatisfactory, but the type Permian in European Russia is brackish to nonmarine in its upper part.

In North America, the whole Paleozoic has been provided with more or less independent local stages and other units (see C. O. Dunbar and others, 1942, 1944, 1948, 1954, 1960), with American type sections or localities.

Cenozoic Correlations

The first problem connected with the Cenozoic is its definition, and the definition of its marine subdivisions, in the European type region. Prevalent current practice seems to be to make the Danian of Denmark a part of the Cenozoic and put the top of the Mesozoic at the top of the Maestrichtian Stage in Holland and Denmark (Loeblich and Tappan, 1957, p. 1113; Bramlette and Sullivan, 1961, p. 136). Few if any worldwide marine Cenozoic stages are yet valid, although prospects are bright for success in the Paleogene, through the use of planktonic forams and nannoplankton (Loeblich and Tappan, 1957; Bolli, 1959; Bramlette and Sullivan, 1961). The Cenozoic series—Paleocene, Eocene, Oligocene, Miocene, Pliocene, and Pleistocene—are now well established, at least as names, although there is considerable variation in the number, terminology, and distribution of the stages that make up the series in the European type section (compare Brinkmann, 1954, p. 254, with Gignoux, 1955, pp. 472 and 557). The base of the Miocene is put variously at the base of the Aquitanian, at the Burdigalian-Aquitanian boundary, and at the top of the Burdigalian. For Brinkmann it is sub-Aquitanian, for Gignoux sub-Burdigalian. Drooger (1954, 1956), within two years, dropped the base of the European Miocene from the top of the Burdigalian to the base of the Aquitanian. Overseas correlations are even less definite. Recently Eames and others (1962) suggested that the Vicksburg and certain other North American formations, commonly considered pre-Aquitanian Oligocene, should be raised to positions in the Miocene. In general, Cenozoic intercontinental marine correlations are exceptionally difficult. The difficulties are magnified if correlations involving nonmarine mammals are taken into account.

Divisions of Geologic Time

Systems and stages are divisions of the rocks. If we agree that the procedures by which sedimentary rocks all over the world are assigned to particular systems and subsystems, or even to stages and substages, are, at least in favorable cases, correlations of contemporaneous strata, we can make the transition from the stratigraphic division of the rocks to the division of geologic time. We can then recognize geologic periods and the primary subdivisions of the periods: Early Cambrian time, the time of deposition of the Lower Cambrian rocks; Middle Cambrian time, the time of deposition of the Middle Cambrian rocks; Late Cambrian time, the time of deposition of the Upper Cambrian rocks; etc. Some finer time subdivisions can also be made, especially in the Mesozoic. Callovian time was the time of deposition of the Callovian rocks; early Callovian time was the time of deposition of the Lower Callovian rocks.

Most periods seem to have been between 40 and 70 million years long (compare Holmes, 1960; Kulp, 1961). Subperiods were therefore very roughly 15–25 million years each. The Cambrian subperiods were probably longer; a Chinese Lower Cambrian fauna might have an age uncertainty of 35 million years from vagueness of correlation alone. The Mesozoic stages are more precise. There are about 11 Jurassic stages and about 12 Cretaceous stages. If the Jurassic and Cretaceous periods were respectively 45 and 65 million years long (compare Holmes, 1960; Kulp, 1961), each Jurassic or Cretaceous stage represents, on the average, 4 or 5 million years. The earliest Jurassic stage, the Hettangian, which includes only three zones, may stand for a shorter time. Most Mesozoic substages are thirds or halves of stages and so may represent 1.5 to 2.5 million years each.

Lacunas and the Geologic Column

Recognition and naming of lacunas. Each lacuna in the rock succession represents a lapse of time. The time represented by the lacuna at 135.5 cm Peterborough, between the Jason and Coronatum zones of the Middle Callovian, is part of Middle Callovian time. If, however, one wished to subdivide Middle Callovian time, should the separation be into two parts—Jason time and Coronatum time—or into three parts—Jason time, lacuna time, and Coronatum time? If one is considering a global time scale, this particular problem is unreal, because the European zonal stratigraphy cannot be extended throughout the world. But similar questions have been raised with regard to pairs of periods. Should intervals between periods be recognized? Moreover, if a large lacuna existed between the type Cambrian and Ordovician of Wales or in the more easily handled Cambro-Ordovician section in Scandinavia, should an American stratigrapher with a more complete section insert a new unit between Cambrian and Ordovician? This was in part what Ulrich tried to do with his Ozarkian System (Ulrich, 1911, p. 608). A consensus of opinion now seems to have developed with regard to lacuna fillings. New systems are not to be established. Stratigraphic units with lacuna-filling faunas are to be assimilated into the systems and subsystems of the long-established standard column. Just how to do this is a problem of adjustment or negotiation in each case. To take one example, the marine strata that seem to belong between the highest Russian marine Permian and the lowest Alpine marine Triassic are assigned to the Permian, not to the Triassic (Brinkmann, 1954, opposite p. 132).

The question of "intervals" remains. Are there still any unfilled large lacunas? Unconformities marking lacunas on the continental platforms are no longer pertinent, now that basins near the margins of the platforms have been found to contain more continuous sections. Studies of surface and sub-surface sections in the basin areas have filled in most of the more obvious lacunas of the fossiliferous marine section. Transitions have been found from Precambrian to Cambrian (southeast California—Nelson, 1962), from Permian to Triassic (Newell, 1962), and from Cretaceous to Tertiary (central California —Payne, 1951; Schoellhamer and Kinney, 1953). It now seems probable that somewhere, on some continent or island, or beneath some small or moderate-sized sea, sedimentary strata exist that formed during the time represented by every paleontologically measurable lacuna in the European record.

Faunal changes and lacunas. It should be noted that not every faunal change is proof of a paleontological lacuna. Even where the ecological facies are similar or identical and whole groups of animals disappear at one horizon, as do the ammonites and plesiosaurs at the Cretaceous-Tertiary boundary in California, the stratigraphic and paleontological lacuna may be small. On the west side of the San Joaquin Valley (Schoellhamer and Kinney, 1953), the shales and sandstone of the Moreno formation are overlain with slight uncon-formity by the sandstones, mudstones, and claystones of the Lodo formation, which is glauconitic at the base, but the Cretaceous-Tertiary contact, deter-mined faunally, is in the Moreno formation more than 200 ft below the uncon-formity. The provincial Paleocene guide fossils *Flabellum remondianum* Gabb, a coral, and *Brachysphingus sinuatus* Gabb, a gastropod, were collected from an 80-ft sandstone lens in the Moreno, and the top of the lens was about 200 ft below the Lodo contact. The Moreno shales, 600 ft or more below the sand-stone lens, contain Maestrichtian ammonites and several kinds of large Meso-zoic reptiles: plesiosaurs, a mosasaur, and the dinosaur *Trachydon*. No physical stratigraphic break was found between the lowest Paleocene guide fossils and the highest Cretaceous guides. Regionally, the abundant marine forams of the highest Cretaceous strata are so similar to those of the lowest Paleocene that the assignment of some faunas to the Cretaceous or the Paleocene is somewhat uncertain (compare Goudkoff, 1945, p. 1004).

Summary Discussion

Biostratigraphic generalizations. Stratigraphic correlations through the use of guide fossils are based on repeated observations over a period of 100–150 years, with results so uniform that they may be summarized as empirical generalizations: (1) The fossil species and genera in a single column vary from horizon to horizon. (2) Homotaxis occurs between columns. (3) Within a province, guide species useful in time correlation can be established for horizon after horizon, using the methods described in this paper in connection with the northwestern European Lower and Middle Jurassic zones. (4) More distant correlations, between provinces, can be made through step-by-step correlations, using gradually varying assemblages. Time correlations based on homotaxial evolutionary sequences will become more and more easily distinguishable from the misleading correlations of facies zones as more is learned about the evolution and geologic history of the families involved. Most of the older studies on ammonite groups were weakened by the use of the now discredited biogenetic law: ontogeny recapitulates phylogeny. The kind of study needed is illustrated by Brinkmann's work on the *Kosmoceratidae*, although that work now deserves the compliment of restudy and revision. The extension of such work will be difficult because so few families have their Peterboroughs.

Correlations based on the appearance or disappearance of major groups, such as trilobites, ammonites, or mammals, are inherently unsafe (Huxley, 1870). Consider, for example, the absurdity of a correlation based on the first appearance of eutherian mammals in North America and Australia. This rule does not prevent an ammonite species or genus from being a sound guide to the uppermost Cretaceous.

In favorable circumstances, such as those that prevail for the northwest European Lower and Middle Jurassic, time correlations within a province may be very precise. For significant comparisons with radiometric ages, however, more nearly worldwide interprovincial correlations must be considered. The precision of interprovincial correlations varies from one part of the geologic column to another. In the Jurassic and Cretaceous a time correlation based on numerous well-preserved specimens of ammonite guide species can hardly be in error by more than one substage, perhaps ± 2 million years. The base of the fossiliferous Lower Cambrian, on the other hand, may vary in age by tens of millions of years.

Stratigraphy and time. Geologic stages and systems are second-order units and geologic periods are, in a way, third-order units. Stratigraphy began with the local columns of one region, from which the generalized column of stages and systems has been chiefly derived. The standard time scale is derived directly from the standard column and from no other source, except for Late Pleistocene details. The fossils of the units in the standard column and of other units in other columns are still our principal guides in stratigraphic correlation, although we cordially welcome the statistical calibration of the standard column, in years, from radiometric data.

REFERENCES CITED

ARKELL, W. J., 1947, The geology of the country around Weymouth, Swanage, Corfe, and Lulworth: Great Britain, Geol. Survey Mem., 386 pp.

——, 1956, Jurassic geology of the world: Edinburgh, Oliver and Boyd, 806 pp.

BANDY, O. L., 1953, Ecology and paleoecology of some California foraminifera: J. Paleont., vol. 27, pp. 161–182, 200–203.

BELL, W. C., 1960, Cambrian, in McGraw-Hill Encyc. Sci. Techn.: New York, McGraw-Hill, pp. 424–427.

BENTZ, A., 1928, Über Strenoceraten und Garantianen insbesondere aus dem mittleren Dogger von Bielefeld: Jahrb. Preuss. geol. Landesanst., pp. 138–206.

BERRY, W. B. N., 1961, Chorology, chronology, and correlation: Geol. Soc. Am., program Ann. Mtg., pp. 10A–11A.

BOLLI, H. M., 1959, Planktonic foraminifera as index fossils in Trinidad, West Indies and their value for worldwide stratigraphic correlation: Eclogae Geol. Helvetiae, vol. 52, pp. 627–637.

BRAMLETTE, M. N., and SULLIVAN, F. R., 1961, Coccolithophorids and related nannoplankton of the early Tertiary in California: Micropaleont., vol. 7, pp. 129–188.

BRINKMANN, R., 1929, Statistisch-biostratigraphische Untersuchungen an mitteljurassischen Ammoniten über Artbegriff und Stammesentwicklung: Abh. Ges. Wiss. Göttingen, N. F., vol. 13, no. 3, 249 pp.

——, 1954, Abriss der Geologie: Stuttgart, Enke, 2 vols.

BUCKMAN, S. S., 1901, Bajocian and contiguous deposits in the North Cotteswolds: The Main Hill-mass: Geol. Soc. London, Quart. J., vol. 57, pp. 126–155.

BURCH, J. Q., ed., 1945–1946, Distributional list of the West American marine mollusks from San Diego, California, to the Polar Sea: Conch. Club Sou. Calif. Minutes nos. 45–63, separately paged.

CALLOMON, J. H., 1955, The ammonite succession in the lower Oxford Clay and Kellaways Beds at Kidlington, Oxfordshire, and the zones of the Callovian Stage: Roy. Soc. London, Phil. Tr., s. B., vol. 239, pp. 215–264.

——, 1961, The Jurassic System in East Greenland, in Geology of the Arctic, G. O. Raasch, ed.: Toronto, Univ. Toronto Press, vol. 1, pp. 258–268.

DEAN. W. T., DONOVAN, D. T., and HOWARTH, M. K., 1961, The Liassic ammonite zones and subzones of the North-West European Province: British Mus. (Nat. Hist.), B., Geol., vol. 4, no. 10, pp. 437–505.

DROOGER, C. W., 1954, The Oligocene-Miocene boundary on both sides of the Atlantic: Geol. Mag., vol. 91, pp. 514–518.

——, 1956, Transatlantic correlation of the Oligo-Miocene by means of foraminifera: Micropaleont., vol. 2, pp. 183–192.

DUNBAR, C. O., chm., 1942–1960, Correlation charts prepared by the Committee on Stratigraphy of the National Research Council: Geol. Soc. Am., B., vol. 53, pp. 429–433; Cambrian, vol. 55 (1944), pp. 993–1003; Ordovician, vol. 65 (1954), pp. 247–298; Silurian, vol. 53 (1942), pp. 533–538; Devonian, vol. 53 (1942), pp. 1729–1793; Mississippian, vol. 59 (1948), pp. 91–196; Pennsylvanian, vol. 55 (1944), pp. 657–706; Permian, vol. 71 (1960), pp. 1763–1805.

EAMES, F. E., BANNER, F. T., BLOW, W. H., CLARKE, W. J., and COX, L. R., 1962, Fundamentals of mid-Tertiary stratigraphical correlation: Cambridge, Eng., Cambridge Univ. Press, 163 pp.

ELTON, C. S., 1958, The ecology of invasions by animals and plants: London, Methuen, 181 pp.

ERBEN, H. K., 1956, El Jurásico inferior de México y sus amonitas: XX Int. Geol. Congress, Mexico, 393 pp.

GIGNOUX, M., (1950) 1955, Stratigraphic geology (trans. by G. G. Woodford): San Francisco, Freeman, 682 pp.

GOUDKOFF, P. P., 1945, Stratigraphic relations of Upper Cretaceous in Great Valley, California: Am. Assoc. Petroleum Geol., B., vol. 29, pp. 956–1007.

HOLMES, A., 1960, A revised geological time-scale: Edinburgh Geol. Soc. Tr., vol. 17, pp. 183–216.

HUXLEY, T. H., 1862, The anniversary address: Geol. Soc. London, Quart. J., vol. 18, pp. xl–liv.

——, 1870, Anniversary address: Geol. Soc. London, Quart. J., vol. 26, pp. xxix–lxiv.

IMLAY, R. W., 1953, Callovian (Jurassic) ammonites from the United States and Alaska: U.S. Geol. Survey Prof. Paper 249, 108 pp.

KEEN, A. M., 1958, Sea shells of tropical West America: Stanford, Calif., Stanford Univ. Press, 624 pp.

KULP, J. L., 1961, Geologic time scale: Science, vol. 133, pp. 1105–1114.

LOEBLICH, A. R., and TAPPAN, H., 1957, Correlation of the Gulf and Atlantic Coastal Plain Paleocene and Lower Eocene formations by means of planktonic foraminifera: J. Paleont., vol. 31, pp. 1109–1137.

MODEL, R., and MODEL, E., 1938, Die Lamberti-Schichten von Trockau in Oberfranken: Jahrb. preuss. geol. Landesanstalt, vol. 58, pp. 631–665.

NATLAND, M. L., 1933, The temperature- and depth-distribution of some recent and fossil foraminifera in the southern California region: Scripps Inst. Oceanog., B., Tech. Ser., vol. 3, pp. 225–230.

——, 1957, Paleoecology of West Coast Tertiary sediments: Geol. Soc. Am., Mem. 67, vol. 2, pp. 543–572.

NELSON, C. A., 1962, Lower Cambrian-Precambrian succession, White-Inyo Mountains, California: Geol. Soc. Am., B., vol. 73, pp. 139–144.

NEWELL, N. D., 1962, Paleontological gaps and geochronology: J. Paleont., vol. 36, pp. 592–610.

OPPEL, A., 1856–1858, Die Juraformation Englands, Frankreichs, und des südwestlichen Deutschlands: Stuttgart, Ebner and Seubert, 857 pp.

D'ORBIGNY, A. D., 1842–1851 (1850–1860), Paléontologie française: terrains jurassiques, céphalopodes: Paris, 642 pp.

PAYNE, M. B., 1951, Type Moreno Formation and overlying Eocene strata on the west side of the San Joaquin Valley, Fresno and Merced counties, California: California Div. Mines, Spec. Rept. 9, 29 pp.

RANGHEARD, Y., and THEOBALD, N., 1961, Nouveaux gisements fossilifères dans le Callovien moyen et supérior de Besançon-Palente: Univ. Besançon Ann. Sci., 2me sér., Géol., Fasc. 15, pp. 3–7.

SCHENCK, H. G., and KEEN, A. M., 1936, Marine molluscan provinces of western North America: Am. Phil. Soc. Pr., vol. 76, pp. 921–938.

SCHOELLHAMER, J. E., and KINNEY, D. M., 1953, Geology of portions of Tumey and Panoche Hills, Fresno County, California: U.S. Geol. Survey Oil and Gas Inv. Map 128.

SCOTT, G., 1940, Paleoecological factors controlling the distribution and mode of life of Cretaceous ammonoids in the Texas area: J. Paleont., vol. 14, pp. 299–323.

SMITH, W., 1815, A memoir to the map and delineation of the strata of England and Wales, with part of Scotland: London, J. Cary, 51 pp.

———, 1816, Strata identified by organized fossils: London, W. Arding, 32 pp.

SPATH, L. F., 1933, The evolution of the Cephalopoda: Biol. Rev., vol. 8, pp. 418–462.

STENO, N., 1669, De solido intra solidum naturaliter contento dissertationis prodromus: Florence, 78 pp.

THEOBALD, N., 1957, Documents nouveaux sur l'extension des différentes zones à ammonites d'âge callovien dans le Jura septentrional: Univ. Besançon Ann. Sci., 2me sér., Géol., Fasc. 7, pp. 21–40.

ULRICH, E. O., 1911, Revision of the Paleozoic systems: Geol. Soc. Am., B., vol. 22, pp. 281–680.

WESTERMANN, G., 1954, Monographie der Otoitidae (Ammonoidea): Beihefte z. geol. Jahrb. (Hannover), no. 15, 364 pp.

WOODRING, W. P., BRAMLETTE, M. N., and KEW, W. S. W., 1946, Geology and paleontology of Palos Verdes Hills, California: U.S. Geol. Survey, Prof. Paper 207, 145 pp.

DONALD B. McINTYRE

Pomona College

Precision and Resolution
in Geochronometry

There are probably compensating errors, and the resulting age determination will be very useful to geologists if, for instance, we could say that 9 times out of 10 the age is x ± y million years. (Larsen, Keevil, and Harrison, 1952, p. 1046)

Formerly it was the custom to distinguish between the so-called exact and inexact sciences, an exact science being one which admitted, or perhaps we should say whose practitioners claimed, absolute precision. Nowadays we are more cautious, and most scientists are well aware that absolute precision can be hoped for only when our measuring devices are being used far from their limits. In other words, whether we are determining chemical composition, stratigraphic thickness, or the age of a rock, it is common to find that if we make replicate readings they will not be identical. Recognizing this, authors often follow the report of a measurement by a plus-or-minus quantity which is intended to indicate, in some manner, the degree of confidence which is to be placed in the value given. Unfortunately, the reader is not always informed what the basis for the plus-or-minus quantity is and what confidence is to be assigned to it, and to provide the figure in such cases is obviously an empty gesture.

In this essay the degree of reproducibility is referred to as *precision*; this is not to be confused with *accuracy* which is the approach to a hypothetical "true" value. We will assume that accuracy (or bias) is dependent upon systematic errors, such as faulty adjustment of instruments or the use of incorrect constants, whereas precision is determined by numerous small and independent random errors.[1] Discussion of the existence and possible magnitude of systematic errors and of gross errors lies beyond the scope of this essay.

---

[1] The implied hypothesis of normal distribution may be questioned, but until we are given data demonstrating how the distribution departs from the normal, we have no satisfactory alternative but to accept it.

Geology is rapidly becoming quantitative and it seems worth while to draw attention to the importance of presenting data so that the precision of measurement is clear, for it is this precision that determines the resolving power and hence, in large measure, the utility of the method. Although the topic is relevant to any measurements, geochronometry happens to present convenient examples. It is not the writer's purpose, however, to review the relative merits of different methods of age dating. The two methods which are discussed, potassium-argon and lead-alpha, were chosen as illustrations because they have yielded the majority of dates on the Mesozoic batholithic rocks of western North America. The writer is not a practitioner of geochronometry; his qualifications are those of most members of the geological fraternity, for we have all been addressed on this subject through our professional literature, and it is our responsibility to draw conclusions from the information published.

In 1960 this essay was sent to many who are active in geochronometry, and the writer is grateful for the replies and comments which he has received. In the meantime considerable advances have been made in isotopic studies, and some doubt has been expressed regarding the accuracy of the lead-alpha method. Nevertheless, because the purpose of the essay is to encourage other readers to draw their own conclusions from any data presented to them, it does not seem necessary to substitute other examples for those originally included.

Since Rutherford's suggestion, in 1905, that the accumulation of decay products in radioactive minerals might provide a means of measuring geological time, great numbers of minerals and rocks have been "dated." Indeed, the rate of output of new "dates" is now so high that it is difficult for evaluation to keep abreast of production. Many geologists have all but given up the attempt and are ready to accept without question any age correlation or distinction made by such methods.

A date quoted for a rock is no better than its precision; hence readers are entitled to expect every author to pass on, in unambiguous terms, his best quantitative evaluation of this date. Because the precision of the age is a function of the precisions of each variable entering into the computation, we must begin by analyzing the random errors in each of these variables.

Precision of the Lead-Alpha Method

"A mineral to be usable for determining the age of rocks by this method should have only radiogenic lead, should have lost no lead, should have only primary radioactive elements, and should have lost none of them." (Larsen *et al.*, 1952, p. 1046) The ionic radius of Pb^{2+} (1.32 A) is very close to that of K^+ (1.33) and very different from that of Zr^{4+} (0.87); hence it is reasonable to suppose that primary lead will be preferentially captured (Goldschmidt,

TABLE 1

TWENTY-FIVE REPLICATE DETERMINATIONS OF PB IN STANDARD
SAMPLE SAID TO CONTAIN 30 PPM
ANALYSES BY C. L. WARING AND H. WORTHING (1953)

Observation number i	Pb, ppm x_i	x_i^2*
1	31	961
2	30	900
3	33	1089
4	30	900
.	34	.
.	30	.
.	29	.
	30	
	28	
	28	
	28	
	29	
	30	
	30	
	32	
	28	
	31	
.	30	.
.	35	.
.	32	.
21	30	900
22	29	841
23	30	900
24	31	961
25	32	1024
$n = 25$	$\sum_{i=1}^{n} x_i = 760$	$\sum_{i=1}^{n} x_i^2 = 23184$

$$s^2 = \frac{1}{n(n-1)}\left[n\sum x^2 - (\sum x)^2\right] = 3.33,$$

$$\bar{x} = \frac{1}{n}\sum x = 30.4,$$

$$s = 1.82 \text{ ppm} \quad \text{or} \quad 1.82 \times 100/30.4 = 6.0\%.$$

* In practice the figures in column i and x_i^2 are not recorded, for only the totals are used and these are obtained on a desk calculator as by-products of entering the values x_i.

1944; Gottfried, et al., 1959) in orthoclase, whereas any lead found in zircon is likely to be radiogenic from a U^{4+} (1.05) or Th^{4+} (1.10) parent. Isotopic analyses confirm that the proportion of primary lead in zircon is often small (Gottfried, et al., 1959, Table 14), although there are notable exceptions. On the assumption that the mineral has had a history which makes the method a valid one, it is necessary to determine (a) the radioactivity, by means of an alpha counter, (b) the thorium/uranium ratio, which for accessory zircons is usually considered known from earlier work, and (c) the amount of lead by spectrographic analysis.

Precision of lead determination. In the application of the method to zircon concentrates from Mesozoic rocks, it is necessary to determine the lead content when it ranges from 1.8–180 ppm (Larsen, et al., 1958). In order to estimate the precision of the lead determinations, Waring and Worthing (1953) made 25 replicate measurements (Table 1) on a standard sample said to contain 30 ppm lead in a silica base. We consider these 25 measurements as a *sample* (size $n = 25$) which is representative of the *population* of all possible measurements. Each individual measurement is termed a *variate*, x_i, $i = 1$, . . . , n; and the *statistics* of the sample are:

the *mean*, $\quad \bar{x} = \dfrac{1}{n} \sum_{i=1}^{n} x_i = 30.4$ ppm,

the *variance*, $\quad s^2 = \dfrac{1}{n-1} \sum_{i=1}^{n} (x_i - \bar{x})^2 = \dfrac{1}{n(n-1)} \left[n \sum x^2 - (\sum x)^2 \right]$,

and the *standard deviation*, $\quad s = 1.82$ ppm or 6.0%.[2]

These definitions are in forms suitable for use with a desk calculator on which the sums of x^2 and of x can be accumulated simultaneously. They give the best estimates of the *parameters*[3] of the population from which the sample has been drawn. From the table prepared by Eleanor G. Crow (*in* Crow, et al., 1960, Table 8), the standard deviation of the population is $\sigma = 4.9$–7.9% with 90% confidence or 4.7–8.4% with 95% confidence. This gives a meaningful measure of the precision of the method.

---

[2] $100s/\bar{x}$ is the coefficient of variation. It is often denoted by C, but here we will use simply $s\%$, and, by analogy, $\sigma\%$. The transformation is justified if s is proportional to $\bar{x}$; in some of the examples this may not be the case.

[3] It is convenient to use italic letters, such as $\bar{x}$ and s, for the statistics of a sample and to use Greek letters, such as μ and σ, for the parameters of a population. In practice we are interested in the statistics only as estimates of the parameters.

In 1959, Gottfried, Jaffe, and Senftle (1959, Table 8) presented a table showing how the precision of the lead determination (at confidence level of 90%) varies with the amount of lead present. If the percentage standard deviation is plotted on semilog paper against the geometric mid-points of the lead ranges given by these authors, we may estimate[4] the precision of all lead determinations on zircons published in U. S. Geol. Survey B. 1070-B (Larsen, *et al.*, 1958, Tables 5–11). The mean value of the standard deviations estimated in this way is 10%. However, many of the lead-alpha dates on rocks of the Mesozoic batholiths were determined on the basis of average values of several lead determinations. In these cases the precision is that of the mean, $\sigma_{\bar{x}} = \sigma_x/\sqrt{n}$, where n is the number of replicate determinations included in the mean. The mean value of all the standard deviations estimated in this manner is 8.8%.

An independent evaluation of the precision of the lead determinations can be obtained from an analysis of the duplicate results themselves. A pooled estimate of the mean precision of the individual lead determinations, i.e., a mean value giving increased weight to larger values of s and of n was computed as s_p where N is the number of samples on which replicate determinations were made and

$$s_p^2 = \frac{\sum_{i=1}^{N} (n_i - 1)s_i^2}{\sum_{i=1}^{N} (n_i - 1)} = 122.8.$$

Hence we estimate $\sigma = 9.4$–13.6% with 90% confidence. This is consistent with the value of 10% obtained above on the basis of the application of Gottfried, Jaffe and Senftle's Table 8 (1959) to the data in U. S. Geol. Survey B. 1070-B, Tables 5–11. We therefore adopt $\sigma = 9$–13% as a tentative[5] measure of the precision of lead determinations for the evaluation of the dates obtained on the Mesozoic batholithic rocks of western North America. That this value is reasonable is further borne out by the fact that replicate analyses of lead in accessory zircons from eastern Massachusetts granites (Webber, *et al.*, 1956, Table 2) yield a pooled estimate of $\sigma = 9.2$–12.0% with 90% confidence (see Table 2).

---

[4] The interpretation of Table 8 of Gottfried, *et al.* (1959) is ambiguous, but the writer believes that any other method of plotting will give higher values for σ. He has assumed that 1.645σ = precision at 90% confidence.

[5] Since this essay was written, the work of Rose and Stern has suggested that a better precision ($<6\%$) may be obtained; but whether the values published in U. S. Geol. Survey B. 1070–B justify this higher confidence is another matter. This illustrates one of the difficulties faced by the reader who wishes to evaluate published dates.

TABLE 2

ANALYSIS OF REPLICATE LEAD DETERMINATIONS ON ACCESSORY ZIRCONS
FROM EASTERN MASSACHUSETTS GRANITES
BASED ON DATA IN WEBBER, HURLEY, AND FAIRBAIRN, 1956

n	$\overline{Pb}$, ppm	s, ppm	$s\%$	n	$\overline{Pb}$, ppm	s, ppm	$s\%$
6	46.5	2.6	5.6	6	68.3	8.6	12.6
6	21.3	1.0	4.9	3	73.0	2.0	2.7
6	19.2	1.9	10.1	4	70.2	3.3	4.7
3	141.0	20.4	14.5	2	89.5	0.7	0.8
6	85.8	2.7	3.2	3	77.0	5.0	6.5
2	58.0	18.4	31.7	3	117.0	6.1	5.2
6	37.2	6.4	17.3	3	116.3	14.8	12.7
4	28.0	0.8	2.9	5	81.8	10.1	12.3
4	46.8	2.1	4.4	3	75.3	3.8	5.0
3	76.3	9.7	12.7	5	65.6	7.4	11.3
3	56.3	7.5	13.3	3	55.0	5.3	9.6
7	71.4	8.7	12.2	3	66.0	1.7	2.6

$$\sum(n - 1) = 75 \qquad\qquad \sum(n - 1)s^2 = 8111.5$$

$$s_p^2 = \frac{8111.5}{75} = 108.15$$

Hence $s_p = 10.4\%$, and $\sigma = 9.2\text{–}12.0\%$ with 90% confidence.

Precision of Th/U ratio. Because the decay constants of thorium and uranium differ, it is necessary to know the Th/U ratio in a mineral which is to be dated by the lead-alpha method. Most of the dates obtained by Larsen and his associates on the batholithic rocks of western North America were based on accessory zircon, and it is this case which is treated here. The available data on the Th/U ratio in accessory zircon have been summarized by Gottfried, Jaffe, and Senftle (1959, Table 1). It is interesting to note the following points: (a) none of the data were published prior to 1957, (b) only 13 "localities" are represented, (c) the Mesozoic batholithic rocks of western North America are not included, (d) a considerable variety of analytical methods were employed providing accuracies said to vary from ±1% to ±20%, (e) at only seven of the "localities" were measurements made on more than one sample, and hence these are the only ones for which σ can be estimated, and (f) the number of samples, the range, and the average are given for these seven localities, but s is not given.

Because complete data are not available for calculation of s, we have to estimate it from the range (see Crow, *et al.*, 1960, Table 12). In four cases it is

TABLE 3

Th/U Ratios in Accessory Zircons

Number of samples, n_i	Range, ω	Mean value, Th/U $= x_i$	Estimate of s_i	$(n_i - 1)s_i^2$	90% confidence limits for σ_i
1		0.8			
22	2.2	1.2	0.59	7.31	
1		1.2			
21	2.3	0.9	0.62	7.68	0.37–0.62*
24	0.8	0.5	0.21	1.01	0.16–0.26†
10	0.2	0.2	0.07	0.04	0.06–0.14†
1		0.3			
9	2.4	1.2	0.81	5.25	0.58–1.38‡
1		0.4			
1		0.5			
4	0.32	0.3	0.16	0.08	
2	0.24	0.4	0.21	0.04	
1		1.1			

$\sum n = 98$, where
$n_i > 1, \sum n = 92,$
and $\mathcal{N} = 7.$

$\sum(n - 1)s^2 = 21.41$

Pooled mean for Th/U $= 0.78$

Pooled estimate $s_p^2 = \dfrac{21.41}{92-7}$; hence $s_p = 0.50$, and $\sigma = 0.44\text{–}0.57$ with 90% confidence

Total range $= 2.7$; $\sum n = 98$; hence standard deviation can be estimated as 0.54

Columns 1 through 3 of this table computed from Gottfried, *et al.* (1959), Table 1.
* Figures computed from the data of H. Holland (in Gottfried, *et al.*, 1959).
† Figures computed from Hurley and Fairbairn (1957).
‡ Figures computed from Lyons, *et al.* (1957).

possible to refer to the original data, and for these the writer has computed 90%-confidence limits for σ (see Table 3). In each case the values of standard deviation computed from the range fall within these limits. The pooled mean for Th/U is 0.78 and the unweighted mean is 0.69. These figures do not accord very closely with the claim that: "At present it seems reasonable to assign a thorium-uranium ratio of 1 for the average accessory zircon." (Gottfried, *et al.*, 1959, p. 12) If the wrong ratio has been used, it is quite possible that this would produce a systematic error only, and that the relative ages of the rocks of a single province might not be affected. However, it is obvious from Table 3 that even within a single province the Th/U ratio in accessory zircon can vary considerably. Thus, the variability of Th/U must be estimated, for it will affect the precision of the date. Because 2.7 is the total range of all 98 values on which Table 3 is based, we can estimate the standard deviation as 0.54. This agrees with the pooled estimate of the standard deviation, $s = 0.50$, giving $\sigma = 0.44$–0.57 with 90% confidence.

Now, the Th/U ratio enters into the age computation by way of the factor c, where

$$c = \frac{2632 + 624 \text{ Th/U}}{1 + 0.312 \text{ Th/U}}.$$

(See Gottfried, *et al.*, 1959, Fig. 1.) We have determined that the mean value of Th/U is about 0.78 and that the standard deviation of the possible values for this ratio is likely to be about 0.50. Hence a Th/U range of $\pm\sigma$ would be 0.28–1.28, giving a range of 2581 through 2452 for c. Hence σ for factor c can be estimated as about 2.6%, or approximately 3%.

Precision of alpha measurement. The radioactivity is measured by the ion-chamber method and is given as the number of alpha counts per milligram per hour. Gottfried, Jaffe, and Senftle (1959, p. 22) report: "... the activity determined by counting methods agrees on the average within 5 percent with the alpha activity calculated from the thorium and uranium content ... In general, the interlaboratory checks agree within 5 percent. From these checks, and also from the alpha-counting experience in this and other laboratories, the alpha-counting data probably are accurate to within 5 percent." Lyons, *et al.*, (1957, p. 528) have recorded their precision in the statement: "Duplicate measurements of alpha activity on the same sample are reproducible to within 5% of the measured value." Webber, Hurley, and Fairbairn (1956, Table 3) have given figures for "standard-deviation precision error based on replicate alpha counts"; their data as published yield a mean value, $s\%$, of 7.8 with $\sigma = 6.4$–10.1% with 90% confidence. Our conclusion must therefore be vague, with σ for alpha determination surely somewhere in the range from 3–10%.

Resulting precision of age determination. If the age is less than 200 million years (m. y.), it is determined from the equation $t = (c \cdot \text{Pb})/\alpha$, where t is the age in millions of years, c is the factor depending upon the Th/U ratio, Pb is the lead content in parts per million, and α is the radioactivity in alpha counts per milligram per hour. If the partial errors in t due to given errors in c, Pb, and α are E_c, E_{Pb} and E_α respectively, then the total error in t is $E_t = E_c + E_{\text{Pb}} + E_\alpha$. In practice we know only the probability distributions of these partial errors and not their actual values. Thus, although it is true that the total error is the sum of the partial errors, the parameters of the probability distribution of t cannot be obtained by summation of the parameters of the probability distributions of the individual variates; i.e., $\sigma_t \neq \sigma_c + \sigma_{Pb} + \sigma_\alpha$. When we make an age determination, what we do in effect is to pick at random the magnitudes of the errors in c, Pb, and α and then add their effects. Assuming that there is no correlation between E_c, E_{Pb}, and E_α, i.e., that there is no reason to expect a particularly large error in c to occur along with a particularly large error in Pb or in α, then we have $\sigma_t^2 = \sigma_c^2 + \sigma_{Pb}^2 + \sigma_\alpha^2$.[6] (If this assumption is not correct then the correlation coefficients must be determined and used to derive σ_t^2.) As a consequence of this relationship, if σ_{Pb} is considerably greater than σ_c or σ_α, as may be the case, then σ_t will be only a little larger than σ_{Pb}. Using the best estimates which we have derived above, we obtain

$$\sigma_{Pb} \sim 9\text{–}13\%, \qquad \sigma_\alpha \sim 3\text{–}10\%, \qquad \sigma_c \sim 3\%.$$

Hence, the predicted precision of dates on the Mesozoic batholithic rocks by the lead-alpha method is $\sigma \sim 10.0\text{–}16.7\%$, or about 9.8–13.6% if allowance is made for the replicate determinations of lead.

The observed precisions (based on Larsen, *et al.*, 1958, Table 12) are as follows:

n		$s\%$	σ, 90%-confidence limits
35	Mexico and Southern California	10.3	8.6–12.9
15	Sierra Nevada	10.8	8.3–15.7
16[7]	Idaho	11.1	8.6–16.0
16	Coast Range	12.4	9.6–17.8
82	All 82 specimens taken together	11.2	9.9–12.9

We conclude that (a) the observed and predicted precisions are the same, within the limits imposed by the data available to us, and (b) all 82 specimens from the Mesozoic batholiths of western North America have the same age, within the limits of the method.

In their work on the accessory zircon from the eastern Massachusetts granites, Webber, Hurley, and Fairbairn (1956, Table 4) state "standard deviation precision errors" for the ages determined. From their data we estimate $\sigma = $ -7.7–12.3% with 90% confidence.

---

[6] One reason for the common use of standard deviations is that their units can be those of the original observations. But in practice there are advantages when variances are employed; the additivity referred to here is one of these.

[7] Incorrectly given in *loc. cit.*

The Potassium-Argon Method

The potassium-argon method is based on the assumption that all potassium in nature contains the same percentage of radioactive K^{40} and, further, that the mineral to be dated has neither gained nor lost any potassium or any radiogenic A_r^{40} since its crystallization. The method and the history of its development have been outlined by Carr and Kulp (1957) and by Lipson (1958), and possible sources of systematic error have been discussed by Curtis, Evernden and Lipson (1958), Curtis and Reynolds (1958), and by Gentner and Kley (1958).

The source of the greatest practical difficulty which is encountered in this method is that 99.6% of atmospheric argon is A^{40}, identical with the minute amount of radiogenic argon which has to be extracted from the mineral and measured. Hence the A^{38} and A^{36}, together forming only 0.4% of atmospheric argon, provide the only means by which the amount of contamination by atmospheric argon can be determined. In practice a "spike" of pure A^{38} is added to the sample as an isotopic tracer and the A^{40}/A^{38} and A^{38}/A^{36} ratios are each measured on the mass spectrometer.

Total potassium is usually determined by flame photometry and the amount of K^{40} is then computed using 0.000119 as the atom fraction of K^{40} in potassium and 39.100 as the atomic weight.

Precision of radiogenic A_r^{40}/K^{40} *ratio.* The writer has found great difficulty in discovering just what some authors mean in their statements regarding precision. Some use standard deviation or probable error explicitly ($\sigma = 1.4826 \times$ PE), but others refer vaguely to "maximum error," do not distinguish clearly between precision and accuracy, or make statements such as "duplicate measurements are usually reproducible to within $p\%$." Frequently even the number of determinations and the range are not stated. In many instances it is obvious that the authors had data from which useful measures of the precision could have been obtained. By not sharing them with their readers, they have diminished the value of their work, for confident inferences cannot be drawn unless the precision is known.

An explicit statement regarding precision has been given by Lipson (1958, p. 144):

The A_r^{40}/K^{40} ratio may now be computed with a probable error of from 5 percent to 7 percent, depending upon the percentage of atmospheric argon in the sample. The total probable error arises from a probable error of 3 percent in the potassium determination and a probable error of 4 percent in the radiogenic argon determination exclusive of error in the atmospheric argon correction. The error in the determination of the A^{36}/A^{40} abundance ratio is taken to be 3 percent, but the effect of this error on the radiogenic

argon determination varies with the percentage of atmospheric argon.   If
we let

e = the percentage error in A^{36}/A^{40},
f = percentage of atmospheric argon in the sample,
E = the percentage error in the radiogenic argon due to the error in
$\quad\;$ A^{36}/A^{40},

then

$$E = \frac{ef}{100 - f}.$$

Applying this equation by using the percentages of atmospheric argon which
are tabulated for each sample, the total probable error can be calculated.

If the percentage of atmospheric argon rises above 50, then, as a consequence
of the relationship cited, the error in A_r^{40}/K^{40} increases very rapidly.   Unfortunately, the percentage of atmospheric argon is not always stated, and not
infrequently, it is impossible to tell whether this error has been included in
the precision given for A^{40}/K^{40}.   Gentner, Jensen, and Mehnert (1954) report
10–15% of atmospheric argon in the determination of a feldspar from a pegma-
tite in the Black Forest.   Such a percentage gives an error of only $\sigma = $ 0.5–0.8%
in the A_r^{40}/K^{40} ratio.   On the other hand, for the 10 New Zealand glauconites
dated by Lipson (1958), the atmospheric argon varied from 37–68%, corresponding to a range in precision for A_r^{40}/K^{40} of $\sigma = $ 2.6–9.5%.   In the
dating of 10 granitic rocks from Yosemite (Curtis, Evernden, and Lipson,
1958), the range in percentage of atmospheric argon was 8.5–63.2, which
corresponds to a range of precision for the A_r^{40}/K^{40} ratio of $\sigma = $ 0.4–7.6%.
Yet, referring to the Yosemite analyses, Evernden, Curtis, and Lipson (1957,
pp. 2120–2121) wrote:

> The major error in our technique is concerned with the absolute calibra-
> tion of the argon-38 spikes used for isotope dilution.   This calibration error
> may give rise to a probable error of 2 or 3 per cent.   However, it must be
> emphasized that, with the spike preparation procedure now being used, the
> argon-38 spike quantities are known relative to one another to less than
> 1 per cent.   Thus it is believed, if the error introduced by uncertainty in the
> absolute-spike calibration constant is negligible, that the analytical technique
> has an inherent probable error of less than 1.5 per cent.   Repeat runs on split
> fractions of biotite concentrates substantiate this conclusion.

No data on these reproducibility tests are given.   The Yosemite dates are
stated as ±1–2%.   With reference to the same rocks, Curtis, Evernden, and
Lipson (1958) state that, for the potassium analyses, if duplicate determinations do not check within 1.5%, they are rejected.   However, this does not

tell us what the precision of a potassium analysis is. Precision can be improved only by perfecting the method or increasing the number of replicate determinations; it cannot be improved by arbitrary rejection of supposedly extreme values (See for example Crow, *et al.*, 1960, Table 16).

In 1954, Wasserburg (*in* Faul, 1954, p. 342) wrote: "Since argon[40]: potassium[40] ratios can be determined to within 4 percent, it should be quite possible to resolve Paleozoic intrusions separated by one geological period." If 4% is the probable error, then $\sigma = 6\%$. In 1956, Folinsbee, Lipson, and Reynolds (1956, Table I) gave the A^{40}/K^{40} ratio as ±5%, although they did not show how the figure was derived. Presumably $\sigma = 7.5\%$. Aldrich, *et al.*, (1956, p. 217) make the following statement: "From the reproducibility of the results by the two methods, it is believed that the error in the potassium analyses is 5 percent or less. From the determinations of argon in air and minerals, the accuracy of the argon determinations is believed to be 3 percent. The error in the ratio, A^{40}/K^{40}, is believed to be less than 6 percent." Presumably $\sigma < 9\%$. Carr and Kulp (1957, p. 777) report: "The numerous repeat runs on the same powder show that the reproducibility in the A^{40} determination lies in the range of ±1–3 percent in most cases. Since this is also the range of variation of the replicate potassium analyses, the analytical error in the A^{40}/K^{40} ratio probably does not exceed 5 percent."

With reference to the dating of basement rocks from the Black Forest, Gentner and Kley (1958, p. 103) give the following values for the nonsystematic errors: potassium analysis 1–2%; argon determination 2%; atmospheric argon correction 1–2%. If these figures are probable errors, then $\sigma A_r^{40}/K^{40}$ is in the range 3.6–5.1%. These authors also state (p. 103) that the individual measurements can fluctuate through a maximum of ±10% on a relative time scale. If by "maximum" is meant "with 95% probability," then we can conclude that $\sigma A_r^{40}/K^{40}$ is about 5.1%, whereas if "with 99% probability" is meant, then σ turns out to be about 3.9%.

These examples are sufficient to indicate how difficult it is to determine from the literature what standard deviation should be accepted for the ratio of radiogenic A_r^{40}/K^{40} on which the age of a rock may depend. The obvious conclusion is that authors should be sure that their readers know exactly what is meant by the precision stated, what it is based on, and what confidence should be attached to it. The writer suggests that until this important question is clarified the most reasonable theoretical precisions to adopt for the purposes of evaluating dates are as follows:

	$\sigma\%$
Potassium analysis	3–6
Total argon determination	3–6
Atmospheric argon correction	0.5–8
Spike calibration	1.5

Assuming that there is no correlation between these errors, we find that the precision is in the range $\sigma = 4.5-11.8\%$. It is unfortunate that this important parameter is not better known.

Resulting precision of potassium-argon age. K^{40} decays into Ca^{40} with a constant denoted by λ_β, as well as into A^{40} with a constant λ_K (sometimes written λ_e). The ratio between these two constants, λ_K/λ_β, is designated R, the branching ratio. The total rate of decay of K^{40} is given by $\lambda = \lambda_K + \lambda_\beta$. The conversion of K^{40} into Ca^{40} is accompanied by emission of β-rays (electrons), which are easily detected; hence λ_β is comparatively well known. On the other hand, the conversion of K^{40} into A^{40} is effected within the nucleus by transformation of a proton into a neutron by capture of one of the electrons from the K-shell. In the consequent rearrangement of the remaining electrons, which is necessary in order that the vacancy in the K-shell be filled, there is emission of low-energy x-rays, the characteristic K-radiation of potassium. Thus λ_K can be determined only indirectly, and the uncertainty in the value of this constant is one of the major sources of systematic error in the method at the present time. Gentner and Kley (1958) claim that whereas λ, the total disintegration constant of K^{40}, is known to within $3-4\%$, the branching ratio, R, may be in error by as much as 10%.

However, any errors in the constants will not affect relative age measurements, provided that the same values are used for all determinations. Because we take as an example the granitic rocks of Yosemite, reported on by Evernden, Curtis, and Lipson (1957) and by Curtis, Evernden, and Lipson (1958), we adopt the values used by these authors:

$$\lambda_\beta = 0.472 \times 10^{-9} \text{ yr}^{-1},$$
$$\lambda_K = 0.557 \times 10^{-10} \text{ yr}^{-1},$$
$$R = 0.118,$$
$$\lambda = 0.528 \times 10^{-9} \text{ yr}^{-1}.$$

Now the equation used in calculating the age of a potassium-bearing mineral is

$$T = \frac{1}{\lambda} \ln\left[1 + \frac{A_r^{40}}{K^{40}} \frac{1+R}{R}\right],$$

where T is the age in years. Letting $x = A_r^{40}/K^{40}$ and $t =$ age in millions of years, we have $dt/dx = 2.12/(0.118 + 1.118x)$ million years per 10^{-3} unit of A_r^{40}/K^{40}. Even after 100 m.y., A_r^{40}/K^{40} is still less than 0.006, and thus the gradient changes only very slowly with increasing age. A 1% error in A_r^{40}/K^{40} produces about the same error in the age if the rock is less than some 200 m.y. old. If the rock is older than about 800 m.y., then the error produced in the age is appreciably less than the error in A_r^{40}/K^{40}. Thus, unless we are dealing with Precambrian rocks, or the precision is known with great confidence, it can be assumed that a given percentage error in A_r^{40}/K^{40} will produce about the same percentage error in the age.

If replicate age determinations are made on one or more rocks, then the results can yield a value for the "observed precision" of the age, which can be compared with the "theoretical precision" determined from consideration of the analytical techniques. It appears that the data on a suite of rocks from the Black Forest (Mehnert, 1958) may be used in this way, but it is unfortunate that experiments have not been undertaken with this goal specifically in view. Fourteen specimens were collected from the basement rocks of the Black Forest, and from some of these, feldspars and micas were separated so that 19 preparations were available for dating, and on these, a total of 66 determinations were made. For the present purposes, we are concerned solely with the degree of reproducibility. An analysis of Mehnert's data is given in Table 4. For each preparation we compute the standard deviation as a percentage of the mean so that the effect of variation in the means may be eliminated. A pooled estimate of the standard deviation is $s_p = 10.8\%$, with $\sigma_t = 9.0\text{--}13.5\%$ with 95% confidence, which is to be compared with the predicted precision of $\sigma_t = 4.5\text{--}12\%$. If the analyses given by Mehnert are truly replicate, it would seem reasonable to suppose that the precision of age determinations by the potassium-argon method could be as much as $\sigma_t = 10\%$.

Statistical Inference

Sampling distributions. If a random sample of size n is drawn from a normal population with mean μ_x and standard deviation σ_x, then, in general, the mean of the sample is $\bar{x} \neq \mu_x$. But the number of possible samples of size n which could be drawn from the population may be large, and the assemblage of all these possible samples forms a second-order population whose parameters are related to those of the original population as follows:

$$\text{the mean value of } \bar{x} = \mu_{\bar{x}} = \mu_x,$$

the standard deviation of the sampling distribution

$$(\text{standard error of } \bar{x}) = \sigma_{\bar{x}} = \sigma_x/\sqrt{n}.$$

For example, suppose we draw a sample of size 10 from a population of 100 individuals with $\mu_x = 12$ and $\sigma_x = 4$. Our sample is one out of $100!/(10! \times 90!)$ or more than 10^{13} possible samples. The mean of this sampling distribution (population of samples) is $\mu_{\bar{x}} = 12$, and its standard deviation (standard error) is $\sigma_{\bar{x}} = 4/\sqrt{10} = 1.26$. Similarly, if the standard deviation s is deter-

TABLE 4

REPLICATE AGE DETERMINATIONS ON 19 ROCKS AND MINERALS FROM
THE BLACK FOREST BY THE POTASSIUM-ARGON METHOD
BASED ON DATA PUBLISHED BY MEHNERT, 1958

Number of determinations	Mean age	$s\%$
5	249	2.0
2	254	0.3
3	243	2.4
3	268	2.6
5	253	4.5
3	269	3.5
4	287	1.6
5	241	16.1
3	273	0.9
2	306	0.1
3	303	3.8
3	280	2.7
2	260	1.1
6	256	25.5
5	278	15.1
3	344	2.4
3	304	1.3
3	283	1.5
3	310	6.6

Hence $s_p = 10.8\%$ and $\sigma = 9.0\text{–}13.5\%$ with 95% confidence

mined for all possible samples of size n, then the standard deviation (standard error) of this sampling distribution is $\sigma_s = \sigma_x/\sqrt{2n}$. For the example given, we would expect the standard deviations of samples of size 10 to have a distribution with a mean of $\mu_s = \sigma_x = 4$ and a standard deviation of

$$\sigma_s = 4/\sqrt{20} = 0.9.$$

Suppose we have two populations defined by parameters μ_x and σ_x, and μ_y and σ_y, respectively, and we draw a pair of variates, one from each population, and take the difference $(x - y)$. If we continued to draw pairs until we had determined all possible values of $(x - y)$, then we would have a new second-order population (sampling distribution) with parameters

$$\mu_{x-y} = \mu_x - \mu_y \quad \text{and} \quad \sigma^2_{x-y} = \sigma^2_x + \sigma^2_y,$$

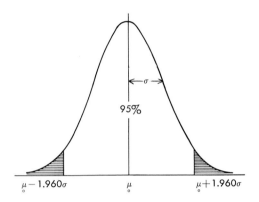

FIG. 1. If the precision of an analytical method is given by σ, we have 95% confidence that a single determination will not differ from the mean, μ_0, by more than $\pm 1.960\sigma$.

provided that there is no correlation between members of the pairs. Thus if

$$\sigma_x = \sigma_y = \sigma, \qquad \text{then} \qquad \sigma_{x-y} = \sigma\sqrt{2}.$$

If we are concerned with differences between means instead of between variates, then we have

$$\mu_{\bar{x}-\bar{y}} = \mu_{\bar{x}} - \mu_{\bar{y}},$$

$$\sigma^2_{\bar{x}-\bar{y}} = \sigma^2_{\bar{x}} + \sigma^2_{\bar{y}} = \frac{\sigma^2_x}{n_1} + \frac{\sigma^2_y}{n_2}$$

$$= \sigma^2 \left(\frac{1}{n_1} + \frac{1}{n_2} \right), \qquad \text{if} \quad \sigma_x = \sigma_y = \sigma,$$

$$= \frac{2\sigma^2}{n}, \qquad \text{if, in addition,} \quad n_1 = n_2 = n.$$

Critical value. Suppose that the precision of chemical analysis of an element is already known and is given by σ, and further, let us assume that the distribution of numerous replicate analyses would yield a normal curve with mean μ_0 and standard deviation σ (Fig. 1). Because we find, from tables of areas under the normal curve, that 95% of the distribution lies between -1.960σ and $+1.960\sigma$, the probability is only 0.05 that a single determination will fall outside the range $\mu_0 \pm 1.960\sigma$. Accordingly, with 95% confidence, we reject the hypothesis that a determination outside this range belongs to this population. Now at this confidence level, five times out of one hundred, we will make a mistake and reject a measurement erroneously, claiming that it does not belong to the population when in fact it does, as we would discover if we were to make more determinations. The error of rejecting the null hypothesis when in fact it is true is called a type I, or producer's, error, for when it is made, a perfectly "good" sample is rejected. In our example, the chance of making a type I error is $\alpha = 0.05$; this is called the significance level. Now it may be that the cost of producing each measurement is so high, or other consequences of making this error are such that we cannot afford to reject such a high percentage of good determinations. If this is so, we can decrease the critical rejection area, say by setting $\alpha = 0.01$, with 0.005 at each tail of the distribution, or even less. From tables of percentiles of the normal distribution we find the following:

Probability of making Type I error	Critical value for $\lvert \bar{x} - \mu_0 \rvert$
0.10	$1.645\sigma/\sqrt{n}$
0.05	$1.960\sigma/\sqrt{n}$
0.01	$2.576\sigma/\sqrt{n}$
0.001	$3.291\sigma/\sqrt{n}$

We can also make use of these relations in the following way: if we have determined $\bar{x}$ from a sample of size n and we already know σ, then we can state confidence limits for the mean, μ_0, of the population to which $\bar{x}$ belongs. For example, with 95% confidence, we can say[8] $\mu_0 = \bar{x} \pm 1.960\sigma/\sqrt{n}$. Alternatively, the sample size required to specify μ_0 to the range $\pm h$ with 95% confidence is $n = (1.960\sigma/h)^2$.

Resolution. We have seen that we can always lessen the probability of making a type I error (i.e., claiming that the null hypothesis is false when it is actually true) merely by decreasing the rejection area α. This is true even when the sample size is as small as two. Whatever value of α we decide upon, we calculate the critical value and agree to reject the null hypothesis if $\lvert \bar{x} - \mu_0 \rvert$ is greater than this. Now, clearly the smaller we have made α (to avoid type I errors), the more likely it will be that we accept the null hypothesis when it is false. This would be a type II error, and the probability of making it is given by β (Fig. 2). We see that, although $\lvert \mu_1 - \mu_0 \rvert$ is greater than our critical value, the probability of overlooking this difference is β. This error is often called a consumer's error, for it will result in the acceptance of measurements which should be rejected. Our confidence in avoiding this error is $1 - \beta$ and is the *power* of the test. Clearly β, and hence the power, depends upon $\lvert \mu_1 - \mu_0 \rvert$, σ, n, and α. If four of these variables are given, then the fifth is fixed. Let us suppose that σ and n are given and α has been assigned the value 0.05, so that

---

[8] If σ were not known, we would use the t-distribution (see, for example, Crow *et al.*, 1960, p. 47).

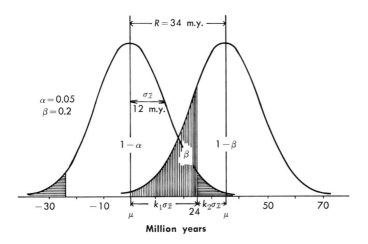

FIG. 2. α is the probability that we will reject, in error, the null hypothesis that a sample mean belongs to population μ_0 because it is greater than $\mu_0 + h$ or less than $\mu_0 - h$. $(1 - \alpha)100\%$ is our confidence that we will not make this error. β is the probability that we will accept, in error, the null hypothesis that a sample mean belongs to population μ_0 because it is less than $\mu_0 + h$ when an alternative hypothesis, namely, that the sample mean belongs to population μ_1, is true. $(1 - \beta)100\%$ is our confidence that we will avoid this error. The diagram is drawn with $\alpha = 0.05$ and $\beta = 0.2$.

the critical value for rejection is $k_1\sigma_{\bar{x}} = 1.960\sigma/\sqrt{n}$. It is clear that β must be much larger than α unless $|\mu_1 - \mu_0|$ is made extreme. Let us suppose that β is not to exceed 0.2; then, from normal curve tables,

$$k_2\sigma_{\bar{x}} = \frac{0.842\sigma}{\sqrt{n}}.$$

Hence

$$|\mu_1 - \mu_0| = \frac{2.802\sigma}{\sqrt{n}}$$

for $\alpha = 0.05$ and $\beta = 0.2$. Similarly,

$$|\mu_1 - \mu_0| = \frac{3.242\sigma}{\sqrt{n}}$$

for $\alpha = 0.05$ and $\beta = 0.1$. These values of $|\mu_1 - \mu_0|$ are called the *resolution*[9] *differences*. The values of α and β that we use will depend upon the penalty attached to these errors in each particular case and on the economics involved. In what follows, we adopt the values $\alpha = 0.05$ and $\beta = 0.2$, thus indicating

---

[9] The analogy with the resolving power of an optical system will be obvious.

that we expect to make a type I error (i.e., to claim a difference $|\mu_1 - \mu_0| > 0$ when the difference is actually zero) once in 20 times and a type II error (i.e., fail to detect an actual difference $|\mu_1 - \mu_0| > 0$) once in 5 times. It does not seem worthwhile to make statements which have lower degrees of confidence, but on the other hand if these risks seem too great, then they can be reduced: the price is an increased value for the minimum difference, R, which can be resolved, and this penalty can be avoided only by improving the precision of the individual measurements (thereby reducing σ) or increasing n, the size of the samples used in determining $\bar{x}$.

Summarizing these conclusions we can make the following statements:

(1) With 80% confidence, we can claim that if $|\mu_1 - \mu_0|$ exceeds $2.802\sigma/\sqrt{n}$, we will detect this at the 0.05-significance level.

(2) With 95% confidence, we can claim that if $|\bar{x} - \mu_0|$ exceeds $1.960\sigma/\sqrt{n}$, then $\mu_1 \neq \mu_0$.

(3) The number of variates to be included in each sample in order to establish a given degree of resolution $= (2.802\sigma/R)^2$.

In geochronometry we commonly have data on two samples and wish to know whether the populations from which they were drawn have a common mean. For instance, two samples are analyzed for potassium: the number of replicate determinations made on the first is n_1, and on the second n_2; the respective means are $\bar{x}$ and $\bar{y}$. Let us suppose that the precision for the method is already established so that $\sigma_x = \sigma_y = \sigma$ which is known. Then we have the following results.

For $|\mu_x - \mu_y|$:

$$\text{Resolution, } R = 2.802\sigma \left(\frac{1}{n_1} + \frac{1}{n_2}\right)^{1/2} = 3.963 \frac{\sigma}{\sqrt{n}} \quad \text{if} \quad n_1 = n_2 = n;$$

for $|\bar{x} - \bar{y}|$:

$$\text{Critical value} = 1.960\sigma \left(\frac{1}{n_1} + \frac{1}{n_2}\right)^{1/2} = 2.772 \frac{\sigma}{\sqrt{n}} \quad \text{if} \quad n_1 = n_2 = n;$$

and

$$n = \left(\frac{3.963\sigma}{R}\right)^2 \quad \text{to establish a given resolving power.}$$

These values used in testing the hypothesis $|\mu_1 - \mu_2| = 0$ are greater by the factor $\sqrt{2}$ than the comparable values for the hypothesis $|\mu_1 - \mu_0| = 0$. The reason is that whereas μ_0 was given, neither μ_1 nor μ_2 is known.

We may therefore state criteria for decision-making as follows. If μ_0 is known and $\sigma_x = \sigma_y = \sigma$ is known but μ_1 and μ_2 are unknown, then (1) with $100(1 - \beta)\%$ confidence, we can claim that if a difference exceeds the resolution, we will detect this at the α significance level:

$100(1 - \beta)\%$	Difference	Resolution	α
80	$\|\mu_1 - \mu_0\|$	$2.802\sigma/\sqrt{n}$	0.05
80	$\|\mu_1 - \mu_2\|$	$3.963\sigma/\sqrt{n}$	0.05
90	$\|\mu_1 - \mu_0\|$	$3.858\sigma/\sqrt{n}$	0.01
90	$\|\mu_1 - \mu_2\|$	$5.456\sigma/\sqrt{n}$	0.01

(2) with $100(1 - \alpha)\%$ confidence we can claim that if a difference exceeds the critical value for rejection, then $\mu_1 \neq a$:

$100(1 - \alpha)\%$	Difference	Critical value	a
95	$\|\bar{x} - \mu_0\|$	$1.960\sigma/\sqrt{n}$	μ_0
95	$\|\bar{x} - \bar{y}\|$	$2.772\sigma/\sqrt{n}$ or $1.960\sigma\left(\dfrac{1}{n_1} + \dfrac{1}{n_2}\right)^{1/2}$	μ_2
99	$\|\bar{x} - \mu_0\|$	$2.576\sigma/\sqrt{n}$	μ_0
99	$\|\bar{x} - \bar{y}\|$	$3.643\sigma/\sqrt{n}$ or $2.576\sigma\left(\dfrac{1}{n_1} + \dfrac{1}{n_2}\right)^{1/2}$	μ_2

Examples

Let us suppose that we have two rocks which have been selected as meeting the specifications that qualify them for radioactive age dating. If a single determination is to be made on each, then, if we are to have an 80% confidence in our ability to distinguish between them at the 0.05 significance level, the difference will have to exceed 3.963σ; apparently this is somewhere between 43% and 66% for lead-alpha, and between 18% and 48% for K-A ages. These are rough figures, but apparently our best estimates of the current resolving powers of the methods. It is certainly hoped that more reliable measures of the resolution will soon become available, and at that time the reader can bring up to date the conclusions presented here.

Suppose now that a single age determination has been made on each of the two rocks, then with 95% confidence we can say that there is indeed a difference between their actual ages if the observed difference between the two determinations exceeds 2.772σ, that is, it seems, 30–46% for lead-alpha and 12–33% for K-A ages. If the two determinations are each the mean of four replicate[10] measurements, then the critical value is halved. It should be noted that it is possible to detect a difference which is smaller than the resolution,

---

[10] There is obviously a practical limit to the extent to which we should endeavor to improve the precision of a method by increasing the number of replicate readings.

but the *a priori* confidence in our ability is less than 80%; indeed we may "detect" a difference which is actually zero, but we may make a type I error in doing so!

The mean age of 11 specimens of tonalite from the batholith of southern California is 114 m.y., whereas the mean of 7 specimens of granodiorite from the same plutonic complex is 105 m.y. (Larsen, *et al.*, 1958, Tables 6 and 7). If we take $\sigma = 10\%$ then $\sigma_{\bar{t}_1} - \sigma_{\bar{t}_2} = 10(\frac{1}{11} + \frac{1}{7})^{1/2} = 4.8\%$. Hence the resolution is $2.80 \times 4.8 = 13.5\%$ or nearly 15 m.y. The critical value is $1.96 \times 4.8 = 9.5\%$ or nearly 10.5 m.y. Thus we conclude that if there is any difference between the actual mean ages of the tonalites and granodiorites in the batholith of southern California then, with 80% confidence, the difference is less than 15 m.y.

Of all the Mesozoic batholiths of western North America which have been dated by the lead-alpha method (Larsen, *et al.*, 1958, Table 12) the widest range of apparent mean ages is between the Sierra Nevada ($n = 15, \bar{t} = 102$) and Idaho ($n = 16, \bar{t} = 108$) batholiths. Taking $\sigma = 10\%$[11], we have $\sigma_{\bar{t}} = 2.5\%$. Hence the resolution is $3.96 \times 2.5 = 9.9\%$ or nearly 10.5 m.y. The critical value is $2.77 \times 2.5 = 6.9\%$ or nearly 7.5 m.y. Thus we must conclude that if there is any difference between the mean ages of these batholiths, then, with 80% confidence, it is less than 11 m.y.

The relative ages of the granitic rocks of Yosemite (Sierra Nevada) are believed to be known from their field relationships. Ten of these rocks have been dated by the potassium-argon method (Evernden, Curtis, and Lipson, 1957). The ages are given to 0.1 m.y., and it is reported that "The agreement between field and experimental determinations of relative age of the various plutons is remarkable. It can be seen that the average interval of time between intrusions is approximately two million years." (Curtis, *et al.*, 1958, p. 12)

Apparently replicate determinations were not made, with the exception that three specimens of the Half Dome quartz monzonite were dated. That this number is too small to yield a satisfactory estimate of the precision is seen from the fact that, whereas $s = 0.8\%$, the 99%-confidence range for $\sigma = 0.4$–13.3%. Until a better estimate of the precision is published, then, largely for the purpose of illustration, we will adopt $\sigma = 10\%$ as a tentative estimate. The resolution would then be about 34 m.y., and the critical value about 24 m.y. (see Fig. 2). If the resolution were to equal the range of observed ages, 18.4 m.y., the analytical precision would have to be more than twice as good or else at least five replicate determinations would have to be made on each specimen. To bring the resolution down to one million years, the analytical precision would have to be about 30 times as good as it now appears to be.

---

[11] The confidence levels quoted do not reflect the present uncertainty in the values of σ.

We conclude therefore that there is about a 70% probability that the observed range of dates (about $\pm\sigma$) on the Yosemite rocks is due to random errors in the analytical methods; or alternatively, with the customary confidence levels, if there is any difference between the actual ages of the rocks, it is less than 34 m.y. If σ is as low as 5%, then the resolution would be 20 m.y. or almost equal to the apparent range.

In this field, reproducibility tests are very costly; however, the results are not useful until we have some estimate of their precision. Science is a rational activity and authoritarianism is out of place; hence potential users of published dates are entitled to know the nature, extent, and findings of any reproducibility tests which have been made. Given certain assumptions and a knowledge of precision, we can hope to detect discrepant observations; but without better knowledge than seems to exist currently, it would be disquieting to find circumstantial evidence suggesting that dates may be discarded on the basis that they do not fit expectation. If a rock, which was acceptable *a priori*, is rejected *a posteriori* because of its age, then full details regarding the precision must be given. Quite apart from judgment of the harder problems of relevancy and accuracy, no one should use a date until he has satisfied himself that the resolution of the method justifies the use intended.

REFERENCES CITED

ALDRICH, L. T., DAVIS, G. L., TILTON, G. R., and WETHERILL, G. W., 1956, Radioactive ages of minerals from the Brown Derby Mine and the Quartz Creek granite near Gunnison, Colorado: J. Geophys. Res., vol. 61, pp. 215–232.

CARR, D. R. and KULP, J. L., 1957, Potassium-argon method of geochronometry: Geol. Soc. Am., B., vol. 68, pp. 763–784.

CROW, E. L., DAVIS, F. A., and MAXFIELD, M. W., 1960, Statistics manual: New York, Dover, 288 pp.

CURTIS, G. H., EVERNDEN, J. F., and LIPSON, J., 1958, Age determination of some granitic rocks in California by the potassium-argon method: California Div. Mines, Sp. Report 54, 16 pp.

——— and REYNOLDS, J. H., 1958, Notes on the potassium-argon dating of sedimentary rocks: Geol. Soc. Am. B., vol. 69, pp. 151–160.

EVERNDEN, J. F., CURTIS, G. H., and LIPSON, J., 1957, Potassium-argon dating of igneous rocks: Am. Assoc. Petroleum Geol., B., vol. 41, pp. 2120–2127.

FAUL, HENRY, 1954, Nuclear geology: New York, John Wiley, 414 pp.

FOLINSBEE, R. E., LIPSON, J., and REYNOLDS, J. H., 1956, Potassium-argon dating: Geochim. et Cosmochim. Acta., vol. 10, pp. 60–68.

GENTNER, W., JENSEN, F., and MEHNERT, K. R., 1954, Zur geologischen Altersbestimmung von Kalifeldspat nach der Kalium-Argon-Methode: Zs. Naturforschung, Bd. 9a, 176 pp.

——— and KLEY, W., 1958, Argonbestimmungen an Kaliummineralien-V: Geochim. et Cosmochim. Acta., vol. 14, pp. 98–104.

GOLDSCHMIDT, V. M., 1944, Crystal chemistry and geochemistry: Chemical Products, vol. 7, pp. 29–34.

GOTTFRIED, D., JAFFE, H. W., and SENFTLE, F. E., 1959, Evaluation of the lead-alpha (Larsen) method for determining ages of igneous rocks: U. S. Geol. Survey, B., 1097-A, 63 pp.

HURLEY, P. M. and FAIRBAIRN, H. W., 1957, Abundance and distribution of uranium and thorium in zircon, sphene, apatite, epidote, and monazite in granitic rocks: Am. Geophys. Union, Tr., vol. 38, pp. 939–944.

LARSEN, E. S., JR., KEEVIL, N. B., and HARRISON, H. C., 1952, Method for determining the age of igneous rocks using the accessory minerals: Geol. Soc. Am. B., vol. 63, pp. 1045–1052.

———, GOTTFRIED, D., JAFFE, H. W., and WARING, C. L., 1958, Lead-alpha ages of the Mesozoic batholiths of western North America: U. S. Geol. Survey, B., 1070-B, 62 pp.

LIPSON, J., 1958, Potassium-argon dating of sedimentary rocks: Geol. Soc. Am., B., vol. 69, pp. 137–150.

LYONS, J. B., JAFFE, H. W., GOTTFRIED, D., and WARING, C. L., 1957, Lead-alpha ages of some New Hampshire granites: Am. J. Sci., vol. 255, no. 8, pp. 527–546.

MEHNERT, K. R., 1958, Argonbestimmungen an Kaliummineralien-VI: Geochim. et Cosmochim. Acta, vol. 14, pp. 105–113.

ROSE, H., JR., and STERN, T., 1960, Spectrochemical determination of lead in zircon for lead-alpha age measurements: Am. Mineralogist, vol. 45, pp. 1243–1256.

WARING, C. L. and WORTHING, H., 1953, A spectrographic method for determining trace amounts of lead in zircon and other minerals: Am. Mineralogist, vol. 38, pp. 827–833.

WEBBER, G. R., HURLEY, P. M., and FAIRBAIRN, H. W., 1956, Relative ages of eastern Massachusetts granites by total lead ratios in zircon: Am. J. Sci., vol. 254, pp. 574–583.

J. HOOVER MACKIN

University of Texas

Rational and Empirical Methods of Investigation in Geology[1]

Most of us are concerned, and some of us have strong feelings, pro or con, about what has been happening to geology in the past 25 years: greatly increased use of nongeologic techniques in the solution of geologic problems, such as dating by radioisotope methods; the tendency for what were special fields of interest to become nearly or wholly independent disciplines, with separate journals and jargon; and most of all, because it penetrates every field, what may be called the swing to the quantitative.

At meetings of our societies, when the elder brethren gather together in hotel rooms after the technical sessions, the discussion usually comes around to these changes. There are apt to be sad postmortems for certain departments, once powerful, which are now, owing to the retirement or flight of their older stalwarts, largely staffed by dial twisters and number jugglers. It is stated, as a scandalous sign of the times, that in certain departments geologic mapping is considered to be, not research, but a routine operation—something like surveying from the point of view of an engineer—and therefore not suitable as a basis

[1] A preliminary draft of this paper was given as an address at the banquet of the Branner Club during the meeting of the Cordilleran Section of the Geological Society in Los Angeles, April 17, 1962. The text has benefitted in substance and form from criticisms by the other authors of papers in this volume. I would like also to express my gratitude to the following, who have read parts or all of the manuscript: Charles Bell, Richard Blank, Howard Coombs, Ronald DeFord, Ken Fahnestock, Peter Flawn, John Hack, Satish Kapoor, William Krumbein, Luna Leopold, Mark Meier, H. W. Naismith, and Dwight Schmidt. Special thanks are due Frank Calkins, who did his best to make the paper readable.

for the doctoral thesis. There is almost always at least one sarcastic remark per evening along the line of what our equation-minded youngsters think is the function of the mirror on a Brunton compass; a comment or two on their ignorance or disregard of the older literature; some skepticism as to whether the author of a new monograph on the mechanism of mountain building had ever been *on* a mountain, *off* a highway; and so on. This is partly banter, because we are aware that these are merely the usual misgivings of every older generation about the goings-on of every younger generation. But sometimes there is evidence of real ill-feeling, which in part at least reflects a defensive attitude; and there may be a few who seem to think that the clock ought to be stopped—that nothing new is good.

Though I am one of the elders, I often cross the hall to a concurrent session of another group, our avant-garde, where there is an almost evangelical zeal to quantify, and if this means abandoning the classical geologic methods of inquiry, so much the better; where there are some who think of W. M. Davis as an old duffer with a butterfly-catcher's sort of interest in scenery; where there is likely to be, once in a while, an expression of anger for the oldsters who, through their control of jobs, research funds, honors, and access to the journals, seem to be bent on sabotaging all efforts to raise geology to the stature of a science; where, in the urgency for change, it seems that nothing old is good.

This picture is not overdrawn, but it applies only to a small number: the blacks and the whites, both sure of their ground. Most geologists are somewhere in the gray between, and are beset with doubts. As for myself, I have sometimes thought that the swing to the quantitative is too fast and too far, and that, because a rather high percentage of the conclusions arrived at by certain methods of manipulating numerical data are superficial, or wrong, or even ludicrous, these methods must be somehow at fault, and that we do well to stay with the classical geologic methods. But at other times I have been troubled by questions: why the swing has been so long delayed in geology as compared with physics and chemistry; and whether, with its relative dearth of quantitative laws, geology is in fact a sort of subscience, as implied by Lord Kelvin's pronouncement that what cannot be stated in numbers is not science. (For original wording, and a thoughtful discussion, see Holton, 1952, p. 234.) Even more disturbing is the view, among some of my friends in physics, that a concern with cause-and-effect relations merely confuses the real issues in science; I will return to this matter later. If only because of the accomplishments of the scientists who hold these views, we must wonder whether our accustomed ways of thinking are outmoded, and whether we should not drastically change our habits of thought, or else turn in our compasses and hammers and fade away quietly to some haven reserved for elderly naturalists.

Preparation for a talk on quantitative methods in geomorphology, as a visiting lecturer at the University of Texas last year, forced me to examine these conflicting appraisals of where we stand.[2] I suggest that two changes, quite different but closely interlocking, are occurring at the same time and have become confused in our thinking.

One of these changes includes an increase in the rate of infusion of new ideas and techniques from the other sciences and from engineering, an increase in precision and completeness of quantitative description of geologic features and processes of all kinds, and an increased use of statistics and mechanical methods of analyzing data. This change fits readily within the framework of the classical geologic method of investigation, the most characteristic feature of which is dependence on reasoning at every step; "Quantitative Zoology," by Simpson, Roe, and Lewontin (1960) shows the way. In so far as it merely involves doing more completely, or with more refinement, what we have always been doing, it is evolutionary; and it is axiomatic that it is good. Some of us may find it hard to keep abreast of new developments, but few oppose them even privately, and even the most reactionary cannot drag his feet in public without discredit to himself.

The other change is the introduction, or greatly increased use, of an altogether different method of problem-solving that is essentially empirical. In its purest form this method depends very little on reasoning; its most characteristic feature, when it functions as an independent method, is that it replaces the reasoning process by operations that are largely mechanical. Because in this respect and others it is foreign to our accustomed habits of thought, we are inclined to distrust it. By "we" I mean, of course, the conservatives of my generation.

At least a part of the confusion in our thinking comes from a failure to distinguish between the evolutionary quantification, which is good, and the mechanical kind of quantification, which I think is bad when it takes the place of reasoning. It is not easy to draw a line between them because the empirical procedures may stand alone, or they may function effectively and usefully as parts of the classical geologic method; that is, they may replace, or be combined in all proportions with, the reasoning processes that are the earmarks of that method. When this distinction is recognized it becomes evident that the real issue is not qualitative versus quantitative. It is, rather, rationality versus blind empiricism.

---

[2] I was only dimly aware, until some library browsing in connection with methodology in the other sciences, of the extent of the scholarly literature dealing with the history and philosophy of science. And I was surprised, as was Claude Albritton (1961), to find that with a few noteworthy exceptions (for example, Conant, 1951, p. 269–295) geology is scarcely mentioned in that literature. I should like to make it plain at the outset that I am not a scholar—I have only sampled a few anthologies of the history of science. I should emphasize also that I do not presume to speak for geology; what I say expresses the viewpoint of a single field geologist.

Although the timing has been influenced by such leaders as Chayes, Hubbert, Leopold, Krumbein, and Strahler, we are now in the swing to the quantitative because of the explosive increase in the availability of numerical data in the last few decades (Krumbein, 1960, p. 341), and because basic descriptive spadework has now advanced far enough in many fields of geology to permit at least preliminary formulation of significant quantitative generalizations. The quantification of geology will proceed at a rapidly accelerating rate no matter what we do as individuals, but I think the rate might be quickened a little, and to good purpose, if the differences between the two groups on opposite sides of the hall, at least those differences that arise from misunderstanding, could be reduced. An analysis of certain quantitative methods of investigation that are largely empirical will, I hope, serve to bring out both their merits and limitations, and may convince some of our oldsters that although disregard of the limitations may produce questionable results, it does not follow that there is anything wrong with quantification, as such, nor with blind empiricism, as such. But this is not very important—time will take care of the oldsters, soon enough. This essay is for the youngsters—the graduate students—and its purpose is to show that as they quantify, which they are bound to do, it is neither necessary nor wise to cut loose from the classical geologic method. Its message is the not very novel proposition that there is much good both in the old and the new approaches to problem-solving. A brief statement of what I am calling the rational method will point up the contrast between it and the empirical method, with which we are principally concerned.

The Rational Method

I'm sure that most American geologists are acquainted with our three outstanding papers on method: G. K. Gilbert's "Inculcation of the Scientific Method by Example," published in 1886; T. C. Chamberlin's "Method of Multiple Working Hypotheses," published in 1897; and Douglas Johnson's "Role of Analysis in Scientific Investigation," published in 1933. I do not need to describe the so-called scientific method here; for present purposes I need only remind you that it involves an interplay of observation and reasoning, in which the first observations suggest one or more explanations, the working hypotheses, analysis of which leads to further observation or experimentation. This in turn permits a discarding of some of the early hypotheses and a refinement of others, analysis of which permits a discarding of data now seen to be irrelevant to the issue, and a narrowing and sharpening of the focus in the search for additional data that are hidden or otherwise hard to obtain but which are of special diagnostic value; and so on and on. These steps are spelled out in formal terms in the papers just mentioned, and it was useful to do that, but those who use the method all the time never follow the steps in the order stated; the method has become a habit of thought that checks reasoning against other lines of reasoning, evidence against other kinds of evidence, reasoning against evidence, and evidence against reasoning, thus testing both the evidence and the reasoning for relevancy and accuracy at every stage of the inquiry.

It now seems to be the vogue to pooh-pooh this method, as differing in no essential way from the method of problem-solving used by the man in the street. I've been interested in watching the way in which men in the street, including some medical doctors—practitioners, not investigators—arrive at conclusions, and I can only suggest that the scientists who insist that all persons arrive at conclusions in the same way should reexamine their conviction. There are, of course, rare intellects that need no disciplining, but for most of us with ordinary minds, facility in the operations that I have just outlined must be acquired by precept, example, and practice.

The objective of the scientific method is to understand the system investigated—to understand it as completely as possible. To most geologists this means understanding of cause and effect relations within the system (Garrels, 1951, p. 32). Depending on the nature of the problem and its complexity, quantitative data and mathematical manipulations may enter the investigation early or late. In general, the larger the problem, the more many-sided it is, the more complicated by secondary and tertiary feedback couples, and the more difficult it is to obtain the evidence, the more essential it is to the efficient prosecution of the study that the system first be understood in *qualitative* terms; only this can make it possible to design the most significant experiments, or otherwise to direct the search for the critical data, on which to base an eventual understanding in quantitative terms.

A problem—any problem—when first recognized, is likely to be poorly defined. Because it is impossible to seek intelligently for explanations until we know what needs explaining, the first step in the operation of the scientific method is to bring the problem into focus. This is usually accomplished by reasoning, i.e., by thinking it through, although we will see shortly that there is another way. Then, if it is evident that the problem is many-sided, the investigator does not blast away at all sides at once with a shotgun; he shoots at one side at a time with a rifle—with *the* rifle, and *the* bullet, that he considers best suited to that side.

This means that the investigator admits to his graphs, so to speak, only items of evidence that are relevant to the particular matter under investigation, and that are as accurate as practicable, with the probable limits of sampling and experimental error expressed graphically. In reading answers from the graph, he does no averaging beyond that required to take those limits into account. And once an item of information has been admitted to the graph, it cannot be disregarded; as a rule, the items that lie outside the clusters of points are at least as significant, and usually much more interesting, than those that lie within the clusters. It is from inquiry as to why these strays are where they are that most new ideas—most breakthroughs in science—develop.

The scientific method tries to visualize whole answers—complete theoretical structures—at the very outset; these are the working hypotheses that give direction to the seeking-out and testing of evidence. But one never rushes ahead of the data-testing process to a generalization that is regarded as a conclusion. This is not because there is anything ethically wrong with quick generalizing. It is only that, over a period of 500 years, investigators have found that theoretical structures made in part of untested and ill-matched building blocks are apt to topple sooner or later, and that piling them up and building on them is therefore not an efficient way to make progress. The need to test the soundness of each building block *before* it gets into the structure— to determine the quality and the relevance of each item of evidence *before* it gets onto the graph—is emphasized by Douglas Johnson (1933). His approach was the antithesis of that to which we may now turn.

The Empirical Method

What I have long thought of as the engineering method or the technologic method (we shall soon see that it needs another name) deals almost exclusively with quantitative data from the outset, and proceeds directly to a quantitative answer, which terminates the investigation. This method reduces to a minimum, or eliminates altogether, the byplay of inductive and deductive reasoning by which data and ideas are processed in the scientific method; this means that it cannot be critical of the data as they are gathered. The data are analyzed primarily by mathematical methods, which make no distinction between cause and effect; understanding of cause and effect relations may be interesting, but it is not essential, and if explanations are considered at all, there is usually only one, and it is likely to be superficial. All of the reasoning operations that characterize the so-called scientific method depend on a fund of knowledge, and on judgment based on experience; other things being equal, the old hand is far better at these operations than the novice. But the operations of the "engineering method" are much less dependent on judgment; in applying this method the sharp youngster may be quicker and better than the experienced oldster. For this reason and because of its quick, positive, quantitative answers, it makes a strong appeal to the younger generation. I would like now to explain the logic of this method, as it operates in engineering.

Many engineers feel that unless a relation can be stated in numbers, it is not worth thinking about at all. The good and sufficient reason for this attitude is that the engineer is primarily a doer—he designs structures of various types, and supervises their building. In the contract drawings for a bridge he must specify the dimensions and strength of each structural member. Nonengineers may be able to think of a drawing that indicates the need for a rather strong beam at a given place in the bridge. But a young man who has spent five years in an engineering school is incapable of thinking seriously of a "rather strong" beam; all of the beams of his mind's eye have numerical properties. If the strength of a beam cannot be put in numerical terms, thinking about it is mere daydreaming.

The matter of stresses in a steel structure is fairly cut and dried. But the engineer is confronted with many problems for which there are no ready answers; he must deal with them—he must complete his working drawings— against a deadline. If he is charged with the task of designing a canal to carry a certain flow of irrigation water without either silting or erosion of the bed, or with the immensely more complex task of developing and maintaining a 10-foot navigable channel in a large river, he cannot wait until he or others have developed a complete theory of silting and scouring in canals and rivers. It may be 50 or a 100 years before anything approaching a complete theory, in quantitative terms, can be formulated; and his drawings, which must be entirely quantitative, have to be ready within a few days or weeks for the contractors who will bid the job. So he has to make certain simplifying assumptions, even though he realizes that they may be wide of the mark, and he has to make-do with data that are readily available, even though they are not entirely satisfactory, or with data that can be obtained quickly from experiments or models, even though the conditions are significantly different from those existing in his particular canal or river.

He is accustomed to these expedient operations, and he is not much concerned if, in plotting the data, he mixed a few oranges with the apples. In fact, he wouldn't worry much if a few apple *crates* and a few orange *trees* got onto his graph. He cannot scrutinize each item of evidence as to quality and relevancy; if he did, none but the simplest of structures would ever get built. He feels that if there are enough points on a scatter diagram, the bad ones will average out, and that the equation for the curve drawn through the clustered points will be good enough for use in design, always with a goodly factor of safety as a cushion. And it almost always is. This method is *quantitative, empirical*, and *expedient*. As used by the engineer, it is logical and successful.

It is of course used by investigators in many fields other than engineering. Friends in physics and chemistry tell me that it accounts for a large percentage of the current research in those sciences. A recent paper by Paul Weiss (1962) with the subtitle "Does Blind Probing Threaten to Displace Experience in Biological Experimentation?" calls attention to its increasing use in biology. The approach and examples are different, but the basic views of Dr. Weiss correspond so closely with those expressed in this essay that I am inclined to quote, not a passage or two, but the whole paper. Because this is impracticable,

I can only urge that geologists interested in this phase of the general problem —whither are we drifting, methodologically?—read it in the original.

In view of its widespread use in science, what I have been calling the engineering or technologic method certainly should not be identified, by name, with engineering or technology as such. And on the other side of the coin, the so-called scientific method is used more consistently and effectively by many engineers and technologists than by most scientists. Besides being inappropriate on this score, both terms have derogatory or laudatory connotations which beg some questions. So, with serious misgivings that will be left unsaid, I will from here on use the term "rational method" for what we are accustomed to think of as the scientific method, and what I have been calling the engineering method will be referred to as the empirical method.[3]

Actually, the method that I am trying to describe is *an* empirical method; it is shotgun or scatter-diagram empiricism, very different from the one-at-a-time, cut-and-try empiricism of Ehrlich who, without any reasoned plan, tried in turn 606 chemical substances as specifics for syphilis. The 606th worked. Both the scatter-diagram and the one-at-a-time types can be, at one extreme, purely empirical, or, if you prefer, low-level empirical. As Conant (1952, pp. 26–30) points out, the level is raised—the empirical approaches the rational —as the gathering and processing of the data are more and more controlled by reasoning.

Use of Examples

The expositions of the rational method by Gilbert, Chamberlin, and Johnson all depend on the use of examples, and having tried several other ways, I am sure that this is the only way to make clear the workings of the empirical method. I have chosen to use actual examples, because these are far more effective than anything I could invent. They could have been selected from any field in geology. My examples are from recent publications dealing with the geologic work of rivers; I know of no other field in which the two approaches to problem-solving stand in such sharp contrast. "Horrible examples" are available, analysis of which would have a certain entertainment value; I shall draw my examples from publications that rank as important contributions. The principal example is from a paper that is unquestionably the outstanding report in this field, "The hydraulic geometry of stream chan-

---

[3] So many friends have objected to these terms that I should say that I am fully aware that they are unsatisfactory, chiefly because they have different connotations in different fields of study. I use them in their plain English meaning. They seem to me to be less objectionable than any other terms, but I will not take issue with those who think otherwise.

nels," by Luna Leopold and Thomas Maddock (1953). I have discussed the methodology of geologic investigation with Leopold on numerous occasions, and we have, in effect, agreed to disagree on some points.[4]

Examples are essential in a discussion of methods, but it is difficult to work with them. The problems of fluvial hydraulics are so complex that if the examples are to be comprehensible they must be simplified, and we must treat them out of context. This may irritate the few who are familiar with these matters at the technical level; I can only ask their indulgence on the ground that I am steering a difficult course between nonessential complexity and oversimplification. I should acknowledge, moreover, that I am an interested party; about 15 years ago I published an article in this field (Mackin, 1948). Finally, and most important, I will be deliberately looking at the way data are handled from the point of view of the conservative geologist, unaccustomed to this manner of handling data and highly critical of it. But I will come around full circle in the end, to indicate that the operations I have been criticizing are those of a valid method of investigation which is here to stay.

Downstream Change in Velocity in Rivers

All of us have seen the white water of a rushing mountain stream and the smooth-surfaced flow of the streams of the plains, and we are prepared by the contrast to suppose that the velocity of the flow decreases downstream. We are aware, moreover, that slope commonly decreases downstream and that velocity tends to vary directly with slope. Finally, we know from observation that the grain size of the load carried by rivers tends to decrease downstream, and that the grain size of the material carried by a river varies directly with some aspect of the velocity. For these reasons, we have always taken it for granted that velocity decreases downstream.

So in 1953, when Leopold and Maddock stated that velocity in rivers *increases* downstream, the statement came as a first-rate shock to most geologists. Three graphs (Fig. 1) from that article are good examples of the sort of evidence, and the manner of handling evidence, on which this generalization is based. They are log-log plots of several parameters; at the top, width of channel against discharge in cubic feet per second; in the middle, depth against discharge; and at the bottom, velocity against discharge. Each point represents data obtained from a U. S. Geological Survey gaging station in the Yellowstone-Big Horn drainage system. The points at the far left, such as 13 and 16, are on small headwater tributaries, and those at the far right, such as 19, are on the main stem of the Yellowstone. The upper and middle graphs show that, as should be expected, both width and depth increase with increase in dis-

---

[4] Leopold states his position elsewhere in this volume.

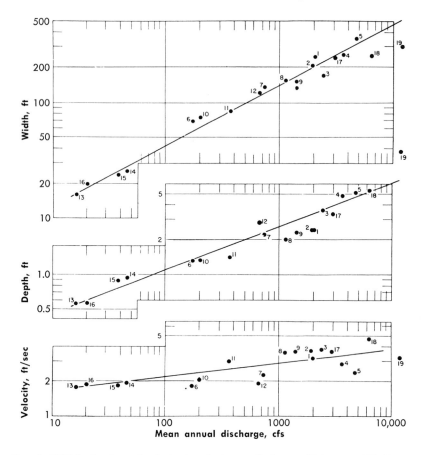

Fig. 1. Width, depth, and velocity in relation to discharge, Bighorn and Yellowstone Rivers, Wyoming and Montana (Leopold and Maddock, 1953, Fig. 6).

charge; the line in the lower graph also slopes up to the right; that is, velocity increases with increase in discharge.

Some may wonder why we have moved over from increase in velocity downstream, which is the exciting issue, to increase in velocity with increase in discharge. While it is true that discharge increases downstream in most rivers, it is at best only an approximate measure of distance downstream—the distance that would be traveled, for example, by the grains composing the load. The answer given in the Leopold-Maddock paper is that there were not enough gaging stations along the rivers to provide a sufficient number of points. Use of discharge, rather than distance, makes it possible to bring onto one graph the main stream and its tributaries of all sizes; or, for that matter, since "main stream" is a relative term, all the neighboring streams in an area large enough to provide enough points to bring out the significant relationships.

This explanation does not quite answer the question, unless expediency is an answer, but it raises another question.

Velocity at any given place—at any gaging station, for example—varies with variations in discharge from time to time during the year; as discharge and depth increase, usually in the spring, velocity at a given place increases very markedly. We may ask, then, *what* discharge is represented by the points on the lower graph? The question is pertinent, because we know that in most rivers much of the year's transportation of bed load—the sand and gravel that move along the bed—is accomplished during a relatively brief period of maximum discharge. But these graphs show mean annual discharges, and the velocities developed at those discharges. The reason for using mean annual discharge is said to be that this parameter is readily available at a large number of gaging stations. This explanation does not answer the question: what is the relevance of mean annual discharge in an analysis of the geologic work of rivers?

This general question, which applies to each of the stations considered individually, takes on another meaning when the relations between mean annual discharge and maximum discharge on streams are considered. Reference to Water Supply Paper 1559 (1960, p. 169) indicates that at point 13 (Fig. 1), which represents a gaging station on the North Fork of Owl Creek, the average annual discharge for the 14-year period of record was 15 cfs (cubic feet per second), whereas the maximum discharge during the same period was 3200 cfs; that is, the maximum was about 213 times the average. The same paper (p. 234) indicates that at point 19, which represents the Yellowstone River at Sidney, Montana, the average annual discharge over a 46-year period was 13,040 cfs, whereas the maximum during the same period was 159,000 cfs; here the maximum was about 12 times the average. The noteworthy thing about this graph—the thing that makes it so exciting—is that it shows that velocity *increases* downstream although we know from observation that grain size *decreases* downstream. The significance of the graph is more readily understood when we remember: (1) that the larger grains move only at times of maximum discharge; (2) that this graph shows mean annual discharge; and (3) that in the small rivers on the left side, the maximum discharge may be more than 200 times as great as the discharge shown on the graph, while in the big rivers on the right, it is less than 20, and usually less than 10 times the discharge shown, that is, that the critical ratios on the two sides are of a different order of magnitude. The slope of the line is an important statistical fact, but it does not bear directly on transportation of bed load by rivers.

One more thought in this connection. The depth at average annual discharge at point 13, on the North Fork of Owl Creek, is shown in the middle graph as being something less than 0.6 foot. I know the general area, and, although I have no measurements at this gaging station, it is my recollection that the larger boulders on the bed of the North Fork are more than 0.6 foot in diameter—the boulders on the bed have diameters that are of the same order of magnitude as the depth at which the very low velocity shown for this point was calculated. Similar relationships obtain for other small headwater streams, the points for which anchor down, so to speak, the left end of the line.

Let us look briefly at one more aspect of the case. The velocity is lower near the bed of a river than near the surface. Rubey (1938) and others have shown that the movement of bed load is determined, not by the average velocity, but by the velocity near the bed. And it has also been established that the relation between average velocity and what Rubey calls "bed velocity" varies markedly with depth of water, roughness of channel, and other factors. We may reasonably ask, then, *what* velocity is represented by the points on the graph? The answer is spelled out clearly by Leopold and Maddock (1953, p. 5).

> Velocity discussed in this report is the quotient of discharge divided by the area of the cross section, and is the mean velocity of the cross section as used in hydraulic practice . . . This mean velocity is not the most meaningful velocity parameter for discussing sediment transport, but it is the only measure of velocity for which a large volume of data is available. Although the writers recognize its limitations, the mean velocity is used here in lieu of adequate data on a more meaningful parameter.

There are various other similar questions about this graph, some of which are discussed by the authors in the clear and candid style of the last quotation. I will not develop these questions, or the secondary and tertiary questions that spring from the answers. Some of you may be thinking: never mind the individual points; what about the trends? It could be argued that if the conclusions are internally consistent; if they match those for other river systems; if, in short, these procedures get results, this alone justifies them.

Let's look at the results. Figure 2 is the velocity-discharge graph of Fig. 1, modified by use of symbols to identify related points and with dashed lines for individual rivers.

Points 1, 2, 3, 4, and 5, are on the main stem of the Big Horn River. Points 1, 2, and 3 are in the Big Horn Basin; point 4 is about 50 miles downstream from 3, and 5 is about 20 miles downstream from 4. The dashed line, which fits these points quite well, slopes down to the right; it means that on the main stem of the Big Horn, velocity *decreases* downstream.

Points 6, 7, 8, and 9 are on the Wind River, which is actually the upper part of the Big Horn River. I do not know whether points 8 and 9 represent the same types of channel conditions as 1, 2, 3, 4, and 5, as suggested by their positions, or whether they should be grouped with 6 and 7, as called for by the

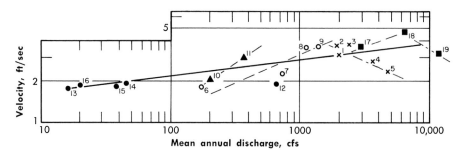

FIG. 2. Same as velocity-discharge graph in Fig. 1, with dashed lines for certain rivers; triangles, Greybull River; open circles, Wind River; X's, Bighorn River; solid squares, Yellowstone River.

geographic usage of the names. Let us say, then, that in what the geographers call the Wind River, velocity at average annual discharge increases downstream.

Points 10 and 11, both on the Greybull River, also suggest by their relative position that velocity increases downstream; the line slopes up to the right. But point 10 is near the mouth of the Greybull, about 40 airline miles downstream from 9; the average annual discharge decreases downstream (Leopold, 1953, p. 612) partly because of withdrawal of water for irrigation. Velocity actually decreases very markedly downstream on the Greybull.

Points 17, 18, and 19 are on the main stem of the Yellowstone. It appears from this graph that velocity increases downstream between 17 and 18, and decreases downstream between 18 and 19.

The generalization that velocity increases downstream, at a rate expressed by the slope of the solid line on this graph, is a particular type of empirical answer. It is what the nonstatistician is likely to think of as an "insurance company" type of statistic—a generalization applying to this group of rivers collectively, but not necessarily to any member of the group. Of the river segments represented on the graph, about half increase in velocity downstream, and about half decrease in velocity downstream. As shown by the different slopes of the dashed lines, in no two of them is the rate of change in velocity the same.

This is really not very surprising. The solid line averages velocity-discharge relations in river segments that are, as we have seen, basically unlike in this respect. Moreover, slope, which certainly enters into velocity, is not on the graph at all. For these reasons the equation of the solid line is not a definitive answer to any geologic question.

But—and here I change my tune—this graph was not intended to provide a firm answer to any question. It is only one step—a preliminary descriptive step—in an inquiry into velocity changes in rivers from head to mouth. This is accomplished by plotting certain conveniently available data on a scatter diagram.

I have indicated earlier how this procedure, which is empirical, expedient, and quantitative, serves the practicing engineer very well in getting answers that are of the right order of magnitude for use in design in deadline situations. Here we see the same procedure operating as a step in a scientific investigation. It is used in this graph to learn something about velocity relations in rivers from a mass of data that were obtained for a different purpose; the purpose of U. S. Geological Survey gaging stations is to measure discharge, not velocity. This gleaning of one kind of information from measurements—particularly long-term records of measurements—that are more or less inadequate because they were not planned to provide that kind of information, is a very common operation in many scientific investigations, and is altogether admirable.

There is another point to be made about this graph. Before the work represented by it was done, there had been no comprehensive investigations of velocity in rivers from head to mouth; this study was on the frontier. In these circumstances, some shots in the dark—some *shotgun* shots in the dark—were quite in order. The brevity with which this point can be stated is not a measure of its importance.

Finally, I wish to emphasize that Leopold and Maddock did not regard the solid line as an answer—its equation was *not* the goal of their investigation. They went on in this same paper, and in others that have followed it, to deal with velocities developed at peak discharges and with many other aspects of the hydraulic geometry of river channels. It is for this reason, and the other two reasons just stated, that I can use the graph as I have without harm to its authors.

But our literature is now being flooded by data and graphs such as these, without any of the justifications, engineering or scientific, that I have outlined. In many instances the graph is simply a painless way of getting a quantitative answer from a hodge-podge of data, obtained in the course of the investigation, perhaps at great expense, but a hodge-podge nevertheless because of the failure of the investigator to think the problem through prior to and throughout the period of data gathering. The equations read from the graphs or arrived at by other mechanical manipulations of the data are presented as terminal scientific conclusions. I suggest that the equations may be terminal engineering conclusions, but, from the point of view of science, they are statements of problems, not conclusions. A statement of a problem may be very valuable, but if it is mistaken for a conclusion, it is worse than useless because it implies that the study is finished when in fact it is only begun.

If this empirical approach—this blind probing—were the only way of quantifying geology, we would have to be content with it. But it is not; the quantitative approach is associated with the empirical approach, but it is not wedded to it. If you will list mentally the best papers in your own field, you will discover that most of them are quantitative and rational. In the study of rivers

I think of Gilbert's field and laboratory studies of Sierra Nevada mining debris (1914, 1917), and Rubey's analysis of the force required to move particles on a stream bed (1938). These geologists, and many others that come to mind, have (or had) the happy faculty of dealing with numbers without being carried away by them—of quantifying without, in the same measure, taking leave of their senses. I am not at all sure that the percentage of geologists capable of doing this has increased very much since Gilbert's day. I suggest that an increase in this percentage, or an increase in the rate of increase, is in the direction of true progress.

We shall be seeing more and more of shotgun empiricism in geologic writings, and perhaps we shall be using it in our own investigations and reports. We must learn to recognize it when we see it, and to be aware of both its usefulness and its limitations. Certainly there is nothing wrong with it as a tool, but, like most tools, how well it works depends on how intelligently it is used.

Causes of Slope of the Longitudinal Profile

We can now turn to a matter which seems to me the crux of the difference between the empirical and the rational methods of investigation, namely, cause-and-effect relations.[5] I would like to bring out, first, an important difference between immediate and superficial causes as opposed to long-term, geologic causes; and second, the usefulness, almost the necessity, of thinking a process through, back to the long-term causes, as a check on quantitative observations and conclusions.

Most engineers would regard an equation stating that the size of the pebbles that can be carried by a river is a certain power of its bed velocity as a complete statement of the relationship. The equation says nothing about cause

---

[5] I am aware that my tendency to think in terms of cause and effect would be regarded as a mark of scientific naiveté by some scientists and most philosophers. My persistence in this habit of thought after having been warned against it does not mean that I challenge their wisdom. Perhaps part of the difficulty lies in a difference between what I call long-term geologic causes and what are sometimes called ultimate causes. For example, a philosopher might say, "Yes, it is clear that such things as discharge and size of pebbles may control or cause the slope of an adjusted river, but what, then, is the cause of the discharge and the pebble size? And if these are effects of the height of the mountains at the headwaters, what, then, is the cause of the height of the mountains"? Every cause is an effect, and every effect is a cause. Where do we stop? I can only answer that I am at the moment concerned with the geologic work of rivers, not with the cause of upheaval of mountains. The question, where do we stop?, is for the philosopher, who deals with all knowledge; the quest for ultimate causes, or the futility of that quest, is in his province. The investigator in science commonly stays within his own rather narrow field of competence and, especially if time is an important element of his systems, he commonly finds it useful to think in terms of cause and effect in that field. The investigator is never concerned with ultimate causes.

and effect, and the engineer might be surprised if asked which of the two, velocity or grain size, is the cause and which is the effect. He would almost certainly reply that velocity controls or determines the size of the grains that can be moved, and that therefore velocity is the cause. To clinch this argument, he might point out that if, by the turn of a valve, the velocity of a laboratory river were sufficiently increased, grains that previously had been at rest on the bed would begin to move; that is, on the basis of direct observation, and by the commonsense test of relative timing, the increase in velocity *is* the cause of the movement of the larger grains. This is as far as the engineer needs to go in most of his operations on rivers.

He might be quite willing to take the next step and agree that the velocity is, in turn, partly determined by the slope. In fact, getting into the swing of the cause-and-effect game, he might even volunteer this idea, which is in territory familiar to him. But the next question—what then, is the cause of the slope?—leads into unfamiliar territory; many engineers, and some geologists, simply take slope for granted.

Our engineer would probably be at first inclined to question the sanity of anyone suggesting that the size of the grains carried by a river determines the velocity of the river. But in any long-term view, the sizes of the grains that are supplied to a river are determined, not by the river, but by the characteristics of the rocks, relief, vegetative cover, and other physical properties of its drainage basin. If the river is, as we say, graded (or as the engineer says, adjusted), this means that in each segment the slope is adjusted to provide just the transporting power required to carry through that segment all the grains, of whatever size, that enter it from above. Rivers that flow from rugged ranges of hard rock tend to develop steep slopes, adjusted to the transportation of large pebbles. Once they are developed, the adjusted slopes are maintained indefinitely, as long as the size of the pebbles and other controlling factors remain the same. Rivers that are supplied only with sand tend to maintain low slopes appropriate to the transportation of this material.

If the sizes of the grains supplied to a given segment of an adjusted river are abruptly increased by uplift, by a climatic change, or by a work of man, the larger grains, which are beyond the former carrying power, are deposited in the upper part of the segment; the bed is raised thereby and the slope is consequently steepened. This steepening by deposition continues until that particular slope is attained which provides just the velocity required to carry those larger grains, that is, until a new equilibrium slope is developed, which the river will maintain thence forward so long as grain size and other slope-controlling conditions remain the same.

Thus in the long view, velocity is adjusted to, or determined by, grain size; the test of relative timing (first the increase in grain size of material supplied to the river, and then, through a long period of readjustment, the increase in velocity) marks the change in grain size as the cause of the change in velocity. Note that because the period of readjustment may occupy thousands of years, this view is based primarily on reasoning rather than on direct observation. Note also that we deal here with three different frames of reference spanning the range from the empirical to the rational.

The statement that grain size tends to vary directly with bed velocity is an equation, whose terms are transposable; neither time nor cause and effect are involved, and this first frame may be entirely empirical. The numerical answer is complete in itself.

The short-term cause-and-effect view, that grain size is controlled by bed velocity, is in part rational, or if you prefer, it represents a higher level of empiricism. As I see it, this second frame has a significant advantage over the first in that it provides more fertile ground for the formulation of working hypotheses as to the mechanical relations between the flow and the particle at rest or in motion on the bed, leading to purposeful observation or to the design of experiments.

The third frame, the long-term view, that velocity is controlled by grain size, has a great advantage over the short-term view in that it provides an understanding of the origin of slope, which the short-term view does not attempt to explain. It is largely rational, or if you prefer, it represents a still higher level of empiricism.

Because I think that the objective of science is an understanding of the world around us, I prefer the second and third frames to the first, but I hope that it is clear that I recognize that all the frames are valid; the best one, in every instance, is simply the one that most efficiently gets the job done that needs doing. The important thing is to recognize that there *are* different frames; and that they overlap so completely and are so devoid of boundaries that it is easy to slip from one to the other.

The difference between the rational and the empirical approach to this matter of river slope, and the need for knowing what frame of reference we are in, can be clarified by a little story. One of the earliest theories of the origin of meanders, published in a British engineering journal in the late eighteen hundreds, was essentially as follows: divested of all geographic detail. Two cities A and B, both on the valley floor of a meandering river, are 50 airline miles apart. City B is 100 feet lower than city A; hence the average slope of the valley floor is two feet per mile (Fig. 3). But the slope of the river, measured round its loops, is only one foot per mile. The British engineer's theory was, in effect, though not expressed in these words, that the river said to itself, "How, with a slope of one foot per mile, can I manage to stay on a valley floor with a slope of two feet per mile? If I flow straight down the middle of the valley floor, starting at A, I will be 50 feet *above* the valley floor at B, and that simply will not do." Then it occurred to the river that it could meet this

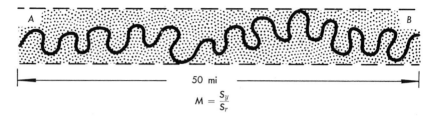

FIG. 3. Diagram illustrating an hypothesis for the origin of meanders.

problem by bending its channel into loops of precisely the sinuousity required to keep it *on* the valley floor, just as a man might do with a rope too long for the distance between two posts. And it worked, and that's why we have meanders.

Note that this theory not only explains meandering qualitatively, but puts all degrees of meandering, from the very loopy meanders of the ribbon-candy type to those that are nearly straight, on a firm quantitative basis—the sinuosity or degree of meandering, M, equals the slope of the valley floor, S_y, over the slope of the river, S_r.

There is nothing wrong with this equation, so long as it only describes. But if its author takes it to be an explanation, as the British engineer did, and if he slips over from the empirical frame into the rational frame, as he may do almost without realizing it, he is likely to be not just off by an order of magnitude, but upside-down—to be not only wrong but ludicrous. This explanation of meanders leaves one item out of account—the origin of the valley floor. The valley floor was not opened out and given its slope by a bulldozer, nor is it a result of special creation prior to the creation of the river. The valley floor was formed by the river that flows on it.

Causes of Downvalley Decrease in Pebble Size

It is a matter of observation that there is commonly a downvalley decrease in the slopes of graded rivers, and it is also a matter of observation that there is commonly a downvalley decrease in the size of pebbles in alluvial deposits. A question arises, then, as to whether the decrease in slope is caused in part by the decrease in pebble size, or whether the decrease in pebble size is caused in part by the decrease in slope, or whether both of these changes are independent or interdependent results of some other cause. My third and last example applies the empirical and rational approaches to a part of this problem, namely, what are the causes of the decrease in pebble size? The reasoning is somewhat more involved than in the other examples; in this respect it is more truly representative of the typical geologic problem.

The downvalley decrease in pebble size could be caused by either of two obvious, sharply contrasted mechanisms: (1) abrasional wear of the pebbles as they move along the bed of the stream, and (2) selective transportation, that is, a leaving-behind of the larger pebbles. The question is, which mechanism causes the decrease, or, if both operate, what is their relative importance?

There is no direct and satisfactory way of obtaining an answer to this question by measurement, however detailed, of pebble sizes in alluvial deposits. The most commonly used approach is by means of laboratory experiment. Usually fragments of rock of one or more kinds are placed in a cylinder which can be rotated on a horizontal axis and is so constructed that the fragments slide, roll, or drop as it turns. The fragments are remeasured from time to time to determine the reduction in size, the corresponding travel distance being calculated from the circumference of the cylinder and the number of rotations. This treatment does not approximate very closely the processes of wear in an actual river bed. Kuenen (1959) has recently developed a better apparatus, in which the fragments are moved over a concrete floor in a circular path by a current of water. Whatever the apparatus, it is certain that the decrease in pebble size observed in the laboratory is due wholly to abrasion, because none of the pebbles can be left behind; there is no possibility of selective transportation.

When the laboratory rates of reduction in pebble size per unit of travel distance are compared with the downvalley decrease in pebble size in alluvial deposits along most rivers, it is found that the decrease in size along the rivers is somewhat greater than would be expected on the basis of laboratory data on rates of abrasion. If the rates of abrasion in the laboratory correctly represent the rates of abrasion in the river bed, it should be only necessary to subtract to determine what percentage of the downvalley decrease in grain size in the alluvial deposits is due to selective transportation.

Field and laboratory data bearing on this problem have been reviewed by Scheidegger (1961) in his textbook, "Theoretical Geomorphology," which is about as far out on the quantitative side as it is possible to get. Scheidegger (p. 175) concludes that "... the most likely mechanism of pebble gradation in rivers consists of pebbles becoming contriturated due to the action of frictional forces, but being assigned their position along the stream bed by a sorting process due to differential transportation."

If I understand it correctly, this statement means that pebbles are made smaller by abrasion, but that the downvalley decrease in pebble size in alluvial deposits is due largely (or wholly?) to selective transportation.

On a somewhat different basis—the rate of reduction of pebbles of less resistant rock, relative to quartzite, in a downvalley direction in three rivers east of the Black Hills—Plumley (1948) concludes that about 25 per cent of the reduction in these rivers is due to abrasion, and about 75 per cent is due to selective transportation.

These two conclusions as to the cause of the downstream decrease in pebble size, solidly based on measurements, agree in ascribing it mainly to selective transportation. Let us try a different approach—let us think through the long-term implications of the processes.

Downstream decrease in pebble size by selective transportation requires that the larger pebbles be left behind permanently. The three-inch pebbles, for example, move downstream to a certain zone, and are deposited there because they cannot be transported farther. The two-inch pebbles are carried farther downstream, to be deposited in an appropriate zone as the slope decreases. These zones may have considerable length along the stream, they may be poorly defined, and they may of course overlap, but there is a downstream limit beyond which no pebbles of a given size occur in the alluvial deposits because none could be carried beyond that limit, which is set by transporting power.

Consider a river carrying a bed load of sand and gravel under steady-state conditions such that the slope and altitude in a given segment are maintained indefinitely without change, and let it be assumed for simplicity that the channel is floored and walled by rock (Fig. 4a). The load moves chiefly

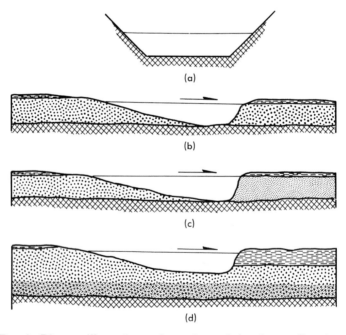

(a)

(b)

(c)

(d)

Fig. 4. Diagram illustrating exchange in graded and aggrading rivers.

during high-water stages and lodges on the bed during low-water stages. The smaller pebbles are likely to be set in motion sooner than the larger pebbles during each rising stage, they are likely to move faster while in motion, and they are likely to be kept in motion longer during each falling stage. In this sense, the transportation process is selective—if a slug of gravel consisting of identifiable pebbles were dumped into the segment, the smaller pebbles would outrun the larger, and this would cause a downstream decrease in the sizes of these particular pebbles in the low-water deposits. But in the steady-state condition, that is, with a continuous supply of a particular type of pebble or of pebbles of all types, all the pebbles deposited on the bed during the low stages must be placed in motion during the high stages; if the larger pebbles were permanently left behind during the seasonal cycles of deposition and erosion, the bed would be raised, and this, in turn, would change the condition. A non-aggrading river flowing in a channel which is floored and walled by rock cannot rid itself of coarse material by deposition because there is no place to deposit it where it will be out of reach of the river during subsequent fluctuations of flow; every pebble entering a given segment must eventually pass on through it. The smaller pebbles move more rapidly into the segment than the larger pebbles, but they also move more rapidly out of it. In the steady-state condition, the channel deposits from place to place in the segment contain the same proportions of the smaller and larger pebbles as though all moved at the same rate. Selective transportation cannot be a contributing cause of a downstream decrease in pebble size in our model river because there can be no selective deposition.

In a real river that maintains the same level as it meanders on a broad valley floor, bed load deposited along the inner side of a shifting bend is exchanged for an equal volume of slightly older channel deposits eroded from the outside of the bend. If these channel deposits were formed by the same river, operating under the same conditions and at the same level over a long period of time (Fig. 4b), the exchange process would not cause a reduction in the grain size of the bed load; insofar as selective transportation is concerned, the relation would be the same as in our model river. But if, by reason of capture or climatic change or any other change in controlling conditions, the older alluvial deposits in a given segment are finer grained than the bed load now entering that segment (Fig. 4c), exchange will cause a decrease in pebble size in a downstream direction, at least until the older deposits have been completely replaced by deposits representing the new regime. Exchange also causes a reduction in grain size if the river, maintaining the same level, cuts laterally into weak country rock that yields material finer in grain size than the load that is being concomitantly deposited on the widening valley floor.

The selective transportation associated with the process of exchange in the graded river, while by no means negligible, is much less effective as a cause of downstream decrease in pebble size than the selective transportation that characterizes the aggrading river. The essential difference is shown in Fig. 4(d); some of the deposits formed by one swing of the aggrading river across its valley floor are not subject to reworking in later swings, because the channel is slowly rising. The largest pebbles in transit in a given segment in a high-water stage are likely to be concentrated in the basal part of the deposit formed during the next falling stage. Thus the aggrading river rids itself of these pebbles, selectively and permanently, and there is a corresponding downstream decrease in pebble sizes in the deposits.

If upbuilding of the flood plain by deposition of overbank material keeps pace with aggradational rising of the channel, the shifting meanders may exchange channel deposits for older alluvium consisting wholly or in part of relatively fine-grained overbank material (Fig. 4d). But in rapidly aggrading rivers this rather orderly process may give way to a fill-spill mechanism in which filling of the channel is attended by the splaying of channel deposits over adjoining parts of the valley floor. On some proglacial outwash plains this type of braiding causes boulder detritus near the ice front to grade into pebbly sand within a few miles; there is doubtless some abrasional reduction in grain size in the proglacial rivers, but nearly all the decrease must be due to selective transportation.

Briefly then, thinking the process through indicates that the downstream decrease in grain size in river deposits in some cases may be almost wholly due to abrasion, and in others almost wholly due to selective transportation, depending primarily on whether the river is graded or aggrading and on the rate of aggradation. It follows that no generalization as to the relative importance of abrasion versus selective transportation in rivers—all rivers—has any meaning.

A different way of looking at this problem has been mentioned in another connection. As already noted, selective transportation implies permanent deposition, for example, the three-inch pebbles in a certain zone, the two-inch pebbles in another zone farther downstream, and so on. If this deposition is caused by a downstream decrease in slope, as is often implied and sometimes stated explicitly (Scheidegger, p. 171), then what is the cause of the decrease in slope? We know that the valley floor was not shaped by a bulldozer, and we know that it was not formed by an act of special creation before the river began to flow. As we have seen in considering the origin of meanders, rivers normally shape their own valley floors. If the river is actively aggrading, this is usually because of some geologically recent change such that the gradient in a given segment is not steep enough to enable the river to move through that segment all of the pebbles entering it; in this (aggrading) river, the size of the pebbles that are carried is controlled in part by the slope, and the larger pebbles are left behind. But if the river is graded, the slope in each segment is precisely that required to enable the river, under the prevailing hydraulic conditions, whatever they may be, to carry the load supplied to it. The same three-inch pebbles that are the largest seen on the bed and banks in one zone will, after a while, be the two-inch pebbles in a zone farther downstream.

We cannot wait long enough to verify this conclusion by direct observation of individual pebbles, because the pebbles ordinarily remain at rest in alluvial deposits on the valley floor for very long intervals of time between jogs of movement in the channel. We are led to the conclusion by reasoning, rather than by direct observation. In the long-term view, the graded river is a transportation system in equilibrium, which means that it maintains the same slope so long as conditions remain the same. There is no place in this self-maintaining system for permanent deposits: if the three-inch pebbles entering a given zone accumulated there over a period of geologic time, they would raise the bed and change the slope. As the pebbles, in their halting downvalley movement in the channel, are reduced in size by abrasion, and perhaps also by weathering while they are temporarily at rest in the valley floor alluvium, the slope, which is being adjusted to their transportation, decreases accordingly.

Does this reasoning settle the problem? Of course not! It merely makes us take a more searching look at the observational data. Since it is theoretically certain that the mechanisms which cause pebbles to decrease in size as they travel downstream operate differently, depending on whether the river is graded or aggrading, there is no sense in averaging measurements made along graded rivers with those made along aggrading rivers. However meticulous the measurements, and however refined the statistical treatment of them, the average will have no meaning.[6]

The reasoning tells us that, first of all, the rivers to be studied in connection with change of pebble size downstream must be selected with care. Because a steady-state condition is always easier to deal with quantitatively than a shifting equilibrium, it would be advisable to restrict the study, at the outset, to the deposits of graded rivers; when these are understood, we will be ready to deal with complications introduced by varying rates of aggradation. Similarly, it will be well, at least at the beginning, to eliminate altogether, or at least reduce to a minimum, the complicating effects of contributions from tributaries or other local sources; this can be done by selecting river segments without large tributaries, or by focusing attention on one or more distinctive rock types from known sources. There are unavoidable sampling problems, but some of these

---

[6] I owe to Frank Calkins the thought that, like most hybrids, this one would be sterile. The significance of this way of expressing what I have been saying about the averaging of unlike things is brought out by Conant's (1951, p. 25) definition of science as "an interconnected series of concepts and conceptual schemes that have developed as a result of experimentation and observation and are fruitful of further experimentation and observations. In this definition the emphasis is on the word 'fruitful'."

can readily be avoided; for example, there are many river segments in which the alluvial deposits are not contaminated by lag materials. Any attempt to develop sampling procedures must take into account, first of all, the fact that the channel *deposits* in a given segment of a valley differ significantly in gradation of grain size from the material moving through the channel in that segment in any brief period; the investigation may deal with the bed load (trapped in a box, so to speak), or with the deposits, or with both; but if both bed load and the deposits are measured, the measurements can only be compared, they cannot be averaged. Certainly we must investigate, in each river individually, the effects of weathering of the pebbles during periods of rest.

We must also take another hard look at the abrasion rates obtained by laboratory experiments, and try to determine in what degree these are directly comparable with abrasion rates in rivers. It is clearly desirable to develop other independent checks, such as those given by Plumley's measurement of rates of downstream reduction in sizes of pebbles of rock types differing in resistance to abrasion. Finally, it goes without saying that the reasoning itself must be continuously checked against the evidence, and one line of reasoning must be checked against others, to make sure that the mental wheels have not slipped a cog or two.

When we eventually have sufficient data on rates of downstream decrease of pebble size in alluvial deposits along many different types of rivers (considered individually), it will be possible to evaluate separately, in quantitative terms, the effect of special circumstances influencing the process of exchange in graded rivers, rates of aggradation in aggrading rivers, and the other causes of downstream decrease in pebble size. These generalizations will apply to all river deposits, modern as well as ancient, and it may even be that we can draw sound inferences regarding the hydraulic characteristics of the ancient rivers by comparing their deposits with those of modern rivers, in which the hydraulic characteristics can be measured.

This rational method of problem-solving is difficult and tortuous, but the history of science makes it clear, again and again, that if the system to be investigated is complex, the longest way 'round is the shortest way home; most of the empirical shortcuts turn out to be blind alleys.

Whither Are We Drifting, Methodologically?

I would like now to return to some of the questions asked at the outset. Must we accept, as gospel, Lord Kelvin's pronouncement that what cannot be stated in numbers is not science? To become respectable members of the scientific community, must we drastically change our accustomed habits of thought, abandoning the classic geologic approach to problem-solving? To the extent that this approach is qualitative, is it necessarily loose, and therefore bad?

Must we now move headlong to quantify our operations on the assumption that whatever is quantitative is necessarily rigorous and therefore good?

Why has the swing to the quantitative come so late? Is it because our early leaders, men such as Hutton, Lyell, Agassiz, Heim, Gilbert, and Davis, were intellectually a cut or two below their counterparts in classical physics? There is a more reasonable explanation, which is well known to students of the history of science. In each field of study the timing of the swing to the quantitative and the present degree of quantification are largely determined by the subject matter: the number and complexity of the interdependent components involved in its systems, the relative ease or difficulty of obtaining basic data, the susceptibility of those data to numerical expression, and the extent to which time is an essential dimension. The position of geology relative to the basic sciences has been stated with characteristic vigor by Walter Bucher (1941) in a paper that seems to have escaped the attention of our apologists.

Classical physics was quantitative from its very beginning as a science; it moved directly from observations made in the laboratory under controlled conditions to abstractions that were quantitative at the outset. The quantification of chemistry lagged 100 years behind that of physics. The chemistry of a candle flame is of an altogether different order of complexity from the physics of Galileo's rolling ball; the flame is only one of many types of oxidation; and oxidation is only one of many ways in which substances combine. There had to be an immense accumulation of quantitative data, and many minor discoveries—some of them accidental, but most of them based on planned investigations—before it was possible to formulate such a sweeping generalization as the law of combining weights.

If degree of quantification of its laws were a gage of maturity in a science (which it is not), geology and biology would be 100 to 200 years behind chemistry. Before Bucher (1933) could formulate even a tentative set of "laws" for deformation of the earth's crust, an enormous descriptive job had to be well under way. Clearly, it was necessary to know what the movements of the crust *are* before anybody could frame explanations of them. But adequate description of even a single mountain range demands the best efforts of a couple of generations of geologists, with different special skills, working in the field and the laboratory. Because no two ranges are alike, the search for the laws of mountain growth requires that we learn as much as we can about every range we can climb and also about those no longer here to be climbed; the ranges of the past, which we must reconstruct as best we can by study of their eroded stumps, are as significant as those of the present. Rates of growth and relative ages of past and present ranges are just as important as their geometry; the student of the mechanics of crustal deformation must think like a physicist and also like a historian, and these are very different ways of thinking, difficult to combine. The evidence is hard to come by, it is largely circumstantial, and there is never enough of it. Laboratory models are helpful only within narrow limits. So it is also with the mechanism of emplacement of batholiths, and the origin of ore-forming fluids, and the shaping of landforms of all kinds, and most other truly geologic problems.

It is chiefly for these reasons that most geologists have been preoccupied with manifold problems of description of geologic things and processes—*particular* things and processes—and have been traditionally disinclined to generalize even in qualitative terms. Because most geologic evidence cannot readily be stated in numbers, and because most geologic systems are so complex that some qualitative grasp of the problem must precede effective quantitative study, we are even less inclined to generalize in quantitative terms. Everybody knows the story of Lord Kelvin's calculation of the age of the earth.

These things are familiar, but they are worth saying because they explain why geology is only now fully in the swing to the quantitative. Perhaps it would have been better if the swing had begun earlier, but this is by no means certain. A meteorologist has told me that meteorology might be further ahead today if its plunge to the quantitative had been somewhat less precipitous—if there had been a broader observational base for a qualitative understanding of its exceedingly complex systems before these were quantified. At any rate, it is important that we recognize that the quantification of geology is a normal evolutionary process, which is more or less on schedule. The quantification will proceed at an accelerating pace, however much our ultraconservatives may drag their feet. I have been trying to point out that there is an attendant danger: as measurements increase in complexity and refinement, and as mathematical manipulations of the data become more sophisticated, these measurements and manipulations may become so impressive in form that the investigator tends to lose sight of their meaning and purpose.[7]

This tendency is readily understandable. Some of the appealing features of the empirical method have already been mentioned. Moreover, the very act of making measurements, in a fixed pattern, provides a solid sense of accomplishment. If the measurements are complicated, involving unusual techniques

---

[7] The subtitle of a recent article by Krumbein (1962), "Quantification and the advent of the computer open new vistas in a science traditionally qualitative" makes evident the overlap of our interests. Professor Krumbein's article deals explicitly with a mechanical method of processing data; the fact that there is no mention of the use of reasoning in testing the quality and relevance of the data to the specific issue being investigated certainly does not mean that he thinks one whit less of the "rational method" than I do. Similarly, I hope that nothing that I have said or failed to say is construed as meaning that I have an aversion to mechanical methods of analyzing data; such methods are unquestionably good if they bring out relationships not otherwise evident, or in any other way advance the progress of the rational method of investigation. When mechanical processes *replace* reasoning processes, and when a number *replaces* understanding as the objective, danger enters.

and apparatus and a special jargon, they give the investigator a good feeling of belonging to an elite group, and of pushing back the frontiers. Presentation of the results is simplified by use of mathematical shorthand, and even though nine out of ten interested geologists do not read that shorthand with ease, the author can be sure that seven out of the ten will at least be impressed. It is an advantage or disadvantage of mathematical shorthand, depending on the point of view, that things can be said in equations, impressively, even arrogantly, which are so nonsensical that they would embarrass even the author if spelled out in words.

As stated at the outset, the real issue is not a matter of classical geologic methods versus quantification. Geology *is* largely quantitative, and it is rapidly and properly becoming more so. The real issue is the rational method versus the empirical method of solving problems; the point that I have tried to make is that if the objective is an understanding of the system investigated, and if that system is complex, then the empirical method is apt to be less efficient than the rational method. Most geologic features—ledges of rock, mineral deposits, landscapes, segments of a river channel—present an almost infinite variety of elements, each susceptible to many different sorts of measurement. We cannot measure them all to any conventional standard of precision—blind probing will not work. Some years ago (1941) I wrote that the "eye and brain, unlike camera lens and sensitized plate, record completely only what they intelligently seek out." Jim Gilluly expresses the same thought more succinctly in words to the effect that most exposures provide answers only to questions that are put to them. It is only by thinking, as we measure, that we can avoid listing together in a field book, and after a little while, averaging, random dimensions of apples and oranges and apple crates and orange trees.

Briefly, then, my thesis is that the present swing to the quantitative in geology, which is good, does not necessarily and should not involve a swing from the rational to the empirical method. I'm sure that geology is a science, with different sorts of problems and methods, but not in any sense less mature than any other science; indeed, the day-to-day operations of the field geologist are apt to be far more sophisticated than those of his counterpart—the experimentalist—in physics or chemistry. And I'm sure that anyone who hires out as a geologist, whether in practice, or in research, or in teaching, and then operates like a physicist or a chemist, or, for that matter, like a statistician or an engineer, is not living up to his contract.

The best and highest use of the brains of our youngsters is the working out of cause and effect relations in geologic systems, with all the help they can get from the other sciences and engineering, and mechanical devices of all kinds, but with basic reliance on the complex reasoning processes described by Gilbert, Chamberlin, and Johnson.

REFERENCES CITED

ALBRITTON, C. C., JR., 1961, Notes on the history and philosophy of science (1) A conference on the scope and philosophy of geology: J. Graduate Research Center, Southern Methodist Univ., vol. 29, no. 3, pp. 188–192.

BUCHER, W. H., 1933, The deformation of the earth's crust: Princeton, N. J., Princeton Univ. Press, 518 pp.

———, 1941, The nature of geological inquiry and the training required for it: Am. Inst. Mining Metall. Eng., Tech. Pub. 1377, 6 pp.

CHAMBERLIN, T. C., 1897, The method of multiple working hypotheses: J. Geol., vol. 5, pp. 837–848.

CONANT, J. B., 1951, Science and common sense: New Haven, Yale Univ. Press, 371 pp.

———, 1952, Modern science and modern man: New York, Columbia Univ. Press, 111 pp.

GARRELS, R. M., 1951, A textbook of geology: New York, Harper, 511 pp.

GILBERT, G. K., 1886, The inculcation of the scientific method by example, with an illustration drawn from the Quaternary geology of Utah: Am. J. Sci., vol. 31, (whole no. 131), pp. 284–299.

———, 1914, The transportation of debris by running water: U. S. Geol. Survey, Prof. Paper, 86, 263 pp.

———, 1917, Hydraulic-mining debris in the Sierra Nevada: U. S. Geol. Survey, Prof. Paper 105, 154 pp.

HOLTON, G., 1952, Introduction to concepts and theories in physical science: Reading, Mass., Addison-Wesley, 650 pp.

JOHNSON, DOUGLAS, 1933, Role of analysis in scientific investigation: Geol. Soc. Am., B., vol. 44, pp. 461–494.

KRUMBEIN, W. C., 1960, The "geological population" as a framework for analysing numerical data in geology: Liverpool and Manchester Geol. J., vol. 2, pt. 3, pp. 341–368.

———, 1962, The computer in geology: Science, vol. 136, pp. 1087–1092.

KUENEN, P. H., 1959, Fluviatile action on sand, Part 3 of Experimental Abrasion: Am. J. Sci., vol. 257, pp. 172–190.

LEOPOLD, L. B., 1953, Downstream changes of velocity in rivers: Am. J. Sci., vol. 251, pp. 606–624.

———, and MADDOCK, T., JR., 1953, The hydraulic geometry of stream channels and some physiographic implications: U. S. Geol. Survey, Prof. Paper 252, 57 pp.

MACKIN, J. H., 1941, Drainage changes near Wind Gap, Pennsylvania; a study in map interpretation: J. Geomorphology, vol. 4, pp. 24–53.

———, 1948, Concept of the graded river: Geol. Soc. Am., B., vol. 59, pp. 463–512.

PLUMLEY, W. J., 1948, Black Hills terrace gravels; a study in sediment transport: J. Geol., vol. 56, pp. 526–577.

RUBEY, W. W., 1938, The force required to move particles on a stream bed: U.S. Geol. Survey, Prof. Paper 189-E, pp. 120–140.

SCHEIDEGGER, A. E., 1961, Theoretical geomorphology: Berlin, Springer-Verlag, 333 pp.

SIMPSON, G. G., ROE, ANNE, and LEWONTIN, R. C., 1960, Quantitative zoology: New York, Harcourt-Brace, 440 pp.

U. S. Geological Survey, 1960, Surface water supply of the United States, 1958; Part 6A, Missouri River Basin above Sioux City, Iowa: U. S. Geol. Survey Water-Supply Paper 1559, 434 pp.

WEISS, PAUL, 1962, Experience and experiment in biology: Science, vol. 136, pp. 468–471.

MASON L. HILL

Richfield Oil Corporation

Role of Classification in Geology

Goethe said that mineralogy interested him only for two reasons: "I valued it for its great practical utility, and then I thought to find a document elucidating the primary formation of the world, of which Werner's doctrine gave hopes." But he went on to conclude that, "Since this science has been turned upside down by the death of this excellent man, I do not proceed further in it, but remain quiet with my own convictions." (Oxenford, 1882)

This statement, made in 1827, reflects Goethe's melancholy reaction to the triumph of the Plutonists' fruitful classification of rocks over that of Werner's less productive Neptunist school. The statement also illustrates the theme of this essay, which is that modern geologic classifications must be revised as knowledge increases, lest they too prove disenchanting.

Examples of attention to classification in geology are evidenced by an early reclassification of sedimentary rocks (Grabau, 1904), by a more recent symposium on the classification of sediments (Pettijohn, 1948; Shrock, 1948; Krynine, 1948), and by a recent book on the classification of carbonate rocks (Ham, 1962). A discussion of fault classifications is presented here to illustrate the role of classification in geology, to emphasize the usefulness of rules of nomenclature and classification, and more particularly to show the need for a reclassification of faults in order to stimulate progress in structural geology.

Classification and Ordering

According to Webster, a classification is "a system of classes or groups, or a systematic division of a series of related phenomena." To classify, one must recognize differences and likenesses as well as gradations between things, processes, and concepts. Classifications are particularly difficult in geology because geologic things, processes, and concepts are many and complex; they usually need to be fixed in space and time; and they commonly involve the terminology of other natural sciences. Furthermore, since the historical science of geology is concerned with the antecedents of natural phenomena, the most significant classifications are interpretive and are, accordingly, subject to error both in formulation and application.

Although classification is usually conceived as a grouping on the basis of differences and likenesses, much good classification is based on gradations of characteristics. The arrangement of related phenomena in gradational series has been called "ordering" (Hempel, 1952 and 1959), or the continuous variable type of classification (Rodgers, 1950). Ordering is preferred whenever it is a possible means of classification, because both large and small differences can be expressed precisely and quantitatively. Ordering may be compared to a "more-or-less," rather than a "yes-or-no" relationship, where one class (or member) has characteristics which grade into another, instead of having separate characteristics. These gradational characteristics may be expressed either in a relative manner (before or after, larger or smaller, etc.) or quantitatively, in which case mathematical analyses may be applied. Ordering is a common means of classification in geology (e.g. isomorphous mineral series allow quantitative chemical classification, or "late Eocene" provides comparative age classification). Often artificial grouping is employed in a gradational series to facilitate scientific work and communication (e.g., clay, silt, sand, and gravel are useful classes of sediments within a gradational series of clast sizes). Sometimes classes will be separated by nongradational differences in a classification, whereas members within these classes may vary gradationally and thus be subject to ordering. Thus igneous and sedimentary rocks are generally nongradational, whereas members of both classes usually vary gradationally. Ordering is especially adaptable to expressing quantitative relationships in mineralogy, petrology, paleontology, and other geologic fields, by graphs showing two or more gradational variables.

Classifications of Faults

The history of geology records many examples of unproductive as well as fruitful classifications, for the contrast between the Wernerian and Huttonian classifications of rocks finds parallels in many less dramatic cases. Far too many geologic terms are either so misleading or so commonly misused that they actually retard scientific progress. The use of names which imply knowledge that does not exist is particularly reprehensible. Thus genetic terms such as "turbidites" and "slump structures" are often applied to features whose origins are uncertain. This practice not only promulgates error but also discourages further study of the objects under investigation. To the extent that the classifications of faults now in use imply knowledge which usually does not exist, these must be suspected of retarding progress in structural geology.

The terminology of faulting presumably began more than 150 years ago in the British coal mines with the words "at fault" used to express the abrupt termination of coal seams. As experience was gained in locating the displaced continuations of these seams, it was discovered that planar structures along which movement apparently had occurred were responsible for abrupt separations of the coal beds. Such structures have continued to be known as faults, and although defined as fractures along which relative movement has occurred, the concept is not complete without at least some reference to the geometric relations of one fault wall to the other. As geologists mapped other terrains, faults of different characteristics were described. To distinguish between faults of differing characteristics the names *normal, reverse, thrust,* and *lateral* were gradually introduced, and used as a classification of faults. These terms are not only common in English geologic literature, but they have equivalents in most other languages; and the structures they denote are shown by conventional symbols on geologic maps and sections. Unfortunately, these terms do not mean the same things to all geologists, as demonstrated by variations in definition revealed in glossaries, textbooks, periodicals, and in oral discussions. For example, Beloussov (1962) gives a classification of faults based on relative and absolute movements without describing criteria for the determination of slip. Furthermore, the basic concept of fault separation as contrasted to slip is not presented. In another section of the same textbook, a genetic classification of faults is given without any indication as to how it is to be used. Concern over classification is evidenced in a number of recent discussions including those of Boyer and Muehlberger (1960), Crowell (1959), Kelley (1960), and Kupfer (1960).

It is obvious that the sense of movement on faults is of paramount tectonic importance. It is true, but not obvious, that geologists can rarely determine fault slip (actual relative movement). It is also true, and again not generally obvious, that geologists classify most faults on the basis of separations (apparent relative movements) but erroneously use the terms *normal, reverse, thrust,* and *lateral* in relation to slip. This confusion between the concepts of fault separation and fault slip, in the common usage of these terms, is the result of imperfect classification.

Although Reid, *et al.* (1913) did much to standardize and establish modern fault nomenclature, they allowed the terms *normal* and *reverse* to mean ambiguously either slip or separation. Gill (1941) in a committee effort which recognized the difference between slip and separation, recommended the fault names "normal," "reverse," "right," "left," and combinations thereof (e.g., "right reverse fault") on the basis of relative slip, but without proposing complementary terms based on fault separations (the usual evidence for faults). Certainly a logical and progressive fault classification, based on sound rules for good nomenclature and classification, is long overdue.

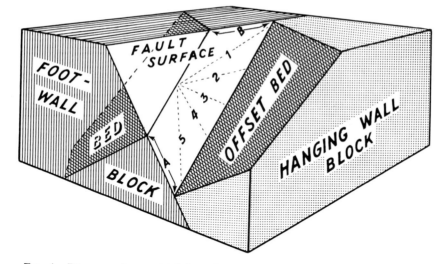

Fig. 1. Diagram of normal left-lateral fault. The dip separation A and the strike separation B are used for the separation-based (apparent relative movement) classification of this fault. The slip-based (actual relative movement) classification would be used as follows, if slips of diagram were approximately determined: (1) reverse left-lateral slip fault; (2) left-lateral slip fault; (3) normal left-lateral slip fault; (4) normal slip fault; and (5) normal right-lateral slip fault.

Dual classification of faults. Most faults are recognized by discontinuities of planar or tabular geologic elements. The accompanying diagram (Fig. 1) shows that the displacement of a tabular geologic element with fixed strike separation (B) and dip separation (A) can be accomplished by slips (1) through (5) and thus demonstrates that separation (apparent relative movement) and slip (actual relative movement) are different concepts. The fault slip (sense and amount of relative movement) is usually indeterminable unless linear geologic elements (e.g., line of intersection of bed and vein) are dislocated. In such cases, and some other rare ones, the net slip is determinable. Therefore, any *generally* useful classification of faults must be based on the geometry of the separations (apparent relative movements) in relation to the fault surface; but in the rare and tectonically important cases where slip can be determined, a kinematic classification is more appropriate. These two natural geologic situations call for two classifications of faults (Hill, 1959) as in Table 1.

These fault types are defined as follows:

Normal fault is an inclined surface along which there has been *apparent* relative depression of the hanging wall.

Reverse fault is an inclined surface dipping 45°, or more, along which there has been *apparent* relative elevation of the hanging wall.

TABLE 1

Separations	Faults	Slips	Faults
Dip separation (measured in dip of fault)	Normal Reverse Thrust	Dip slip (measured in dip of fault)	Normal slip Reverse slip Thrust slip
Strike separation (measured in strike of fault)	Right-lateral Left-lateral	Strike slip (measured in strike of fault)	Right-lateral slip Left-lateral slip
Dip and strike separations (measured in both dip and strike of fault)	Named after principal separation or appropriate combined term (e.g., normal left-lateral fault of diagram)	Oblique slip (measured in fault surface)	Named after principal slip component or appropriate combined term (e.g., reverse left-lateral slip fault, 1 of diagram)

Thrust fault is a surface dipping less than 45° along which there has been *apparent* relative movement of the hanging wall over the footwall. (Some workers use this term either as synonymous with, subordinate to, or inclusive of reverse fault, but there is a good case for reverse and thrust as equal and separate categories in order to distinguish between the ratios of apparent horizontal shortening to apparent relative uplift.)

Right-lateral fault is a surface along which, as viewed in plan, the side opposite the observer has had *apparent* relative movement to the right. (Note that the single word "lateral" is not used in the dual classification of faults, whereas right-lateral and left-lateral faults are as different from each other as normal and reverse faults.

Left-lateral fault is a surface along which the side opposite the observer has had *apparent* relative movement to the left.

Normal slip fault, reverse slip fault, thrust slip fault, right-lateral slip fault, and *left-lateral slip fault* are defined as the separation-based terms above, with the omission of the word "apparent," to show that information on *actual* relative movement (slip) has been obtained.

These two sets of fault names, one classifying faults according to commonly determined *apparent* relative movement (the strike and/or dip separations), and the other by occasionally determined *actual* relative movement (the strike and/or dip components of slip), are needed for comprehensive and practical fault classification. The great advantage of the twofold classification is that connotation of *slip* (actual relative movement) on a fault is avoided when only *separation* (apparent relative movement) is known. Although the separation-based terms can usually be employed, the slip-based terms have greater tectonic significance, and therefore should be used whenever possible.

Rules of Nomenclature and Dual Classification of Faults

Rules for providing good scientific classification must be formulated and applied. First, however, rules of nomenclature (the system of names used in a classification) must be considered. The following rules, in part modified from Wadell (1938), are proposed, and the application of each to the dual classification of faults is presented.

RULE 1. A name should be widely understood and used by scientists, or it should be so appropriate that it is likely to become widely understood and used.

Application. The separation-based fault names are widely used by geologists, but too often in the sense of denoting slip. The terms *wrench* or *transcurrent* are frequently used instead of *lateral;* but, in this writer's opinion, wrench is objectionable because of its dynamic implication; transcurrent improperly implies transection of other structures; and both terms refer to slip without benefit of complementary terms for use when only separations are known. A wider understanding of the difference between separation and slip is required before the names of faults can be commonly understood.

RULE 2. A name should be descriptive or explanatory. If the significance (such as genesis) of the thing, action or concept is adequately known, a name expressing such significance is desirable. However, if doubt of this significance exists, or if the term may be used when doubt does exist, it is better to use a purely descriptive name. A combined descriptive and explanatory name is likely to be ambiguous and should therefore be avoided. If possible, a descriptive name should be subject to operational definition (Bridgman, 1927), whereby others may verify by reobservation or experimentation.

Application. The fault names are descriptive rather than explanatory, although *normal* is not rational, and *thrust* is dynamic rather than geometric. *Right-* or *left-lateral* are particularly good descriptive words for apparent sidewise movements, as right- or left-lateral slip are for relative sidewise movements. These names also aptly express important geometric (or kinematic) differences. Kelley (1960) and others have objected to naming faults on the basis of separations, because these can vary along the fault (in plan or section). Obviously in some such cases, due to complicated structural or stratigraphic situations, the separation-based terms characterize only local segments of the fault. But in many of these cases such variations of separation provide evidence for fault slip. For example, separations resulting from the displacement of an anticline may clearly indicate either dip slip, strike slip, or some combination thereof. In these cases the fault can be named according to the slip, which is descriptive of the kinematics and thus is tectonically more significant than a name based upon the separation alone.

> RULE 3. If possible, a name should be a common word, with modifying words as required; it should approximate a definition of a class, with modifiers to distinguish between members of the class. Proper names and terms combining roots of different linguistic origins are permissible only if they are more practical. When a common or vernacular name is used in a scientific sense, its meaning must be defined. It is better to adopt a new name that is precisely defined than to use a common name whose meaning is inexact.

Application. The fault names are precisely defined common nouns with appropriate adjectives. It has been suggested by Gill (1935) and others, that the qualifying word "separation" be added to the fault term when slip has not been determined. However, experience indicates that this limiting word will seldom be appended, whereas if slip had been determined the author would be eager to add the word "slip" to the fault name as evidence of additional information. It has been suggested by Kelley (1960) that right and left slip be substituted for right- and left-lateral slip, respectively. If these terms are accepted, it would be logical to change the separation-based terms to right fault and left fault, or right-separation and left-separation faults. Furthermore, if the term *separation* were used in the dual classification, it would also be logical to refer to normal separation, reverse separation, and thrust separation faults. These and other reasonable suggestions for fault names, including wrench and transcurrent, need to be accepted or rejected so that one set of names can be employed. Recommendations from a duly appointed international committee may be required to establish standards.

> RULE 4. A name should be rational and appropriate to the science involved, although a new name should not be used if an appropriate old one exists within the science or if an acceptable one from another science is available. However, new and precisely defined terms are preferable to old terms that are imprecise or commonly misused.

Application. The fault names are, in context, rational and appropriate to the science of geology. New names are not used in the dual classification of faults, although more precise and restricted definitions are employed. If the names were not in common usage, new names for both separation-based and slip-based classifications might be preferred.

RULE 5. A foreign term should be used when appropriate, but unless it is a common word it should be used in its original rather than in its translated form.

Application. Foreign names are not used in the classification, although some are properly used in fault terminology.

RULE 6. Symbolic and/or mnemonic terms may be used if properly defined, and if more practical than descriptive terms.

Application. Since the terms are few and short, symbolic or mnemonic terms are not justified.

RULE 7. The same thing should not be given two different names, nor should two different things be given the same name. It is, however, less objectionable for a thing to have two names than for two different things to have the same name.

Application. The fault names of the dual classification are not ambiguous. If slip is determined, only the slip-based nomenclature is used, even though the fault may have previously been classified according to separation. The common usage of a single set of fault terms in a slip sense when only separation is known is ambiguous, and has conspired to prevent a search for criteria determining fault slip. For example, in common usage *"reverse fault"* can mean either that reverse slip or that reverse separation is known. This usage has also encouraged ill-founded tectonic interpretations, and has generally retarded progress in structural geology. Use of the dual nomenclature can preclude ambiguity and encourage determination of fault slip.

RULE 8. A name should represent a group of things, processes, or concepts and, if possible, should also be a part of a greater group (e.g. granite represents a mineralogical and textural group of rocks and it is also a class of igneous rocks).

Application. The names of the dual classification represent groups of faults, and faults are only one group of earth structures.

Rules of Classification and Dual Classification of Faults

RULE A. A classification (including its nomenclature) should be appropriate to the knowledge of the subject, and to the purposes for which it is devised.

Application. The dual classification of faults is appropriate for current knowledge of faulting and for the purposes for which it is devised. There are other ways of classifying faults, and for special purposes some of these may be better than the dual classification. For example, bedding-plane, dip, strike, and oblique faults, or longitudinal and transverse faults, or epi-anticlinal faults provide grouping according to associated structures. But since such classifications are not based on the characteristics of the faults themselves, they cannot be considered as significant classes of faults. Although fault classifications based on presumed origins (Clark, 1943) or on presumed stress fields (Anderson, 1951) have had considerable acceptance, it appears that genetic or dynamic classifications are either too theoretical or too subjective for present knowledge of structural geology (Hill, 1947). The dual classification allows appropriate classification of most faults on the basis of apparent relative movement (separation), and in addition provides a classification for faults when actual relative movement (slip) is determined.

Rule B. A classification should be comprehensive and exclusive. Thus the categories of the classification should be collectively complete and individually separate.

Application. The classification is comprehensive and exclusive. All recognized cases of fault separation and slip are included, and the five rational categories in each (normal, reverse, thrust, and right- and left-lateral) are mutually exclusive.

Rule C. A classification should be flexible. Provision should be made for intercalation of new terms and for expansion of existing terms. Classification based on ordering of gradational characteristics should be used where possible, because greater precision in differentiation is allowed without preventing broad grouping.

Application. The classification is such that all the principal fault types are named, all combination types can be expressed (e.g. normal left-lateral fault), and all possible components of separation or slip are included. No expanded connotation of the terms can be conceived until dynamic and/or genetic fault characteristics are commonly recognized. Ordering of all gradations of strike and/or dip of the fault, all variations of separation, and all variations in sense of slip may be expressed within the categories of the dual classification. Although, for example, normal and reverse (or normal-slip and reverse-slip) faults are gradational through the vertical, ordering across a vertical surface is not good classification because this dip divides apparent (or actual, if slip is known) horizontal extension from shortening across the fault. On the other hand, ordering of fault dip within one class is significant in order to obtain the proportion of relative uplift to either extension or shortening.

Rule D. A classification should be either descriptive or theoretical. Combinations of descriptive and theoretical elements lead to confusion. As the science progresses theoretical classifications become more useful.

Application. The dual classification of faults is based entirely on the descriptive elements of separation (geometric) or slip (kinematic), although it is possible that future advancements in the knowledge of faulting may allow dynamic or even genetic classifications.

Conclusions

In geology, as in all other sciences, progress is facilitated by precise nomenclature and logical classification. All geologic classifications should be scrutinized in the light of current knowledge. To stimulate advancements in their science, geologists must be as willing to revise their classifications as they are to make new observations and new interpretations. The rules proposed here for naming and classifying geologic phenomena are thought to be useful, although they may not be complete or mutually exclusive, are not of equal importance or scope, and could be expressed in different terms.

Present classifications of faults have retarded progress in structural geology because the names commonly given to faults so often falsely imply knowledge of fault slip. The dual classification of faults recommended here is analogous to the dual classification of strata into rock-stratigraphic and time-stratigraphic categories. In stratigraphy progress was stimulated by a classification which distinguished between lithologic and chronologic units. A classification which distinguishes between the concepts of fault separation and fault slip might likewise stimulate progress in structural geology.

REFERENCES CITED

Anderson, E. M., 1951, The dynamics of faulting and dyke formation with applications to Britain, 2nd ed.: London, Oliver and Boyd, 206 pp.
Beloussov, V. V., 1962, Basic problems in geotectonics (Am. Geol. Inst. translation): New York, McGraw-Hill, 816 pp.
Boyer, R. E., and Muehlberger, W. R., 1960, Separation versus slip: Am. Assoc. Petroleum Geol., B., vol. 44, pp. 1938–1939.
Bridgman, P. W., 1927, The logic of modern physics: New York, Macmillan, 228 pp.
Clark, S. K., 1943, Classification of faults: Am. Assoc. Petroleum Geol., B., vol. 27, pp. 1245–1265.
Crowell, J. C., 1959, Problems of fault nomenclature: Am. Assoc. Petroleum Geol., B., vol. 43, pp. 2653–2674.

GILL, J. E., 1935, Normal and reverse faults: J. Geol., vol. 43, pp. 1071–1079.

———, 1941, Fault nomenclature: Roy. Soc. Canada, Tr., 3rd ser., vol. 35, sec. 4, pp. 71–85.

GRABAU, A. W., 1904, On the classification of sedimentary rocks: Am. Geologist, vol. 33, pp. 228–247.

HAM, W. E., ed., 1962, Classification of carbonate rocks, a symposium: Am. Assoc. Petroleum Geol., Mem. 1.

HEMPEL, C. G., 1952, Fundamentals of concept formation in empirical science: Internat. Encyclopedia of Unified Sciences, vol. 2, no. 7, Chicago, Univ. Chicago Press, 93 pp.

———, 1959, Some problems of taxonomy: unpublished manuscript.

HILL, M. L., 1947, Classification of faults: Am. Assoc. Petroleum Geol., B., vol. 31, pp. 1669–1673.

———, 1959, Dual classification of faults: Am. Assoc. Petroleum Geol., B., vol. 43, pp. 217–221.

———, 1960, Fault symbols: GeoTimes, vol. 5, no. 3, pp. 23–24.

KELLEY, V. C., 1960, Slips and separations: Geol. Soc. Am., B., vol. 71, pp. 1545–1546.

KRYNINE, P. D., 1948, The megascopic study and field classification of sedimentary rocks: J. Geol., vol. 56, pp. 130–165.

KUPFER, D. H., 1960, Problems of fault nomenclature: Am. Assoc. Petroleum Geol., B., vol. 44, pp. 501–505.

OXENFORD, JOHN, 1882, Conversations of Goethe: London, George Bell and Sons.

PETTIJOHN, F. J., 1948, A preface to the classification of sedimentary rocks: J. Geol., vol. 56, pp. 112–117.

REID, H. F., DAVIS, W. M., LAWSON, A. C., and RANSOME, F. L., 1913, Report of the Committee on the Nomenclature of Faults: Geol. Soc. Am., B., vol. 24, pp. 163–183.

RODGERS, JOHN, 1950, The nomenclature and classification of sedimentary rocks: Am. J. Sci., vol. 248, pp. 297–311.

SHROCK, R. R., 1948, A classification of sedimentary rocks: J. Geol., vol. 56, pp. 118–129.

WADELL, HAKON, 1938, Proper names, nomenclature and classification: J. Geol., vol. 46, pp. 546–568.

CHARLES A. ANDERSON

U. S. Geological Survey

Simplicity in Structural Geology[1]

In 1951, I made the statement that "Until more precise correlations of the older Precambrian rocks can be made, based on radioactivity or other methods, the *simplest* explanation is that only one period of orogeny, corresponding to Wilson's Mazatzal Revolution, has occurred in Arizona during early Precambrian time." (Anderson, 1951, p. 1346; italics added) This explicit reference to the use of simplicity in correlating structural events and reconstructing geologic history led the Chairman of the Anniversary Committee to ask for an essay on simplicity in structural geology.

Principle of Simplicity

The principle of simplicity has been called Occam's (or Ockham's) razor, the principle of parsimony, or the principle of economy. Allusions to simplicity in the literature are innumerable and varied in intent and nuance. A revival of interest in this principle among philosophers of science has been partly inspired by the work of Nelson Goodman.

All scientific activity amounts to the invention of and the choice among systems of hypotheses. One of the primary considerations guiding this process is that of simplicity. Nothing could be much more mistaken than the traditional idea that we first seek a true system and then, for the sake of elegance alone, seek a simple one. We are inevitably concerned with simplicity as soon as we are concerned with system at all; for system is achieved just to the extent that the basic vocabulary and set of first principles used in dealing with the given subject matter are simplified. When simplicity of

---

[1] I wish to thank my two colleagues, James Gilluly and Walter S. White, for helpful and critical comments in their review of this essay.

basis vanishes to zero—that is, when no term or principle is derived from any of the others—system also vanishes to zero. Systematization is the same thing as simplification of basis. (Goodman, 1958, p. 1064)

William of Occam, known as *Doctor Invincibilis* and *Venerabilis Inceptor*, was born around 1300 and became a member of the Franciscan order while still a youth. He was an intellectual leader in the period that saw the disintegration of old scholastic realism and the rise of theological skepticism. The famous dictum attributed to him, "*Entia non sunt multiplicanda praeter necessitatem*," has appeared in nearly every book on logic from the middle of the nineteenth century. It is doubtful that the "Invincible Doctor" used these words (Thorburn, 1918), but he did use similar words such as *Frustra fit per plura quod potest fieri per pauciora* (Laird, 1919, p. 321). The "razor" is commonly used now without special reference to the scholastic theory of entities, and Laird believes that the precise form in which Occam stated it is irrelevant.

Russell (1929, p. 113) states that Occam's razor, "entities are not to be multiplied without necessity," is a maxim that inspires all scientific philosophizing, and that in dealing with any subject matter, one should find out what entities are undeniably involved, and state everything in terms of these.

The concept of simplicity is a controversial topic in the philosophy of science according to Kemeny (1953, p. 391). One school believes it involves an assumption about the simplicity of nature, whereas others justify it as a matter of convenience, "a labor-saving device." Jevons (1883, p. 625) objected to the generalization that the laws of nature possess the perfection which we attribute to simple forms and relations, and suggested that "Simplicity is naturally agreeable to a mind of limited powers, but to an infinite mind all things are simple."

Mill (1865, p. 461) questioned Hamilton's belief that "Nature never works by more complex instruments than are necessary," stating that "we know well that Nature, in many of its operations, works by means which are of a complexity so extreme, as to be an almost insuperable obstacle to our investigations." Mill (1865, p. 467) believed that we are not justified in rejecting an hypothesis for being too complicated, but "The 'Law of Parcimony' needs no such support; it rests on no assumptions respecting the ways or proceedings of Nature. It is a purely logical precept; a case of the broad practical principle, not to believe anything for which there is no evidence . . . The assumption of a superfluous cause, is a belief without evidence." Mill (*ibid.*) emphasizes that the principle which forbids the assumption of a superfluous fact, forbids a superfluous law and "The rule of Parcimony, therefore, whether applied to facts or to theories, implies no theory concerning the propensities or proceedings of Nature."

Feuer (1957, p. 121), like Mill, emphasized that the scientific principle of simplicity does not rest on the assumption that the laws of nature are simple, and he pointed out that the simplicity of nature has had a long philosophical history which he would call the *metascientific principle of simplicity*, to distinguish it from the scientific methodological principle of Occam's razor. Verifiability is the important element in Occam's razor; the principle of simplicity is thus a straightforward basis for rejecting theories if they are unverifiable (Feuer, 1957, p. 115). The verified theory is the simplest because every unnecessary component is an unverified item.

Demos (1947) expresses some skepticism about the use of simplicity and suggests that the scientific philosopher tries to evade the charge of fallacious reasoning by introducing the principle of simplicity, thereby enabling him to choose among the several theories consistent with the observed facts. The scientist then selects the theory that explains the greatest number of phenomena with the fewest assumptions. Bridgman (1961, p. 10) regarded Occam's razor:

> ... as a cardinal intellectual principle, ... I will try to follow it to the utmost. It is almost frightening to observe how blatantly it is disregarded in most thinking ... To me it seems to satisfy a deep-seated instinct for intellectual good workmanship. Perhaps one of the most compelling reasons for adopting it is that thereby one has given as few hostages to the future as possible and retained the maximum flexibility for dealing with unanticipated facts or ideas.

Simplicity and Geology

A recent issue of "Philosophy of Science" contains a symposium on simplicity, but only one paper mentions its application to geology. Barker (1961, p. 164) revives the old problem of the meaning of fossils: are they remains of organisms that actually existed on earth millions of years ago, or were they placed there by the Creator to test our faith? Barker concluded that unless there is independent evidence in favor of a Creator, the simple theory is that plants and animals existed in the past in circumstances similar to those in which we find them today. This leads to uniformitarianism, a topic discussed elsewhere in this volume.

An excellent geologic example of simplicity is given by Woodford (1960) in discussing the magnitude of strike slip on the San Andreas fault. In 1906, the right-lateral slip along this fault was 22 feet in central California, and in southern California offset streams indicate right-lateral movement of thousands of feet during Quaternary time. But for pre-Quaternary movements, it is necessary to distinguish between separation and slip. A structurally complex succession of granodiorite, Paleocene, and Miocene rocks north of the San Gabriel Mountains is offset in a way that seems to require 30 miles of right-lateral slip since the middle Tertiary. Displacements may have been even greater (a range from 160 to 300 miles has been suggested), but Woodford prefers a working hypothesis that includes some dip slip and so he limits strike slip on the San Andreas fault to 30 miles, right lateral. "The tentative choice of short slips, if these will do the business, is an example of the use of the principle *Disjunctiones minimae, disjunctiones optimae.* This rule may be considered a quantitatively parsimonious relative of Ockham's law: *Entia non sunt multiplicanda praeter necessitatem.*" (Woodford, 1960, p. 415)

The preparation of a geologic map is the essential first step in structural geology, and one of the first steps is the building up of the stratigraphic sequence. The law of superposition is vital to the success of this study. Even where we have "layer-cake" stratigraphy, Albritton (1961, pp. 190–191) has pointed out that it is not clear how the principle of simplicity operates in geology:

> ... [given] two nearby mesas of three formations conformably arranged in similar sequence from bottom to top. Without evidence to the contrary, most stratigraphers would recognize only three formations in all, perhaps on the ground that it is in vain to do with more what can be done with fewer. But if a three-formation column is simpler than a [six-formation] column, would it not be simpler still to lump the three formations into one group, and then have a single entity?

Of course the answer is that to do so is to lose information. The purpose of the geologic study has an important bearing on the choice of stratigraphic units. Fundamentally, selection is made to focus attention on the environment of deposition of the sediments, to indicate the various stages in the geologic history. For structural interpretations, delineation of thin units may help the geologic map to elucidate the structure. The objective is to use the map as a means of showing as many as possible of the elements that bear on the geologic history and structure, and something about the basis on which these elements have been verified.

In regions of complex structure, particularly if the rocks are nonfossiliferous and folded isoclinally, stratigraphy and structure are determined concurrently by mapping distinctive lithologic units whether they are beds, zones, or formations. Structural elements and data on the direction that the tops of beds are now facing are diligently searched for in all exposures. In this manner, the stratigraphy and structure unfold together, and the final interpretation results from the integration of both. The interpretation may be complex, but the principle of simplicity will be followed if no unverifiable facts are essential to the interpretation. In actual practice there are few situations in which a geologic interpretation does not require some unverified assumptions, and in general the use of the principle of simplicity involves the acceptance of the interpretation that has the maximum of verifiable facts and minimum of assumptions.

Prediction is an important facet of structural geology; in mapping, a field geologist commonly predicts what will be found on the next ridge, valley, or mountain range. In a sense, this is a field test of the interpretations developing in the mind of the geologist. No doubt it is a frequent experience with a geologist, mapping in a region of complex geology, to find his predictions erroneous; the geology may be more complex than the interpretation of the moment. But this is a part of the accumulation of field data and in no way conflicts with the use of simplicity in the final interpretation. Prediction is the end product of many studies in structural geology in proposing exploration programs, and in the search for new mineral deposits and petroleum accumulations.

Many examples could be cited where early expositions of the geologic history of a particular region are less complex than later explanations based on additional field studies. Probably most geologists would accept as axiomatic that new information leads to a more complex story. In a sense, it is a mark of progress as we build upon the experience of those who worked before us on similar problems. This is to be expected, particularly in regions where the rocks have been acutely deformed by past tectonic activity. The geologic history becomes more complex as we build up a storehouse of "verifiable elements," even though each succeeding historical account does not introduce entities beyond necessity.

In regions where heavy vegetation and thick soil cover the rocks, it is a time-consuming process to assemble the facts that are needed to reconstruct the story of the stratigraphy and structure. The early interpretations are likely to be simple because of meager data. Trenching, drill holes, and painstaking studies of the saprolites may in time add to the verifiable elements to give a more complete and more complex history.

Older Precambrian in Arizona

I would like to discuss in more detail the older Precambrian geology in Arizona as an example of the workings of the principle of simplicity in structural geology. By 1951, sufficient geologic mapping had been done in the older Precambrian rocks of the Grand Canyon, Globe-Miami, Mazatzal Mountains, Little Dragoon Mountains, Bagdad, and Prescott-Jerome areas to indicate that only one period of orogeny, followed by the intrusion of granitic rocks, could be recognized in each of these areas.

> The natural temptation is to assume that the orogenies in these five separate areas occurred at the same time, particularly because of the general parallelism of the folds where the trends were determined, and Wilson (1939) has termed this probable widespread orogenic disturbance, the Mazatzal Revolution. From a purely academic view, one might question

this conclusion, for it is well known that the Precambrian covers an immense period of time, and it would be surprising if only one period of orogeny occurred in Arizona during the early Precambrian time. Hinds (1936) has suggested that two periods of orogeny and two periods of granitic invasion occurred in Arizona prior to the deposition of the Younger Precambrian Grand Canyon series and Apache group, the Mazatzal quartzite marking the period of sedimentation between these orogenies. Because no positive angular unconformities have been found between the Mazatzal quartzite and Yavapai schist, some doubt exists regarding the validity of this older period of orogeny and granitic invasion. (Anderson, 1951, p. 1346; thereupon followed the sentence quoted in the introductory paragraph.)

Philip M. Blacet of the U.S. Geological Survey has recently mapped, south of Prescott, a basement of granodiorite gneiss older than the Yavapai Series. This gneiss underlies a basal conglomerate containing angular blocks of the granodiorite and abundant well-rounded boulders of aplite. The basal conglomerate grades upward into feldspathic sandstone, gray slate, pebble conglomerate, and beds of rhyolitic tuffaceous sandstone (now recrystallized to quartz-sericite schist) of the Texas Gulch Formation, described by Anderson and Creasey (1958, p. 28) as possibly the oldest formation in the Alder Group of the Yavapai Series. Similar slate, pebble conglomerate, and tuffaceous sandstone occur in the type section of the Alder Group in the Mazatzal Mountains (Wilson, 1939, p. 1122) and were deformed during Wilson's Mazatzal Revolution. The unconformable relation between the Texas Gulch Formation and the granodiorite gneiss south of Prescott is important as proving the existence of a granitic rock older than the Yavapai Series, and therefore older than the granitic rocks intruded during the Mazatzal Revolution. Therefore two periods of granitic intrusion in the older Precambrian of Arizona are proved by normal stratigraphic relations, superposition, and transgressive intrusive contacts. Hinds was correct in suggesting the two periods, but he placed his second period after the Mazatzal Revolution rather than before. He did not have verifiable data to support his conclusion, and following the principle of simplicity, his contribution had to be ignored.

Progress is being made in the use of radiometric measurements to correlate rocks and structural events in the older Precambrian of Arizona. Some of these data are shown in Table 1; the ages indicated for the gneisses, granites, and pegmatites from which mica samples were collected range from around 1200 to around 1500 million years (m. y.).

Mica from the pre-Yavapai granodiorite gneiss south of Prescott gave K-Ar and Rb-Sr measurements indicating an age of about 1250 m. y. (Carl Hedge, written communication). Measurements of the isotopes of lead in the zircon from the granodiorite gneiss indicate a minimum age of 1700 m. y. (E. J. Catanzaro, oral communication). These data indicate that the mica in the granodi-

TABLE 1

RADIOMETRIC AGES OF ROCKS
FROM THE OLDER PRECAMBRIAN OF ARIZONA

Sample locations*	Ages in million years	
	K-Ar	Rb-Sr
1. Gneiss, Grand Canyon	1390	1370
2a. Lawler Peak granite, Bagdad	1410	1390
2b. Pegmatite in Lawler Peak granite	1410	1500
3. Pegmatite, Wickenburg	1160	1300
4. Pegmatite in Vishnu schist, Grand Canyon		1550 1530
5. Migmatite zone in Vishnu schist, Grand Canyon		1390
6. Granite near Valentine		1300
7. Diana granite, Chloride		1350
8. Chloride granite, Chloride		1210
9. Oracle granite, Oracle		1450

* Samples 1 through 3 are from Aldrich, Wetherill, Davis, 1957, p. 656, and samples 4 through 9 are from Giletti and Damon, 1961, p. 640.

orite gneiss recrystallized during the deformation of the Yavapai Series, corresponding in a general way to the time Aldrich, Wetherill, and Davis (1957) have called the 1350-m.y. period of granitic rocks. The zircon gives an older age, more in keeping with the stratigraphic relations. It should be noted that Silver and Deutsch (1961) have reported an age of 1650 m. y. for zircon from a granodiorite in southeastern Arizona (Cochise County).

It is tempting to assume that the 1350-m.y. period corresponds to the Mazatzal Revolution; unfortunately no reliable radiometric dates have been obtained from granitic rocks clearly related to the Mazatzal orogeny, that is, from the Mazatzal Mountains or adjacent areas. The available age data clearly demonstrate the need for systematic work, for there is much to be learned from radiometric measurements of the Precambrian rocks in Arizona. I predict that such studies will ultimately show that the structural history is more complex than can be documented from present data.

Most structural geologists would infer that there are, in Arizona, metamorphic rocks older than the granodiorite gneiss south of Prescott and that such rocks were deformed prior to or during the intrusion of the granodiorite made gneissic during the deformation of the Yavapai Series. Using the principle of simplicity, we can say with assurance that the simplest explanation in 1962 is that there were at least two periods of orogeny and granitic intrusion in the older Precambrian history of Arizona. As more verifiable elements are discovered, the story may well become even more complex.

Concluding Statement

Much of my discussion has been limited to the use of the principle of simplicity in explanatory or interpretive aspects of structural geology rather than in developing theories or laws. It is appropriate to refer to Mario Bunge, who raises doubts about simplicity in the construction and testing of scientific theories. A theory must at least be consistent with the known facts and should predict new and unsuspected facts (Bunge, 1961, p. 133). Bunge (1961, p. 148) believes that simplicities are undesirable in the stage of problem finding, but desirable in the formulation of problems, and much less so in the solution of problems. His advice is that "Ockham's razor—like all razors—must be handled with care to prevent beheading science in the attempt to shave off some of its pilosities. In science, as in the barber shop, better alive and bearded than dead and cleanly shaven."

It seems to me that when a structural geologist is formulating explanatory hypotheses, the principle of simplicity should not restrict his imagination; complex hypotheses may stimulate and guide the work toward new and different data. For this phase of a study, Bunge has made an excellent point; it is only in the final selection of the hypotheses that the assortment should be pared by Occam's razor.

REFERENCES CITED

ALBRITTON, C. C., JR., 1961, Notes on the history and philosophy of science. (1) A conference on the scope and philosophy of geology: J. Graduate Research Center, Southern Methodist Univ., vol. 29, no. 3, pp. 188–192.

ALDRICH, L. T., WETHERILL, G. W., and DAVIS, G. L., 1957, Occurrence of 1350 million-year-old granitic rocks in western United States: Geol. Soc. Am., B., vol. 68, pp. 655–656.

ANDERSON, C. A., 1951, Older Precambrian structure in Arizona: Geol. Soc. Am., B., vol. 62, pp. 1331–46.

———— and CREASEY, S. C., 1958, Geology and ore deposits of the Jerome area, Yavapai County, Arizona: U. S. Geol. Survey, Prof. Paper 308, 185 pp.

BARKER, S. F., 1961, On simplicity in empirical hypotheses: Phil. Sci., vol. 28, pp. 162–171.

BRIDGMAN, P. W., 1961, The way things are: New York, Viking (Compass Books Edition) 333 pp.

BUNGE, MARIO, 1961, The weight of simplicity in the construction and assaying of scientific theories: Phil. Sci., vol. 28, pp. 120–149.

DEMOS, RAPHAEL, 1947, Doubts about empiricism: Phil. Sci., vol. 14, pp. 203–218.

FEUER, L. S., 1957, The principle of simplicity: Phil. Sci., vol. 24, pp. 109–122.

GILETTI, B. J. and DAMON, P. E., 1961, Rubidium-strontium ages of some basement rocks from Arizona and northwestern Mexico: Geol. Soc. Am., B., vol. 72, pp. 639–644.

GOODMAN, NELSON, 1958, The test of simplicity: Science, vol. 128, pp. 1064–1069.

HINDS, N. E. A., 1936, Uncompahgran and Beltian deposits in western North America: Carnegie Inst. Washington, Pub. 463, pp. 53–136.

JEVONS, W. S., 1883, The principles of science: London, MacMillan, 786 pp.

KEMENY, J. G., 1953, The use of simplicity in induction: Phil. Rev., vol. 62, pp. 391–408.

LAIRD, JOHN, 1919, The law of parsimony: The Monist, vol. 29, p. 321–344.

MILL, J. S., 1865, An examination of Sir William Hamilton's philosophy: London, Longmans, Green, 561 pp.

RUSSELL, BERTRAND, 1929, Our knowledge of the external world: New York, W. W. Norton, 268 pp.

SILVER, L. T. and DEUTSCH, SARAH, 1961, Uranium-lead method on zircons: New York Acad. Sci., Ann., vol. 91, pp. 279–283.

THORBURN, C. C., JR., 1918, The myth of Occam's Razor: Mind, vol. 27, pp. 345–353.

WILSON, E. D., 1939, Pre-Cambrian Mazatzal Revolution in central Arizona: Geol. Soc. Am., B., vol. 50, pp. 1113–1164.

WOODFORD, A. O., 1960, Bedrock patterns and strike-slip faulting in southwestern California: Am. J. Sci., vol. 258A, pp. 400–417.

LUNA B. LEOPOLD
WALTER B. LANGBEIN
U.S. Geological Survey

Association and Indeterminacy in Geomorphology

You find a rock. It looks like an ordinary piece of flint, broken and rough. On a part of it is a patina whose soft grey color contrasts with the shiny brownish surfaces of conchoidal fracture. You could have found this rock in nearly any kind of an environment almost anyplace in the world. There is nothing distinctive about it.

You hand this same piece of rock to a colleague and ask what he can make of it. He considers it soberly before he says, "You know, that could be an artifact." There springs to mind then a picture of a primitive man, squatting barefoot before a fire warming his hands. The firelight casts his shadow against the cliff below which he crouches.

The difference between the reaction before and after the passing thought that this might indeed be the tool of ancient man is the difference between mild disinterest and a kaleidoscope of mental pictures. This difference reflects differences in the associations of thoughts.

The present essay is concerned with how associations are used in geologic reasoning, and then with certain philosophic considerations which seem to be influencing the methodology and direction of geomorphology.

When you picked up the piece of flint the associations which flashed through your mind were specific to the limits of your knowledge regarding the object itself. This stone was unusual only in that it appeared to have been worked by human hands. The mental pictures which were projected by the thought process stemmed only from an intellectual interest. The specimen itself is valueless. If, however, the rock had been a sample of ore, the chain of thought might have led to interest of quite a different kind. Our everyday experience in geology emphasizes that the purposes of this branch of natural science are twofold—intellectual and utilitarian—being constituted of the two principal elements which generally tend to stimulate the mind of man.

In geomorphology, as in other branches of science, mental pictures depicting associations in the natural world have an intrinsic value which stems from the wonderment that a knowledge of nature seems to produce nearly uniformly among thoughtful human beings. But associations in the natural world are not only objects of interest in themselves; they are also tools of the art.

The association of different observations is a form of logic. What is here called "association" might be viewed by some merely as another word for reasoning. But this type of reasoning which is used in geology is so extensively elaborated that it bears but little resemblance to mathematical logic, even if the logician may be able to discern in geologic reasoning the same precepts and, indubitably, the same methods which constitute the bases for any kind of logical reasoning. If the reader, then, wishes to equate the word "association" as used here with logic or with reasoning, we pose no objection, but it is the basis for this reasoning that is here being examined.

The simplest and most fundamental type of association deals with the process acting. When one observes in an outcrop a uniformly bedded sandstone he associates this with his general knowledge of the way in which sand may be deposited. A sand deposit usually implies that there was a source of quartz materials, a process by which these materials were reduced to relatively uniform size and sorted, and a physical situation leading to progressive accumulation of the materials in a depositional environment. The outcrop is interpreted, then, by means of a general knowledge of the processes of weathering and subsequent transportation by water or wind.

In contrast to the observations of materials in a vertical section, another line of associations relates a feature of the landscape to particular processes. The occurrence of an alluvial fan at the mouth of a canyon is interpretable in terms of the form and location of the materials, in this case both indicating that the sediment making up the fan had its source in the canyon and that it was transported from there to its present position, presumably by water or by gravitational flow lubricated by water.

Implicit in the utilization of associations is the principle of uniformitarianism: geologic processes presently observed are presumed to be the same as those operating throughout geologic time. The association of a cropping of uniformly bedded sandstone with presently observed conditions under which sand may be so deposited stems from the assumption that processes presently observed are the same ones that operated in the distant past.

The concept of association goes far beyond a principle even so general as that of uniformity. That principle in itself does not necessarily suggest sequential operations, nor does it treat of the relationship between individual observations and the generality to which these observations may be applicable. For example, in the sample case cited, let it be supposed that the sandstone is transected by a dike of igneous material. The knowledge of process leads to the conclusion that the sand must have been deposited at a time previous to that in which the igneous material was intruded.

The idea of uniformitarianism does not in itself deal with time relationships. The geologist studies the bones of a dinosaur. In the same formation where the bones were discovered the footprints of a beast are found preserved as casts. The bones of the feet can be compared with the footprint and, let us say, the print seems to have been made by the animal whose bones are now fossilized. There is nothing at the present time quite like this creature, and it is by the use of association rather than by reasoning stemming from uniformitarianism that the bodily form of the dinosaur can be shown to be compatible with the casts of his footprints. It would seem, then, that the use of associations provides an indispensable extension to uniformitarianism in geologic reasoning.

Whole fields of geology, particularly paleontology, are based more on association than on any principle which relates presently observable processes to those which occurred in previous epochs. Interpretations must be made of phenomena unlike any known to occur under present conditions. This implies that the concept of association is of no lower an order of generality than is the principle of uniformitarianism.

To summarize, then, geologic reasoning is based on a logic called here the use of associations. Associations are useful in four different ways. First, particular associations may indicate the sequence of events in time. Second, an association found locally may indicate a general relation having limits far beyond the immediate locality or scope of the observation. Third, a particular association may be indicative of the processes acting. Fourth, synthesis of a variety of observations is, in effect, a broadening of the scope of associations considered in a given context.

Generalization may be thought of as a synthesis of individual bits of knowledge into a broader framework, but synthesis is merely the broadening of a context of association. The number of associations which are involved in a particular thought process is possibly one measure of the degree to which synthesis is achieved. Thus the use of association, much in the manner indicated by the simple examples cited above, constitutes the methodology of synthesis, or integration. From this point of view the utilization of the concept of association represents one of the fundamental bases of geology.

In the inductive method, the purpose of describing a phenomenon may be, for example, to eliminate extraneous details to see what, on the average, is the pattern represented by the data. The generalized description may be either quantitative or qualitative. The question of what data should be included would be determined primarily by the question asked rather than by an *a priori* determination of whether the data apply to the generalized description required. As many cases as possible would be studied to see what patterns are displayed among the examples. Whether quantitative or qualitative, the search for patterns in information is essentially inductive.

The difference between inductive and deductive approaches does not lie in the presence or absence of a working hypothesis or multiple hypotheses, but these approaches may differ in the stage at which the hypothesis is derived. The difference does not dispense with the need, at some stage, for developing an hypothesis which must be tested against data and reason.

Those of us working in geomorphology have a particular interest in the philosophy of research, both because of the nature of our subject and the history of its development. The aim of this portion of the geologic science is to understand the forms of the earth's surface. It is not difficult to see, then, that it is a subject which might first have been approached by classifying the observed forms, i.e. devising categories for pigeonholing different types of hills, valleys, scarps, rivers, and drainage patterns. From such classification, certain generalizations were drawn—an inductive approach.

A continued interest in classification, during the first third of the present century, took the form of assigning names to features of the landscape. Streams were designated as subsequent, superimposed, etc., and each such designation carried with it appropriate inference about both operative processes and historical sequence. Little attention was paid to the study of process, which, looking back at the record, now appears to have led to a neglect of field studies as the foundation of geomorphic science. As a result, the subject became one of decreasing interest to other workers in geology. An important aspect of this growing disinterest was that geomorphology, as practiced, seemed to lose its inherent usefulness.

In science usefulness is measured in part by ability to forecast, i.e., to predict relations postulated by reasoning about associations and subsequently subject to verification by experiment or field study. With this in mind, it is apparent that preoccupation with description could lead to decreasing usefulness because classification and description are usually insufficient bases for extrapolation and thus for prediction.

At mid-century there began a revitalization of geomorphology, which has taken the form of a more detailed investigation of processes operative in landscape development. Study of process has been accompanied by increased use of quantitative data and mathematical expression. The trend toward quantitative study in geomorphology, in contrast with description, should not be viewed as a basic difference in method of investigation, as mentioned earlier, but rather as a difference in the type of problem being attacked. Both quantitative and qualitative geologic research are based on the use of associations and the concept of uniformity.

This trend parallels that in geologic research in general. Before 1930, less than one page in a hundred in the "Bulletin of the Geological Society of America" contained mathematical formulation. The percentage now approaches ten in a hundred. Civil engineering shows a similar trend, but the level has always been higher.

Coupled with the forward increase in the quantitative method in geomorphology there is, encouragingly enough, a greater concentration on geologic mapping in many investigations, and in others, at least a detailed study of stratigraphy in the field. The work of John T. Hack (1960) on geomorphology of the central Appalachians is a model which it is hoped a growing proportion of workers in the field will emulate. He made detailed geologic maps of local areas which he then used as the basis for study of form and process in which both qualitative and quantitative arguments were used. Similarly, John P. Miller mapped extensive areas in the Sangre de Cristo Range, New Mexico, and used these as the basis for geomorphic studies (see Miller, 1959).

Among the geologic sciences, geomorphology has, for some time in America, been approached in a manner sufficiently different from other aspects of geology that it may have come to be viewed as different in philosophy. We contend that in philosophy and in method it is one with other geologic sciences. Association, uniformity, working hypothesis, reasoning, quantitative and qualitative data are concepts and tools as much needed here as elsewhere in geology.

At any time the need for a set of questions, implicit or explicit, is paramount. Over and above that, there is a time for new data and there is a time for new theory. Progress depends on both. For several decades governmental authorities had been collecting data on rivers. No one knew just how to apply this store of information to geomorphic inquiry. No one knew what questions to ask. Then, in 1945, Horton set forth a new hydrophysical theory of the landscape that was refreshingly exact in its principles in contrast with the anthropomorphic word pictures of William Morris Davis. The analysis of river data began soon after. There followed a decade and a half of analysis using the data available in conjunction with the ideas stimulated by Horton's theory. Not much more is likely to be gleaned from either. The time is set for new theory and new data.

The shift in interest from description toward process and from the qualitative toward the quantitative in geomorphology appears also to be leading toward an important shift in viewpoint which may have far-reaching effects on the field. New sets of associations are evolving because of the particular questions now being asked. We think we see operating in landscape development a principle long recognized in physics but new to geomorphic thinking—a principle of indeterminacy.

By indeterminacy in the present context we refer to those situations in which the applicable physical laws may be satisfied by a large number of combinations of values of interdependent variables. As a result, a number of individual cases will differ among themselves, although their average is reproducible in different samples. Any individual case, then, cannot be forecast or specified except in a statistical sense. The result of an individual case is indeterminate.

Where a large number of interacting factors are involved in a large number of individual cases or examples, the possibilities of combination are so great that physical laws governing forces and motions are not sufficient to determine the outcome of these interactions in an individual case. The physical laws may be completely fulfilled by a variety of combinations of the interrelated factors. The remaining statements are stochastic in nature rather than physical.

These stochastic statements differ from deterministic physical laws in that the former carry with them the idea of an irreducible uncertainty. As more is known about the processes operating and as more is learned about the factors involved, the range of uncertainty will decrease, but it never will be entirely removed.

An example may be drawn from river processes. Into a given reach of river between tributaries, a certain rate of flow of water and a certain amount of sediment are introduced from upstream. Both change during the passage of a given flood or through a season or a period of years. To accommodate these various rates of discharge of water and sediment, a number of interdependent hydraulic variables will change, including width, depth, velocity, slope, and hydraulic roughness. A particular change in discharge and sediment may be accommodated by several combinations of values of these dependent or adjustable factors.

Specifically, the physical equations which must always be satisfied are equations of conservation, such as the conservation of mass. In the river, this is expressed in the statement,

$$Q = wdv,$$

or discharge is the product of width, depth, and mean velocity. Another physical equation is the relation of velocity, depth, slope, and hydraulic roughness expressed by the Chezy or Manning equation. Another is the relation between shear stress and the sediment load. In a particular case these physical relations can be satisfied by a variety of combinations of values of the dependent variables.

In addition to the physical laws of conservation, another kind of principle is operating, a principle which deals with distribution of energy in time and space and is probabilistic in form. It operates as tendencies guiding the combination of the dependent factors. There is a tendency toward minimum work or minimum rate of energy expenditure and, separately, a tendency toward uniform distribution of energy expenditure.   These are usually opposing tendencies. These tendencies operate through processes which tend to keep an equilibrium among the factors by restraining change.

In the river, such processes, or governors, include scour and fill, changes in bed configuration (ripples, dunes, antidunes), the Bagnold (1956) dispersive stress on the bed. Such processes act in the same manner as the mechanical governor on the old steam engine. Any tendency to change one factor at the expense of another induces a resistance to that change, and so the hydraulic factors hover around a mean or equilibrium. But at any moment in time, the specific relations cannot be forecast except in a statistical sense.

Such governing action is well known in the process of scour and fill. If local deposition occurs on the bed of an alluvial channel, depth tends to decrease slightly, velocity may increase, and slope may tend to increase, the net result of which tends to limit deposition or to induce compensatory scour. The average relation or the most stable relation in river mechanics appears to be one in which total energy expenditure is minimized and energy utilization is uniformly distributed through the channel reach, a consequence of the requirements for a stable open system (Leopold and Langbein, 1962).

In the development of land forms there are many different processes acting at innumerable localities. There are, in other words, a great many hills, rills, valleys, cliffs, and other forms, and on each, a large number of variable factors operate.   Geomorphologists have considered that the variations observed among examples of the same features are due to two principal causes: (a) slight variations in local structure, lithology, vegetation, or other factors, and (b) irreducible errors in measurements. We postulate a third no less important one—statistical variation resulting from the indeterminacy discussed above. At first blush, this addition may seem trivial, obvious, or implied in the first two causes, but philosophically it seems important. The following example may illustrate the point.

Imagine a broad hill slope of uniform material and constant slope subjected to the same conditions of rainfall, an ideal case not realized in nature. Assume that the slope, material, and precipitation were such that a large number of rills existed on the surface in the form of a shallow drainage net. Would it be supposed that rills comparable in size and position were absolutely identical? The postulate of indeterminacy would suggest that they would be very similar but not identical.   A statistical variation would exist, with a small standard deviation to be sure, but the lack of identity would reflect the chance variation among various examples, even under uniform conditions.

In addition to known physical relationships there are other relations of a stochastic nature that can be used to explain certain geomorphic forms (Langbein, 1963), and they imply that variance in form is an inherent property. It is here suggested that the same principle may have general applicability to many aspects of geologic science. The landscape, in other words, exhibits a variability which may be expected as a result of incomplete dynamic determinacy. General physical laws are necessary but not sufficient to determine the exact shape of each land form. Some scatter of points on graphs showing interrelations between factors is expected, although the mean or median condition is reproducible in different sets of samples.

The same set of conditions, for example the same climate, the same lithology, and the same structure, can lead to a spectrum of different dimensions and positions of the otherwise identical aspects, for example, the rills just mentioned. These variations exist even though there are (a) common climatic and geologic environment, and (b) a common set of hydraulic principles.

Hence we conclude that there remain certain unsatisfied conditions, certain degrees of freedom (excess of unknowns over number of equations that can be written to connect these unknowns). Implicit in this observation is the possibility of applying principles of probability to an interpretation of those aspects of the landscape subject to variance. The analysis is helped by the central-limit theorem that a mean condition exists. The variance about the mean is a function of the degrees of freedom.

Thus it appears that in geomorphologic systems the ability to measure may always exceed ability to forecast or explain. The better to account for variations in land forms, it may be possible to introduce new relationships, each deriving importance in proportion to the extent that they satisfy nature, i.e. agree with reality in the field. These new or alternative relationships may be stochastic rather than physically deterministic. Thus probabilistic relationships may provide better agreement with actual conditions than the direct physical relationships which have previously been used. The stochastic statements, which may at times enlarge upon physical relations based on Newtonian laws of mechanics, will differ from the latter in having an inherent variance implicitly or explicitly stated. But this probabilistic or stochastic statement may turn out to be the more important element and lead to more specific understanding of processes than the previous approximation which supposed exact physical laws.

What we believe will be an example of the substitution of a probabilistic statement for a physical one, and thus of an improvement in understanding is in the much-studied logarithmic distribution of velocity in turbulent flow. The approximation to field observation provided by momentum theory is deterministic in nature, but it is well known that it contains implicitly a variance. It now begins to appear that explanation of the logarithmic velocity distribution based on stochastic principles may be more basic in leading to understanding and will agree as well or better with actuality than the physical models previously used. Further, the stochastic relation will lead directly not only to mean values but also to a statement of the variance about the mean.

Equilibrium in geomorphology, from this point of view, can be achieved in a variety of ways and is fixed or definable for a large number of cases only by their means. Those cases which deviate from the mean are not necessarily in any less perfect equilibrium than other cases which coincide with the mean. In this sense geomorphology inherently involves variance, which is an intrinsic property of geomorphic forms.

In this light, statistical processes and statistical treatment are necessary objects of study and tools of the science. They can be studied only quantitatively. This is, if need be, justification enough for the growing emphasis on a quantitative rather than a descriptive treatment of land forms.

But justification of our tools, our methods, or our emphasis, should not occupy attention in geomorphology. If results are of intellectual interest, or lend themselves to practical prevision or forecasting, the science will prosper. To this end, geomorphologists might best look to the scope of the associations in our reasoning processes.

Any aspect of science may founder temporarily on the shoals of small questions, of details, as well as on the dead-end shallows of description. Resurgence of activity and interest can revitalize a subject when the questions posed for investigation are big ones, questions which, if answered, have wide applicability or lead to broad generalization. But generalization is the broadening of associations, the spreading of a foundation for reasoning. The big question is one whose answer might open new or enlarged areas of inference or association.

The measure of a research man is the kind of question he poses. So, also, the vitality of a branch of science is a reflection of the magnitude or importance of the questions on which its students are applying their effort. Geomorphology is an example of a field of inquiry rejuvenated not so much by new methods as by recognition of the great and interesting questions that confront the geologist.

REFERENCES CITED

BAGNOLD, R. A., 1956, The flow of cohesionless grains in fluids: Philos. Trans. Royal Soc. (London), Ser. A, no. 964, v. 249, pp. 235–247.

HACK, J. T., 1960, Interpretation of erosional topography in humid temperate regions: Am. J. Sci., vol. 258-A (Bradley Volume), pp. 80–97.

HORTON, R. E., 1945, Erosional development of streams and their drainage basins, hydrophysical approach to quantitative morphology: Geol. Soc. Am., B., vol. 56, pp. 275–370.

LANGBEIN, W. B., 1964, Geometry of river channels: Am. Soc. Civil Engrs., Jour. Hydraulics Div. (in press)

LEOPOLD, L. B., and LANGBEIN, W. B., 1962, The concept of entropy in landscape evolution: U.S. Geol. Survey, Prof. Paper 500-A, 20 pp.

MILLER, J. P., 1959, Geomorphology in North America: Przeglad Geograficzny, Warsaw, vol. 31, no. 3–4, pp. 567–587.

FREDERICK BETZ, JR.

Geologic Communication

Geology may be viewed as a body of knowledge that grows by additions of observations, verifications, and interpretations. The significant point in all identification of knowledge is that it has no tangibility until it has been expressed in terms which are understandable to at least one individual beyond the discoverer. Thus the vitality of geology—its data, hypotheses, principles, and methods of investigation—is nourished by various modes of communication, which are understood first by those who devote themselves to this science and second by others to whom geologic information is conveyed.

While communication must remain abreast of investigation, it should not become an end in itself. The mass of scientific information has already become greater than any individual can absorb. Soon the scientist will not even be able to deal effectively with the abstracts published as guides to the literature of his special field. To cope with this problem, a "science of communication" has developed, but this separation of communication from subject matter brings with it the threat that the servant may come to dominate the master.

Perhaps the best way for scientists to attack the "information problem" is to become more expert with the tools of communication, which we often use indiscriminately and badly. In the following discussion, the example of geologic communication is considered from several points of view. Among the topics to be considered are the nature of geologic data, the characteristics of the tools used to communicate geologic information, and the influence of communication upon the body of geologic thought.

Data of Geology and Tools of Communication

W. C. Krumbein (1962) classifies the data of geology as observational and experimental. The first type consists of (a) "qualitative observations or statements regarding natural objects or events" and (b) "numerical measurements on those natural objects or events." They are obtained in the field or "measurement" laboratory. The second represents "quantitative measurement data arising under specified and controlled conditions in an experimental laboratory." Krumbein asserts that, although geology is basically a qualitative science and geologists are most concerned with observational data, quantification is advancing steadily in some subfields.

193

The tools used to record and communicate geologic data are language, mathematical and abstract symbols, and graphic representations. They are used individually, but often appear in combination, partly because they are needed to supplement or reinforce one another in providing the most effective communication of different kinds of data, and partly because the capacity of each tool is not fully exploited. There may also be a substitution of tools in different stages of recording and communicating data or interpreting them. The combined use and substitution of tools is illustrated by the geologic map.

Since the beginnings of geology, a major aim of its investigations has been the mapping of geologic objects, mainly units of rock. Krumbein notes that the measurements of the location, distribution, and orientation of units of rock are examples of the long use of numerical data in geology. However, the rocks are defined by physical and chemical properties, not by these "observational" measurements. Some of the properties are examined quantitatively, but others are not or cannot be. The rock type is, therefore, defined by mixed quantitative and qualitative data. Furthermore, the unit of rock that is mapped is established on a qualitative interpretation or judgment of unity, represented either by homogeneity or some peculiar heterogeneity of components. The judgment is often based on the relative age assigned to the rocks by use of a variety of procedures, both qualitative and quantitative. If users of the map or other observers in the field accept the judgment of the mapper, it is credited with being objective. Where there is disagreement, the same area may be mapped more than once with different results, one of which is presumed by each mapper to be correct. The desire to promote quantification and eliminate subjective determinations and evaluations in geologic mapping is understandable, but, as Krumbein warns, quantification raises a problem that pervades all of geology. It "involves making a distinction between those parts of the science that can best be treated wholly on a quantitative basis and those that may actually be weakened by overquantification." The danger lies in attributing regularities to geologic objects, which, to an unknown degree, do not exist or cannot be proved.

In the geologic map, some of the recorded measurements of dimension and orientation are expressed graphically, but others are superposed directly on the map sheet in the form of numbers. The quantitative reliability of the presentation is enhanced by the use of a topographic base, which allows an immediate visual recognition of the relationship between the rocks and the configuration of the surface.

Data on lithology and relative age are expressed by colors, patterns, and symbols. On large-scale maps, graphic presentation of these data need not be a difficult exercise in communication. In maps of medium to small scales, the quantity of data given must be smaller or the detail simplified. Simplification may be preferred because it permits retention of both categories of data. At still smaller scales, the alternative of eliminating one category is often unavoidable. Since the geologic map is primarily an instrument of historical investigation, the data on lithology are sacrificed so as to retain information on relative age.

When the data are not incorporated in the map, they are usually given in texts and tables. When printed on the map sheet, this information can be regarded as the explanation of the map. Frequently, however, the information is contained in a separate pamphlet or book, where it may be combined with material not directly related to the map. Then, instead of serving as an accompaniment to the map, the written material is the main product of the mapping investigation, and the map is secondary. At small scales, which are used for compilations of data covering large regions, or for indices to maps of larger scales, all details must be provided outside the map.

As constituted, then, the map is not a self-contained communication. The information necessary to make it completely useful must be obtained elsewhere or by interpretation based on the user's knowledge and experience. For the nongeologist, the cryptic information on relative age and lithology has little meaning or value.

The question raised by the geologic map is whether it represents the best and most complete use of the cartographic medium for the purpose. The impression created by the geologic map is that the amount and nature of information exceed the capacity of the graphic tool. It might be presumed that the map, because of its fundamental place in geologic science, had been carefully and steadily developed, and that the combined use of the graphic tool and other tools was a refined solution of a problem in communication. The evidence is to the contrary. The map is essentially what it was in its earliest examples, a geographic directory of geologic objects only superficially characterized by graphic devices.

That there is an opportunity for fuller use of the cartographic medium is demonstrated by various types of maps. In geology, progress toward better direct communication of data through maps has been made where a practical purpose is involved. In this case, there is usually a need to make the map usable by and useful to nongeologists. The requirement has forced geologists producing such maps to become aware of the resources of the cartographic medium. In the case of the geologic map, two types of investigations might be undertaken to improve and develop it. One would be to determine whether the map should have additional functions of communication, such as synthesizing the relationships between the objects mapped and placing the geologic data in a more distinct environmental perspective. The other would be to analyze the potential of the cartographic medium to determine whether information now in texts and tables could be expressed graphically.

The reliance on language for communication of geologic knowledge is evident, but as experimental and quantitative procedures become more common, numbers and other systems of abstract symbols will make inroads on the dominance of language.

The advantages of symbolization as a tool of communication are familiar, but may be reviewed briefly here. Baulig (1956) points to mathematical symbolization, especially algebraic, as the most perfect scientific language because it is rigorously precise, unequivocal in meaning, unexcelled in ease of handling, and universal in use. Symbolization also has the obvious advantage of relative economy in use of space. Baulig notes that mathematical symbolization is suited best to expressing relationships, particularly abstract ones. The physical sciences are in a position to avail themselves of this tool, but the natural sciences are still in the process of describing and classifying objects and are not ready to employ symbols exclusively. They must rely on the word to give form and reality to their data and the inferences derived from them. Furthermore, so long as substantial parts of geology are treated better qualitatively or elude quantitative investigation, symbols will not replace language as the primary tool.

The advantages of mathematical symbols are the drawbacks of verbal language. Nevertheless, scientific verbal languages possess a superiority over systems of symbols because they are not limited to their symbols, or terminology, but can make use of words that everyone knows in common languages.

The deficiencies of verbal language can be overcome by accurate and skillful use, which should be desired by the communicator and expected by his audience. Inaccurate and inept use of numbers is censured and casts doubt on the validity of the data being presented and the investigations underlying them. The user of language should search for a similarly strict standard of acceptability. As a group, geologists, who are dependent on language, do not give it such support. Often those geologists and other scientists who use language well are looked upon with suspicion, as though they were guilty of concealing faulty procedure and inadequate data by clever manipulation of words. An equally negative attitude common among geologists ascribes to all an innate inability to use language correctly and effectively. The prevalence of poor writing is, however, not to be excused in a science that requires verbal communication.

Criticism of Geologic Writing

The published criticism of geologic writing focuses on poor grammar, bad habits of style, and abuse of terminology.

The first two charges have been discussed lately by Weber (1957) in respect to German geologic writing. This critic attributes the decline in quality of writing in recent decades to a lack of training of geologists in classical languages. He sees the trend continuing as the poor writing of today becomes the model for tomorrow's authors. To substantiate his claim Weber refers to errors in syntax and spelling, use of dialectal words, and diffuseness. Earlier, Cloos (1933) had protested against the wordiness of German geologic literature, illustrating his complaint by examples that he rewrote in shorter, clearer form. Geologic literature in other languages seems similarly afflicted.

These criticisms can be debated, because grammar and style are themselves not clearly defined. Usage has replaced grammar in some languages, particularly English, as the standard of correctness and acceptability. Bergen Evans (1962) says: "There is no simple rule about English that does not have so many exceptions that it would be folly to rely on it." The obligation of the writer in English has shifted from strict observance of grammatical rules to an awareness of accepted ways of saying things. This obligation rests also on editors, who have the power to destroy good writing by application of bad rules.

Referring to scientific and technical translating, which shares the problems of original writing, Holmstrom (1951) says that the ability to express thought "involves skill in exploiting the possibilities of interplay between words through syntax and accidence, emphasis and cadence, metaphor and simile, sentence and paragraph structure and the indefinable thing called 'style.'" The difficulty of acquiring this skill is stated by E. B. White, who says[1] that "There is no satisfactory explanation of style, no infallible guide to good writing." Evans advises:

> In order to exercise good taste in English one must know the full spread of what is allowable, the great variety of forms that are being used by the best speakers and writers. And one learns this not by mastering rules but by paying careful attention to details in the speech or writing of those whose English seems attractive or compelling.

The advice is given without reference to subject matter or intended audience.

The criteria of good style are as relevant to technical writing as to literary writing and perhaps should be applied more stringently to the former, if one accepts the views of Darlington (1953):

> The theory that scientific discovery is impersonal, or as it is called, objective, has had several evil consequences . . . One should write, one is told, in the third person, in the passive voice, without betraying conviction or emphasis, without allusion to any concrete or everyday object but with the feeblest indifference and the greatest abstraction. This practice has proved to be so readily acquired that it has now, for a whole generation, been debauching the literary language of the world. The result has been that

---

[1] See Strunk and White in the References.

science, instead of being a source of strength and honesty, is fast robbing the common speech of these very qualities. For the style itself is neither strong nor honest.

Several decades ago, Sir James Barrie was quoted by T. A. Rickard (1931) as having said that "the man of science appears to be the only man who has something to say, just now—and the only man who does not know how to say it." Rickard preferred to think that this comment had been a friendly jibe at the pure scientists of the nineteenth century, but was an unpleasant truth when applied to practitioners of "the avowedly utilitarian branches of science" of the present day. A more significant comparison would be made between present-day writing in pure science and applied science. In the case of geologic writing, as with geologic maps, clarity of communication seems to be more and more an attribute of applied science, because it is a necessity. The unfavorable criticism should be aimed at geologists who feel no compulsion to write well, not at branches of their science. Barrie's premise that the scientific writer has something to say is put to a serious test by many writers. As a consolation they may accept White's opinion that there is "no assurance that a person who thinks clearly will be able to write clearly." [2] One may also note that there is no assurance that a person who does not write clearly is able to think clearly.

To combat the weaknesses in grammar and style of geologic writing, Weber (1957) suggests two measures. One is to encourage systematic scrutiny of published literature for offenses, which should be publicly cited. The other is to encourage authors to assume personal responsibility for correcting and improving their writing before submitting manuscripts for publication. The first proposal relies on the efficacy of threats to improve behavior. It would certainly meet with widespread opposition, even from those not found guilty. The second is the more agreeable proposal, but it rests on the dubious assumption that geologists as a group are better critics of writing than they are writers.

An improvement in geologic writing may result from the strain being placed on publication facilities by the constantly increasing number of manuscripts submitted. Among the ways of relieving this strain, several that have been introduced in scientific and technical journals strike at prolixity. The objective is attained by setting maximum limits on the length of manuscripts that will be published or by offering incentives to authors to write as briefly as possible. A promise of more rapid publication is the most persuasive argument. In acceding to self-discipline, more authors may learn to appreciate the weight and value of words.

The third criticism of geologic writing concerns the abuses of terminology. C. W. Washburne (1943) describes them as the use of incorrect terms, contra-

---

[2] See Strunk and White in the References.

dictory terms, pleonasms, and fancy words, and the misuse of valid terms. A distinction can be made between the more and the less serious abuses. Pleonasms are often idiomatic and have a claim to acceptability, especially in the spoken language. The use of fancy words, including foreign-language equivalents and obsolete terms, can be altogether appropriate in places. White treats these offenses under the heading of style rather than correct or acceptable usage. The inexcusable abuse is the use of a valid term that is irrelevant in the context.

Watznauer (1956) sees a twofold purpose in terminology. To the individual, terminology is the means of possessing knowledge in condensed form; to the group, terminology provides the verbal codes that simplify communication. Terminology should be a distinct aid to scientists, but has become increasingly a barrier to understanding. The barrier is heightened by the proliferation of specialized vocabularies. When communication based on the use of terminology breaks down, the special language becomes a jargon.

Challinor (1961) attempts to clarify the problem by differentiating between jargon and acceptable terminology. He calls jargon "Twittering, chattering. Terminology invented or used where ordinary words would do as well." On the other hand, he says "Technical terminology, geological terminology, however uncouth the terms, is not jargon if it fixes meaning shortly and concisely." Regrettably, his attempt fails, for neither gracefulness nor succinctness prevents terminology from being jargon, even when the terms look like ordinary words.

There is also the problem of communication with scientists in other fields and with the general public, which terminology tends to complicate. A drastic view of the barrier that exists here is shown in the following statement from a geologic dictionary for general users by Himus (1954): "It is a common accusation that geologists in common with other scientists are guilty of inventing and using a barbarous and repellent jargon which is incomprehensible to the man in the street and may even be adopted as a protection against criticism."

Such criticism of geologic writing underscores the need for skill and accuracy in the use of language. Leniency may be permissible in judging skill, but accuracy, particularly in the use of terminology, is essential. There must be a commonly held belief in the integrity and inviolability of terminology to which both the user and the creator of terms subscribe. Acceptance of this belief would prevent the user from using terms without knowing their meanings, and the creator from introducing terms for which there was no need. The abuses by the user can be overcome by the conscientious use of dictionaries and other types of wordbooks. The creator has the added obligation of knowing the motivation for terms, the sources of terms, and the terminology of his subject in different languages.

Sources of Geologic Terminology and Implications of Its Growth

In his work on the composition of scientific words, Roland Brown says that these words "originate in three ways: (1) adoption directly with appropriate modifications in spelling from Greek, Latin, and other languages; (2) composition by compounding and affixation; and (3) outright or arbitrary creation without use of evident, antecedent root or stem material."

It is not always easy to determine which of these actions accounts for the origin of a particular term. Some dictionaries explain the etymology of the words they contain, but this information does not tell whether the first user of a term borrowed or derived it from an existing word or invented it. In fact, many terms, especially the older ones, entered the vocabulary without a known formal introduction. The source shown in dictionaries is more often the author of an accepted current definition than the first user or originator of the term. For the user of terminology, the accepted meanings are, of course, far more important than the history of usage, and it would not serve his purpose to have this additional historical information.

F. A. Burt (1949) has examined the origin of geologic terms specifically and found that the commonest source is the vernacular. He cites such terms as *joint, graben, dune, lava,* and *moraine* as examples of ordinary words that have entered the geologic vocabulary, but with more restricted meanings than they had originally. There is an almost endless list of common words with geologic meanings. To add only a few, *ash, axis, basin, bed, bomb, boss, groove, group, habit, head, heave,* and *incompetent* can be mentioned. Burt also refers to terms that come from particular environments, such as *barchan, hamada,* and *nunatak.* Baulig (1956) remarks that the terminology of geomorphology is filled with such words, which come into use as localisms and, in some cases, acquire wider use.

Besides common words, proper nouns are adopted or adapted for use in the geologic vocabulary. Every geologist is familiar with the many stratigraphic and rock names that are derived from specific geographic designations and the fossil names drawn from surnames. Burt cites the following examples of terms of this origin: in geomorphology, *meander* and *monadnock;* in paleontology, *Beltina;* in mineralogy, *labradorite;* in petrology, *syenite;* and in ground-water geology, *artesian.*

It is evident that many cases of adoption or adaptation of ordinary words and proper names involve borrowing from a foreign language. *Decke, fjord, graben, horst, klippe, loess,* and *nappe* are examples of terms, used in geologic vocabularies generally, which have been borrowed from vocabularies of particular languages.

Terms should be borrowed from foreign languages primarily to fill gaps in terminology. A second reason for his kind of borrowing is to take advantage of terms that seem especially suitable to subject-matter specialists. The latter reason is less definite than the former, which can be determined by the inspection of vocabularies in different languages. Gaps are far more frequent, not only in scientific terminology but also in ordinary words, than is usually realized.

To illustrate the gaps in geologic terminology, a sample has been taken from the four-language geologic dictionary edited by Rutten. The section on "tectonic geology" contains 653 terms (not including synonyms), of which only 393 are represented in all four of the languages, 141 in three, 105 in two, and 14 in one. There are 644 terms in Dutch, 561 in German, and 506 in both English and French. Dutch appears to have the richest terminology of this subject, but the relative scarcity of gaps is undoubtedly related to the fact that Dutch was the primary language of the compilers. Furthermore, the dictionary project afforded them an opportunity to discover the gaps in the Dutch terminology, which, according to two of the compilers, were closed by coining terms.

The absence of equivalents in two of the four languages for any term is less significant than a gap in one or three. Where at least two languages contain equivalents, the sense of the knowledge they express is seen to have gained identification beyond its source. A term that has no equivalents in three of the languages may represent a highly restricted identification, although it may also stand for a distinct advance of knowledge in one language area over the other areas. The absence of a term in only one of the languages suggests that the subject has, for some reason, not been pursued actively in that language area. This interpretation is supported by the prevalence of gaps in sequences of related terms. On the other hand, it may indicate that foreign-language terms are being used regularly to discuss the subject.

In the sample, English and French show the same number of gaps, but English is the only missing language in 83 cases, whereas French alone is absent in 42. Based on a study of the terms of geomorphology, Baulig finds that foreign-language terms are used most in English and successively less in German and French. He relates the prevalence of borrowed technical terms in English to the long-time general receptiveness of English-language speakers to words of foreign origin. German, according to Baulig, is more likely to contain translations of foreign-language terms or modifications to a German form. French, he finds, resists German terms because they seem difficult for French speakers to assimilate and pronounce, but is more tolerant of words from other Romance languages. Thus, the indicated gaps in French terminology are more likely to be real gaps than those in English.

Baulig comments on the dangers of borrowing without adequately understanding the source language. Too often, adoptions result in distortions of meaning and incorrect usage. The tendency to borrow freely makes these abuses all the more noticeable in English writing and speech.

Borrowing occurs also between different sciences, particularly to serve the needs of specialists working in border areas. The rapidly developing interdisciplinary fields, such as geophysics and geochemistry, have vocabularies that represent mingling, rather than mere borrowing, of terms from the parent fields. As terms become common to more than one field, they tend to fall within the scope of the general language and appear in standard language dictionaries. The commonly accepted definitions of an increasing number of scientific terms are found today in these dictionaries, which are cited as the authorities for definitions shown in modern technical dictionaries.

Adoption or adaptation of words from any source often involves change in meaning. The scientific usage is subject to further change, with the result that many terms have several different scientific meanings, not just in succession but simultaneously. Watznauer regards change from original meanings as normal deviation caused by the advance of knowledge. A typical example of the history of origin and changes in usage has been traced by Tourtelot, using the word *shale*. He concludes that the present usage of this term in two technical meanings is permissible and justifiable. It would be futile to insist on a single meaning for this kind of term. The user cannot be expected to define his usage of each term with different meanings each time he uses it. The usage, whether technical or vernacular, should be apparent to the reader from the context.

Invention of terms should become necessary only when no terms fulfilling the purpose are available in any language. The need grows as the knowledge of the field increases. The discovery of hitherto unidentified objects demands the creation of new names. There is less frequent need for new common words, since they stand for classes of objects, generalizations, and concepts, which are not newly recognized as often as data are.

Whatever the mode of origin, *need* is the basic justification for terminology. The growth of terminology in modern time suggests that need does not always motivate the introduction of new terms. Watznauer has examined this growth critically and concluded that the purpose of terminology is being destroyed by uncontrolled addition of specialized terms. He argues that a new term should represent an addition to knowledge and that too many terms are unnecessary because they merely reexpress what has been known before. He observes that terms are being introduced without clear-cut definitions and therefore do not serve as a point of reference for the state of knowledge at a given time.

Watznauer (1956) sees the individual scientist unable to cope with the many terms applying to special subfields and abandoning the effort to keep abreast of knowledge in specialties other than his own. He finds terminology threatening to become the master of science and artificially promoting specialization that tends to disunite fields. This argument oversimplifies the explanation of real or apparent fragmentation of sciences. The actual increase in the store of knowledge is still a compelling factor in limiting the scope of individual interest in and capacity for comprehending a science. In the case of geology, specialized vocabularies do not cause the drift of subfields toward affiliation with other sciences, but once the movement has begun they serve to reinforce it.

Monolingual Dictionaries

Dictionaries and other types of wordbooks are a measure of the amount and kind of attention given the subject of terminology. Bibliographic and statistical records of all types of monolingual and multilingual dictionaries throughout the world, published by UNESCO (1961 see also Wüster, 1955, 1959) show geologic dictionaries to be few in number today; and there is no evidence that they were more common in the past.

Dictionaries can be classified as general or specialized by reference to their coverage of fields and degree of completeness within the fields covered. In a strict interpretation, a general dictionary is one that covers the entire terminology of a field at a given time. An all-inclusive geologic dictionary may have been compiled in the past, but none appears to exist now. By design, the modern general geologic dictionary is one with broad coverage of the terminology, but with intentional omissions of some subject areas or categories of terms.

Specialized dictionaries do not have to conform to any standard of coverage or completeness. These dictionaries may be separate publications of considerable size with complete coverage of a stated range of subject matter, but often they are glossaries and vocabularies appended to geologic books, papers, and map explanations.

In English, four general geologic dictionaries published in the nineteenth century—by Roberts in 1839, by Humble in 1840, by Page in 1865, and by Oldham in 1879—are cited in modern dictionaries as predecessors. The modern dictionaries, which have been examined for this discussion, are those prepared by Rice (1940), Himus (1954), Stokes and Varnes (1955), the AGI Glossary Project (1957; second edition containing a supplement, 1960; abridged version, 1962), and Challinor (1961).

The Rice and AGI dictionaries are comprehensive works intended primarily for professional geologists. The Rice dictionary (1940), with an estimated total of 8000 terms, was the largest English-language geologic dictionary at the time of its publication. With 14,000 terms in the original edition and about 4000 more in a supplement, the AGI dictionary is the closest approach to an all-inclusive geologic dictionary available today. Some of those compiled in the nineteenth century may have covered the smaller body of terminology of that time as completely. For example, Humble (1840) defined about 3000 terms in his dictionary published in 1840 and added 300 in the second edition in 1843.

The difference in size of the Rice and AGI dictionaries is partly an indicator of the growth of terminology in a period of less than 20 years. It is also an indicator of the vastly greater resources of manpower applied to the AGI Project. After about four years of planning by representatives of numerous organizations, topical committees, in which more than 80 individuals participated, spent three years and four months in selecting terms and providing definitions. The Rice dictionary was compiled by one person, not a professional geologist, without organized assistance, over a period of many years.

As comprehensive works, both the Rice and AGI dictionaries necessarily contain a broad coverage of geologic fields. The compilers of the AGI dictionary considered 30 fields of geology and related sciences and included all but a few in the final compilation. The terminology of each field covered is complete except in a few cases, for reasons that are stated in the preface to the dictionary. Limited coverage was justified mainly by the existence of accessible specialized dictionaries or other reference works on terms and names of a subject area. In the Rice dictionary, the only announced exclusion was stratigraphic and paleontologic nomenclature. Actually, it contains a great many stratigraphic names.

The Himus dictionary (1954) and the abridged version of the AGI dictionary are classed as selective general dictionaries. Both were published in series of pocket-sized reference books intended for the general reader. The Himus dictionary is the smaller volume, containing about 1800 terms and names. The AGI abridged dictionary, with 7000 entries, or about half the contents of the second edition of the original dictionary, is, despite its format, a comprehensive work. It establishes a new scale for selective geologic dictionaries. Two decades ago the most complete dictionary was less than 10 percent larger than this abridged work of today. The largest selective dictionary published previously contained less than half as many terms.

Stokes and Varnes (1955) selected 2800 terms covering the field of geology broadly, which they considered to be of concern to civil engineers and related specialists. The specific omissions are stratigraphic names, most rock names, and most general and elementary terms of mineralogy and petrology. Whether the intended audience has no use for the information that is omitted is questionable. What Stokes and Varnes have accomplished is to put the problem of abridgment in focus. They have distinguished information that is properly recorded in an abridged general dictionary from that which belongs in unabridged general and specialized dictionaries.

Challinor (1961) explains his purpose in compiling a geologic dictionary with this statement:

There appears to be room among works on geology for one that will probe the subject by examining the meaning and usage of names and terms that stand for the more significant things, facts, and concepts of the science. This small book is an essay towards a critical and historical review of a selected ABC of the subject.

The format of a dictionary is employed by Challinor to present comments on geologic subject matter. Terminology is treated as a manifestation of the state of geologic knowledge and the degree of maturity of the science at different times in its history. Secondarily, Challinor supplies a study on the usage, source, and etymology of geologic words. There is no pretense of complete coverage in this selection of about 1250 terms and 300 names belonging to subfields of geology, to which 250 general geologic words, designation of tools and concepts, and terms borrowed from physics and chemistry are added.

In addition to the five dictionaries mentioned, two other modern dictionaries contain a broad representation of geologic terminology, although they are not specifically geologic. These two are the dictionary of mining- and mineral-industry terms by Fay (1920), and the geographic dictionary prepared by a committee (L. D. Stamp, Chairman) of the British Association for the Advancement of Science (BAAS), which was published in 1961.

The Fay volume (1920) contains 20,000 terms, or 8000 more than appear in the first edition of the AGI dictionary. In this compilation, Fay had six active collaborators and twelve reviewers of definitions. About 4000 of the terms can be considered geologic. Thus the Fay dictionary was also the first major geologic dictionary published in the United States. Only paleontologic terms are specifically omitted, but, in keeping with the purpose of the work, the majority of the geologic terms are mineral and rock names.

The BAAS dictionary (1961) may be regarded as the geographic counterpart of the AGI dictionary, since it, too, is the result of an intensive examination of terminology for the purpose of producing a comprehensive general dictionary. The BAAS project took even more time than the AGI project. In a first stage, an attempt to carry out directions given by the BAAS to a dictionary committee ended in a virtual suspension of effort after three years. The project was resumed by a reorganized committee of twelve members, supported ultimately by fifty-eight collaborators, many of them outside Britain. A research officer was appointed to prepare an initial list of terms and definitions. This task was completed in one year. In the following six years, Stamp, who was also the editor of the dictionary, quadrupled the list of terms and, with the assistance of the other committee members and the collaborators, reviewed definitions and prepared comments on them.

With an estimated total of only 3200 terms, the BAAS dictionary still may be classified as both an unabridged and an abridged dictionary. The size does not indicate selectivity in subject-matter coverage so much as intentional limitation to "terms in current geographical literature written in English."

The criterion of currency is not applied in any of the other dictionaries being considered here.

The BAAS dictionary contains many terms used in geography that are also identified with the vocabularies of geology, climatology, meteorology, soil science, and ecology. In respect to geologic terminology, Stamp notes the following omissions: mineral names; rock names except for some "commonly misused or misunderstood (names) and names applied to broad groups"; all but a few stratigraphic names (but more than 200 are listed in an appendix to the dictionary); and all but some important tectonic terms. These omissions, primarily of nomenclature, do not indicate a narrowness of interest in geologic subject matter among physical geographers. Geologists might presume that the majority of terms in the dictionary were taken from the field of geomorphology. Actually, geomorphic terms amount to less than 10 percent of the total of geologic terms. The coverage of geologic terms is so broad that, according to a review in "The Geochemical News,"[3] the dictionary contains many terms of interest "to geologists, mineralogists, petrologists, and even geochemists."

The fundamental significance of the widespread borrowing and sharing of terminology and subject matter among sciences is that they no longer have completely separate areas of interest. Indeed the boundaries between the major fields are being erased rapidly. The question can be asked: What will be the identifying marks of the individual fields in the future? An answer is given for geology by C. W. Wright (1959), who characterized this field as a group of sciences unified by a special outlook, which he describes as a sense of time and process. Wright mentions only chemistry, biology, geography, and meteorology as sciences joined for a special purpose in geology, but still other sciences are familiar in their geologic orientations. If Wright's interpretation is accepted, then one can ask whether geology was ever anything but an outlook on problems dealt with from other standpoints by other disciplines. Today, the identification of such fields as geophysics, geochemistry, and geohydrology is viewed widely as evidence of the fragmentation of the science of geology. On the contrary, these subfields are interdisciplinary links between geology and other sciences that have always existed but were not recognized formerly. In the process of identifying these links, the concept of geology as a completely separate discipline is becoming obsolete. Like other sciences that have already abandoned an imaginary autonomy, geology will become identified as one important viewpoint influencing investigations in a group of interdisciplinary fields. In them the geologic influence may be dominant, but from time to time and place to place it will undoubtedly be supplanted by influences of other participating disciplines. It is unrealistic to classify these fields as branches of any one of the participating disciplines, even if they were first recognized within

---

[3] See H., in References.

single disciplines. Thus geophysics is as much a branch of geology as it is of physics, geochemistry is not the exclusive property of geology or chemistry, and it is proper for both geographers and geologists to be geomorphologists.

The replacement of distinct sciences by interdisciplines has been foreshadowed by the terminology gathered in modern technical dictionaries. For practical reasons, comprehensive general dictionaries are forced to omit whole vocabularies of existing subfields of the science and interdisciplines in which it participates. Basically the compilers are faced with the problem of defining the limits of the field and are finding the solution increasingly elusive. The general dictionary must, therefore, abandon comprehensiveness, and the burden of recording the complete terminology must be distributed among specialized dictionaries.

A stated function of the BAAS dictionary is to serve those whose native tongue is not English, because English is becoming "increasingly the normal medium for scientific writing and publication." This conclusion was confirmed by the revisers of the Royal Netherlands Geological and Mining Society's multilingual geologic dictionary. As a Dutch publication, in the original edition in 1929 Dutch was the language of reference. In the revision published in 1959, English occupied this position because the compilers found that it was becoming dominant in geologic literature.

These dictionary compilers refer to the dominant medium as English without describing this "English" that is used for scientific communication. In respect to terminology, as was indicated in the earlier discussion of sources of terms, a significant part consists of foreign-language terms adopted with little or no change by English-language speakers. Thus the BAAS dictionary contains about 900 terms, more than one-fourth of the total, from 31 foreign languages or language groups. Presumably these terms have been assimilated into English and are now integral parts of the communication medium called English. In reality, an international terminology is evolving.

The natives of foreign-language areas use the so-called English terminology in a framework that is also referred to as English. On examination, this language is found to be a geologic *lingua franca* composed largely of English words, used frequently in ways unfamiliar to English-language speakers, and of English-like words that seem to be invented more or less spontaneously by the foreign-language speakers. In grammar and style it often bears greater affinity to some foreign language than to English. Foreign-born scientists carry this *lingua franca* into English-language areas, where, unfortunately, too many continue to use it. They complicate the problem of scientific communication by adding negligence to the already prevalent indifference toward, and defiance of, good use of language.

The difficulties created by the use of foreign-language terms and the faulty use of English by foreigners are augmented by the differences between North

American and British English. The BAAS dictionary takes into account these differences in the use of terminology. They occur in both terms and usage. The more troublesome are the differences in usage, which are apt to be overlooked by English-language speakers. The extent to which British terminology differs from American is demonstrated by the Himus geologic dictionary. Roughly 400 of the estimated total of 1800 terms are British terms and names, which are not used regularly, if at all, by Americans and are no more meaningful to them than foreign-language words.

In group projects it is difficult to obtain agreement on definitions. The BAAS instructed its first dictionary committee to prepare "a glossary of geographical terms with agreed definitions in English including references to origin and previous usage and to current use and misuse." The reorganized committee evaluated the charge and concluded that the effort to prepare definitions that would meet with complete approval of the members would have to be abandoned. They discovered further that while original definitions can be found for recent terms, many older terms have gained acceptance without benefit of a specifically recorded first definition. The committee chose to accept from a standard source, usually the Oxford English Dictionary, at least one clear meaning and to obtain variant usages from the technical literature.

The AGI dictionary offers a combination of different types of explanations. Presumably the topical committees adhered to the aim of finding the original or another authoritative definition before writing a new one. The agreement on either accepting an existing definition or preparing a new one was a responsibility of each committee. These committees ranged in size from one member to twelve, with an average of about three. There is visible evidence of a lack of uniformity in handling definitions, which, like the variations in coverage of topics, is probably the result of wide delegation of responsibility. That such irregularities are not desirable was recognized by the compilers, but those that occurred were not corrected because too much time was believed to have been spent on the project to permit further delay in publication. Instead, an immediate review of the dictionary for omissions and errors, in which the readers were invited to participate, was announced. It yielded about 4000 additional and redefined terms. The revision of the dictionary seems to prove that the number of experts who can be expected to reach agreement on the proper selection and definition of terms in their own special vocabularies is very low.[4]

---

[4] The following statement appears on p. iii of the AGI dictionary: "Selection of definitions used was made by the members of the sub-committees listed below. Unaccredited (sic!) definitions were written by these committees or individuals." As printed, the second sentence says that definitions not ascribed to a source are not approved definitions. This expression of no confidence in the committees and their members can be interpreted by each reader to his own satisfaction.

Interlingual Dictionaries

The basic purpose of interlingual dictionaries is to coordinate terminology in different languages as an aid in reading and translating foreign-language writings. The function is to provide equivalents, not definitions. Such dictionaries are, as Holmstrom (1951) points out, "apt to foster the illusion that each word in a language necessarily has its exact and self-sufficient counterpart in other languages." The presence of gaps, or absence of equivalents, has been illustrated earlier in this discussion by the example of geologic terminology in four languages. Where equivalents do not exist, the reader or translator must be prepared to visualize or express the term in some other way, usually by a phrase. He will also have the opportunity of reducing a statement in one language to a word in another.

A technical word or expression is surrounded by other words that create the context. The real unit of equivalence between languages is, therefore, more often a phrase or a sentence than a word. Holmstrom (1951) states that

> the first principle of good translating is to translate not words but ideas organically. The effect of reading a sentence in one language ought to be to generate in the translator's mind an articulated pattern of ideas, so that he may then forget the wording in which they were originally expressed and may himself proceed to reexpress them by making his own professionally educated choice and arrangement of words in the other language.

The scientific reader should also adopt this principle and not be content with knowing approximately what the foreign-language author has said, but require of himself that he know it completely and idiomatically in the other, generally his own, language. To do so, the reader or translator must have at least as good command of his own language as he has of the foreign language.

Most interlingual technical dictionaries, in addition to presenting language in incorrect units, contain an overabundance of irrelevant and unnecessary terms, according to expert opinion cited by Holmstrom (1951). These dictionaries are encumbered by "unwanted" terms, which are ordinary dictionary words, cognates, and compounds with easily identifiable constituents. In a sample of seven bilingual technical dictionaries, Holmstrom found the average content of "unwanted" terms to be 90 percent of the total.

For comparison, Holmstrom's criteria were applied to Huebner's German-English geologic dictionary (1939). It was found to contain as much superfluous material as in any of Holmstrom's samples. Huebner includes countless terms that are identical in German and English or that differ only slightly in spelling; compounds with meanings obvious from their elements; and many words and parts of compounds that are in the German general vocabulary or common scientific vocabulary. By strict adherence to the criteria, Huebner's dictionary would have to be reduced from 25,000 entries to about 3000.

On reappraisal of Holmstrom's criteria, it is clear that they presuppose a higher level of competence in languages than can be expected of scientific readers. It is not realistic to presume that these readers can analyze word structure in foreign languages. The "unwanted" words in interlingual dictionaries may, therefore, be essential to the majority of scientific readers. Translators, as the other main group of users, should be able to get along without common words in a technical dictionary, but they are in need of explicit assistance in deciphering technical terms and their derivatives. The professional translator typically lacks proficiency in technical vocabularies in any language, as published translations amply demonstrate.

When Huebner's dictionary is reexamined in terms of its usefulness to readers with an unequal knowledge of German and English, it emerges as an encyclopedic work of substantial quality and value. Besides its primary function, it gives information on regional usage of both English and German geologic terminology, often with more than a mere word equivalent, and it indicates incorrect usage of German terms in English. Regrettably, the English-German part of this dictionary has never been published.

Bilingual dictionaries commonly have two parts, each with one of the languages as the language of reference. In effect they are pairs of dictionaries in which the contents of both parts are cross referenced. Ideally all terms used in one part should appear in the other, but the purpose of the dictionary may dictate differences. For example, Fischer and Elliott (1950) explain that in their German and English glossary of geographic terms, the English-German part "is not intended primarily for the German student who wants to read English geographical literature, but for the English-speaking geographer who wishes to establish the German equivalent for an English term." Thus, because "many English terms are not easily rendered in German," they "are to be found only in the English-German part." Also, "Terms practically the same in both languages are, in general, included only in the English-German part; English readers usually recognize such words but may hesitate to use them in a foreign language. This is especially true for English terms used in German . . . and for terms from another language . . . used in both languages." For the English-speaking user's benefit, the German-English part is the larger, since his main problem is to understand German literature, not translate English into German.

In multilingual dictionaries, additional dictionaries can be handled in the same fashion as the two languages of bilingual dictionaries. The complete repetition of all terms as many times as there are languages in the dictionary produces the easiest work for the largest audience to use. In a variant on this arrangement, a trilingual geologic dictionary prepared by the military geologic organization of the German army during World War II[5] contains a German-

---

[5] See Wehrgeologenstab Wannsee in the References.

French-English part followed by a French-German and an English-German part. Starting with a French or English term in the second and third parts, respectively, the German equivalent can be used to find the equivalent in either of these other languages in the first part. Thus, although intended for primary users of German and arranged for their convenience, this dictionary can be used effectively by speakers of English or French.

In all dictionaries discussed so far, the terms are listed in alphabetical order. This simple arrangement is replaced in some dictionaries by listings based on some type of association of meanings.

Both editions of the Royal Netherlands Geological and Mining Society's multilingual dictionary (Rutten, 1929; Schieferdecker, 1959) illustrate a non-alphabetical arrangement of terms. In this general dictionary the field of geology is divided into major branches or subjects, which are further subdivided topically.[6] According to Schieferdecker, who edited the second edition, the arrangement of terms is genetic. The characterization is appropriate for various sequences of terms within topical divisions, but it is meaningless for the dictionary as a whole because many of the terms have no genetic connotation and thus their order can have no genetic significance. Schieferdecker commends the so-called genetic arrangement as a convenience for the reader by greatly facilitating the finding of terms. On the contrary, the alphabetical index is the only convenient key to the terms.

In another example of a nonalphabetical arrangement of terms, Challinor (1961) lists his terms in a classified index under 48 group headings. According to Challinor, "within each group an attempt is made to put them into some logical order." Some sequences of terms are familiar and, therefore, appear to be logical, but others are arbitrary and wholly personal. In this case the user can ignore the index and look for terms directly in the alphabetical listing of the dictionary proper.

Despite the weaknesses of nonalphabetical order, it offers the advantage of grouping terminology by subjects and topics. The user with time to browse can obtain a complete picture of terminology of a topic without the distraction of interspersed unrelated terms. The plan converts a general dictionary into a series of specialized dictionaries.

The associative order of terms in a dictionary is an indirect approach to the problem of placing terms in context. The additive effect of sequences of words with related connotations can create an impression of the places in which they are used properly. A direct approach is taken by scientific reading exercise

---

[6] The first edition (1929) contains eight primary divisions and 44 secondary; the second edition (1959) has 74 primary and 107 secondary divisions. The great increase in primary and secondary divisions in the second edition may be due to various causes indicated in the previous discussion of English dictionaries. The effect of the increase is to provide more structure for the allocation of terms in the dictionary.

books designed for use in foreign-language instruction. Selections from foreign-language literature may be translated in their entirety into the user's tongue and printed beside the original text, or only technical terms and other selected expressions or phrases are translated and given in footnotes, sidenotes, or appended vocabularies. These books are not systematic presentations of terminology, but are often used in place of dictionaries for hasty acquisition of a specialized foreign-language vocabulary.

A direct systematic approach to the problem of coordinating terminology in two or more languages demands an effort beyond translation and compilation. In the late nineteenth century, de Margerie and Heim (1888) became concerned by the increasing misunderstanding of terminology of crustal dislocations. They undertook to clarify the concepts of the topic by publishing parallel French and German versions of their text. Where technical terms appeared, the columns of text were interrupted and the special French and German terms were centered on the page. In addition, any English equivalents of the French and German terms were given. The authors also appended references to sources of terms and examples of usage.

Baulig (1956), inspired by this older work, published a study on the terminology of geomorphology in French, English, and German, with incidental attention to other languages, especially Arabic. The text is in French. Baulig divided the subject into many topics, which he discussed systematically in more than 500 numbered paragraphs. Immediately following the appearance of a French special term in the text, equivalents in French, English, and German, and in places dialectal terms and equivalents in other languages, were inserted. The same term may appear in several places in the volume to account for usage in different contexts. A combined index refers to the numbered paragraphs, and the different usages are also signalled by cross references in the text. Baulig summarized the purpose of his study as follows: to reveal to the French user the resources, often unsuspected, of his own language; to help him in reading and possibly translating foreign-language literature; and to contribute to a revision of the international vocabulary of geomorphology.

Both studies attest to the ingenuity and scholarship of their authors. They have produced a combination of monolingual and interlingual dictionaries and explanatory texts that can be used for a variety of purposes. Baulig may have dealt with the largest practical grouping of subject matter in his study. The feasibility of applying this plan to a general dictionary is slight. These studies support an argument for detailed specialized wordbooks, which can portray technical language in meaningful units.

Interlingual dictionaries call attention to the seriousness of the problem of worldwide scientific communication. In the absence of an international language, the primary reporting in one language is not directly usable by those lacking a reading knowledge of that language. A recent examination of the effects of language barriers in earth sciences was made by Emery and Martin (1961), who found that the literature contains references mostly "to sources from the same country as the author, evidently because of familiarity with language and ease of access." They observed that the second most frequent source for non-English writers is American and British literature, "probably because English is the most familiar language of the scientific world."

Language barriers are being lowered, though not eliminated, by the simultaneous publication of abstracts in one or more of the other widely used languages along with the original complete text. Journals and volumes of abstracts issued periodically in various important languages are invaluable guides to worldwide literature. The dependence on abstracts of foreign-language literature is paralleled by the growing reliance on abstracts of literature in the user's own language. The abstract is becoming an ultimate unit of reading, instead of serving just as a guide to publications.

An alternative to abstracting foreign-language literature is complete or substantially complete translation. Whereas abstracts are often prepared by subject-matter specialists, translations are usually the work of professional translators. The value of completeness of a translation can be outweighed by the deficiencies in rendition of technical information. Translation is, therefore, a way of overcoming language barriers that should be adopted only if it can be justified. The primary justification is not the existence of a barrier but the importance of the literature and the need to have its contents known.

Today, in the United States, bulk translation of Russian literature confirms the inability of most American scientists to read Russian. If the translations prepared so far have established the importance of Russian scientific work, then the obvious solution for American scientists is to learn to read Russian and not to depend further on translations. In defense of translation on a grand scale, the limited opportunities for studying Russian in American schools could be cited. On the other hand, the existence of widespread opportunities for studying foreign languages does not guarantee lasting proficiency.

Emery and Martin (1961) show that American earth scientists do not report extensive use of French and German sources, although the literature in these languages is voluminous. A report on proficiency in foreign languages, published by the U.S. National Science Foundation (1961), explains the reason for this surprising observation. The report is based on an inquiry among 100,000 American scientists, who provided the following information: (a) "84 percent stated they could read scientific or technical material in a foreign language"; (b) of this group only "30 percent rated their ability as good"; (c) "Only 12 percent of those reading German rated their ability as 'good'; in French it was 9 percent . . ."

Although many Europeans are competent in the use of several languages, the growing number of languages in which scientific literature is written poses a problem for them, too. In 1927, Salomon in Germany was discouraged by the growing problem in worldwide communication of geologic knowledge. He predicted, perhaps not altogether facetiously, that the future geologist would have to spend his first 80 years in learning languages and then only could he begin with geology. Salomon proposed the adoption of Latin as the language for international geologic communication, but was realistic enough to anticipate strong opposition. The outlook for the success of this proposal has long since faded, but the need for an international language is greater than ever.

The increasing use of English in scientific communication may lead to recognition of English as the international language some day, but there is no prospect that it will displace all other languages in the immediate future. Until that day, geologists and other scientists who depend on language to express much of their knowledge, must keep in mind the grave conclusion stated by Emery and Martin (1961) that:

> ... science is proceeding in each country largely independently of progress in other countries. This is ... extremely wasteful of manpower, facilities, and time, although it does provide independent confirmation of ideas and techniques. Its existence means that probably a majority of scientists tacitly assume that it is easier to make independent discoveries than to learn of other prior work when the latter is reported in an unfamiliar language.

Concluding Remarks

The problems of terminology and its unrestrained growth, of dictionaries and their contents and arrangement, of modes of communication other than language, and of interlingual exchange of scientific information are all overshadowed by the more perplexing problems caused by the rampant growth of literature.

Emery and Martin (1961) remarked that:

> ... a scientist of a given field is faced not only by a flood of publications in his own language but by similar floods in other languages. Since there is a limit to his time and ability to absorb this material, the scientist may choose to specialize in a field so small that he can read most of the literature or he may choose to cover a larger field and ignore most of the literature, particularly that which is difficult to read or obtain.

The problems only appear to have become urgent in our time. Almost 70 years ago, when the flood of literature was a trickle compared with today's outpouring, Archibald Geikie (1897) said much the same [7]:

> I am only too painfully aware how increasingly difficult it is to[8] keep pace with the ever-rising tide of modern geological literature. The science itself has so widened, and the avenues to publication have so prodigiously multiplied, that one is almost driven in despair to become a specialist, and confine one's reading to that portion of the literature which deals with one's own more particular branch of the science. But this narrowing of the range of our interests and acquirement has a markedly prejudicial effect on the character of our work.

Geikie continues with words of admonition that should be repeated today:

> The only[9] consolation we can find is[10] the conviction, borne in upon us by ample and painful experience, that[11] a very[12] large mass of the geological[13] writing of the present time is utterly worthless[14] for any of the higher purposes of the science, and that it may quite safely and profitably, both as regards time and temper, be left unread. If geologists, and especially young geologists, could only be brought to realise that the addition of another paper to the swollen flood of our scientific literature involves a serious responsibility; that no man should publish what is not of real consequence, and that his statements when published should be so clear and condensed as he can make them, what a blessed change would come over the faces of their readers, and how greatly would they conduce to the real advance of the science which they wish to serve.[15]

---

[7] The text is quoted from the first edition (1897, pp. 287–288) of Geikie's "Founders of Geology." Several changes were made in the second edition (1907, pp. 471–472), which are indicated in the footnotes that follow.

[8] Inserted between "to" and "keep" in the second edition: "find time for a careful study of the work of our predecessors, and also to."

[9] "The only" is replaced in the second edition with "There is but slender."

[10] "we can find in" is replaced in the second edition with "to be derived from."

[11] Inserted between "that" and "a" in the second edition: "in the case of geological literature."

[12] "very" is omitted in second edition.

[13] "geological" is omitted in second edition.

[14] "utterly worthless" is replaced in the second edition with "of little or no value."

[15] "." is replaced in second edition with "!."

REFERENCES CITED

American Geological Institute, 1957, Glossary of geology and related sciences: Washington, D. C., Am. Geol. Inst., 325 pp.; 2nd ed. (with supp.), 1960, 420 pp. Abr. ed., 1962, Garden City, N. Y., Doubleday, 545 pp.

BAULIG, HENRI, 1956, Vocabulaire franco-anglo-allemand de géomorphologie: Paris (Soc. d'Edition: Les Belles Lettres) Univ. Strasbourg, Fac. Lettres, Publ., fasc. 130, 230 pp.

BROWN, R. W., 1956, Composition of scientific words: Washington, D. C., U.S. Natl. Mus., The Author, 882 pp.

BURT, F. A., 1949, Origins of geologic terms: Sci. Monthly, vol. 69, pp. 20–22.

CHALLINOR, JOHN, 1961, A dictionary of geology: Cardiff, Univ. of Wales Press, 235 pp.

CLOOS, HANS, 1933, Wie sag ich's meinen Fachgenossen?: Geol. Rundschau, Bd. 24, pp. 225–228.

DARLINGTON, C. D., 1953, The facts of life: London, G. Allen & Unwin, 476 pp.

EMERY, K. O., and MARTIN, B. D., 1961, Language barriers in earth science: GeoTimes (Am. Geol. Inst.), vol. 6, no. 2, pp. 19–21.

EVANS, BERGEN, 1962, Comfortable words: New York, Random House, 379 pp.

FAY, A. H., 1920, A glossary of the mining and mineral industry: U.S. Bur. Mines, B. 95, 754 pp.

FISCHER, ERIC, and ELLIOTT, F. E., 1950, A German and English glossary of geographical terms: Am. Geog. Soc., Lib. Ser. no. 5, 111 pp.

GEIKIE, ARCHIBALD, 1897, The founders of geology: London, Macmillan; 1st ed., 297 pp.; 2nd ed. (1905), 486 pp.

H., E. W., 1962, Book review—A glossary of geographical terms: Geochem. News, no. 3, p. 8.

HIMUS, G. W., 1954, A dictionary of geology: Harmondsworth, Penguin Books, 153 pp.

HOLMSTROM, J. E., 1951, Report on interlingual scientific and technical dictionaries: Paris, UNESCO, Publ. 884, 35 pp.

HUEBNER, WALTHER, 1939, Geology and allied sciences—A thesaurus and a coordination of English and German specific and general terms: New York, Veritas Press, Part 1, German-English, 424 pp.

HUMBLE, WILLIAM, 1840, Dictionary of geology and mineralogy: London, Henry Washbourne; 1st ed., 279 pp.; 2nd ed. (1843), 294 pp.

KRUMBEIN, W. C., 1962, The computer in geology: Science, vol. 136, pp. 1087–1092.

MARGERIE, EMMANUEL DE, and HEIM, ALBERT, 1888, Les Dislocations de l'écorce terrestre—Die Dislocationen der Erdrinde: Zurich, J. Wurster, 154 pp.

OLDHAM, THOMAS, 1879, Geological glossary, for the use of students: London, Edward Stanford, 62 pp.

PAGE, DAVID, 1865, Handbook of geological terms, geology and physical geography: Edinburgh, Blackwood, 506 pp.

RICE, C. M., 1940, Dictionary of geological terms (exclusive of stratigraphic formations and paleontologic genera and species): Ann Arbor, Mich., J. W. Edwards, 461 pp.

RICKARD, T. A., 1931, Technical writing: New York, John Wiley, 337 pp.

ROBERTS, GEORGE, 1839, An etymological and explanatory dictionary of the terms and language of geology; designed for the early student, and for those who have not made great progress in that science: London, Longman, Orme, Brown, Green, & Long-mans, 183 pp.

RUTTEN, L., ed., 1929, Geologische nomenclator: The Hague, G. Naeff, 338 pp.

SALOMON, WILHELM, 1927, Die geologische Literatur und die Sprachen: Geologe, Nr. 41, pp. 1009–1013.

SCHIEFERDECKER, A. A. G., ed., 1959, Geological nomenclature: Gorinchem, J. Noor-duijn, 523 pp.

STAMP, L. D., 1961, A glossary of geographical terms: London, Longmans; New York, John Wiley (1962), 539 pp.

STOKES, W. L., and VARNES, D. J., 1955, Glossary of selected geologic terms with special reference to their use in engineering: Colorado Sci. Soc., Pr., vol. 16, 165 pp.

STRUNK, WILLIAM, JR., and WHITE, E. B., 1959, The elements of style: New York, Macmillan, 71 pp.

TOURTELOT, H. A., 1960, Origin and use of the word "shale": Am. J. Sci., vol. 258-A, pp. 335–343.

UNESCO, 1961, Bibliography of interlingual scientific and technical glossaries: Paris, UNESCO, 4th ed. 236 pp.

U.S. National Science Foundation, 1961, Foreign-language proficiency of scientists reporting to the National Register of Scientific and Technical Personnel, 1960: Washington, D. C., Natl. Sci. Found., Sci. Manpower B., no. 16, 4 pp.

WASHBURNE, C. W., 1943, Some wrong words: J. Geol., vol. 51, pp. 495–497.

WATZNAUER, ADOLF, 1956, Kritische Bemerkungen zur wissenschaftlichen Begriffs-bildung: Zs. angew. Geol., Bd. 2, pp. 64–65.

WEBER, HANS, 1957, Die Sprache in der deutschen geologischen Fachliteratur der neueren Zeit: Neues Jb. Geol. u. Paläont., Mh., no. 6, pp. 274–278.

Wehrgeologenstab Wannsee, Aussenstelle Heidelberg, 1943, Wehrgeologisches Wörter-buch—Deutsch-Französisch-Englisch: (German Army), Oberkomm. d. Heeres, AHA/In Fest (Geol.), 449 pp.

WRIGHT, C. W., 1959, Order and disorder in nature: Geol. Assoc. (London), Pr., vol. 69, pp. 77–82.

WÜSTER, EUGEN, 1955, 1959, Bibliography of monolingual scientific and technical glossaries: Paris, UNESCO, 2 vols.

JAMES GILLULY

U. S. Geological Survey

The Scientific Philosophy of
G. K. Gilbert

The philosophy of G. K. Gilbert has earned a place in this symposium because of his profound influence upon the thinking of geologists everywhere. Other American geologists, notably Hall, Dana, Rogers, Darton, Daly, and perhaps a few others, have contributed nearly or quite as importantly to the body of our science. But Gilbert gave geology a larger dimension and greater vigor through his thoughtful discourses on scientific method, the creation and testing of hypotheses, and the disciplined use of the imagination. Much more influential, however, than all of his essays on method, was the example set by his scientific memoirs. The conscientious, imaginative observation and the judicious weighing of alternatives that these memoirs exemplify have become the ideals by which most of his successors evaluate geologic research to the present day. Because these qualities have become the standards of American geology, many geologists who have never read a line of Gilbert's writings are modeling their work, to the best of their abilities, upon his.

Gilbert's stature and breadth of vision were recognized in his own day. He was the president of seven scientific societies, the recipient of four prizes and medals for scientific accomplishment, and the corresponding or honorary member of many foreign societies. He was the only man ever to serve twice as president of the Geological Society of America—first in 1892 and again seventeen years later in 1909. No one can deny his meriting this unique honor; he was one of the first truly distinguished American geologists.

Gilbert's great powers would have made their impact felt under any circumstances. It is not to denigrate them, then, to point out that his influence was maximized by the scientific climate of his time. He came on the scene at a turning point of American scientific history, when our science was just emerging from the long eclipse that began with the death of Franklin—precisely the right time for him to exercise the greatest influence upon the course of the new day.

218

For the first two-thirds of the nineteenth century, American science lagged far behind our technology and invention. Between the time of Franklin and that of Willard Gibbs, we produced no scientist of the very first rank unless it be Matthew Fontaine Maury. As Tyndall deplored in 1872, many of our better scholars were diverted by lack of support for scientific work either into administration, like Joseph Henry and William Rogers, or into the teaching of other subjects. Gibbs, for a time, had to teach Latin rather than either mathematics or physics, even though Yale paid him no salary. The Drapers, father and son, were perhaps the best of our astronomers, but the father made his living by writing history and the son by teaching physiology, in order to get the money to build their telescopes (Cohen, 1959).[1]

After the Civil War this situation began slowly to change for the better. The great step forward for geology began with the mining boom in the West and the pressures for exploratory surveys as the railroads expanded across the sparsely settled frontier. With negligible exceptions, this was the first time in our history when geologists were able to devote their full time and energies to geologic research. Certainly it was the first time in our history that a considerable group of such men were assembled. To borrow a term from our friends in physics, it is clear, I think, that there is such a thing as a "critical mass" of scientists who, by mutual stimulation, are able to do much more as a group than the same men would have been able to do if each were working alone. Perhaps this generalization would not apply to the very great geniuses, but I believe it is easy to show that it applies to most scientists of more normal competence. Every teacher of graduate students recognizes the application of this rule to a graduate seminar. The blossoming of American geology in the late years of the nineteenth century took place not only because the descriptive geology of half a continent needed to be done and men could spend full time in doing it, nor because the group assembled was one of great geniuses, even though I think the average competence to have been very high. It took place because the great challenge of scientific exploration attracted an unusually able group of men who could devote full time to research in an atmosphere of mutual stimulation.

No wonder this generation produced so many men distinguished in geology: Gilbert, Powell, Dutton, Emmons, Walcott, Hayden, Cross, Becker, Hague, Ward, Iddings, and McGee. This list could be considerably extended by adding the teachers in the new graduate universities who were also a part of the same

---

[1] A hundred years ago many able scientists were diverted from teaching and research into administration because of lack of funds for science; today the plethora of project funds is luring far more scientists away from teaching and research into management and fund solicitation than ever were driven away in the simpler days of the last century. *Plus ça change....*

program: Chamberlin of Chicago, I. C. Russell of Michigan, G. H. Williams of Johns Hopkins, and H. S. Williams of Cornell. That most of these men were exceptionally able is generally agreed, but it seems to me that the impact they made upon the science was even larger than their abilities would normally have justified. The combination of great challenge, mutual stimulus, and the financial support that enabled them to study many facets of geology, not only areally but also in depth, made possible the flowering of the science in America.

Of these men, Powell was the man of broadest vision, perhaps the most far-seeing American statesman of his generation, but there is no question that Gilbert was the man of preeminent influence on geology. His influence was not revolutionary, like that of Gibbs in physical chemistry, but was more akin to that of Richards, our first Nobel prize winner, in setting a high standard of breadth and critical insight into the problem he studied—a standard so high as to form a permanent criterion by which his successors test scientific excellence.

Gilbert's philosophy was, of course, a synthesis of ideas and methods built up by the scientific fraternity over the centuries. The task of science consisted, for him as for others since Bacon, in the observation of natural phenomena and the discovery of orderly relations between them.

In several of his lectures on methodology, he specifically disclaimed any novelty of approach, and, indeed, his philosophy did not contain anything new. That one must have several hypotheses in mind in order to sharpen observation, that sound judgment depends upon testing more than one hypothesis, that the scientist should be reserved as to his own conclusions because every man tends to be partial to his own brain child—all these ideas stressed by Gilbert and beautifully illustrated in his papers had been familiar since the days of John Locke and had been eloquently stated by David Hume a hundred years before Gilbert wrote.

Because the attitude underlying these ideas is so essential to research, Gilbert properly laid stress upon them. He also was fully aware of the pitfalls of semantics and of the danger of mistaking words for ideas, a danger from which the vast rubbish pile of obsolete geologic terms still fails to discourage our too numerous neologists. In the 1880's he was alert to the problem of relating language to meaning. Few others in that day considered the constraints placed on our thinking by language, although Mach in physics and Pearson in statistics were working along similar lines. These constraints are a principal concern of present-day philosophy.

The relation Hume called "cause and effect," Gilbert more noncommittally called "antecedent and consequent." He continually stressed one fact: every antecedent has not one but many consequents. As he put it (Gilbert, 1886, p. 286), "Antecedent and consequent relations are therefore not merely linear, but constitute a plexus; and this plexus pervades nature."

His work gives innumerable examples of his realization that the very complexities of the antecedents and consequents of a particular phenomenon furnish powerful ways of evaluating hypotheses relating to it. The more consequences one can recognize as implied by some hypothesis, the more abundant the opportunities of testing them against the facts; the more diverse the consequences, the more sensitive the test. To quote:

> [An investigator] is not restricted to the employment of one hypothesis at a time. There is indeed an advantage in entertaining several at once, for then it is possible to discover their mutual antagonisms and inconsistencies, and to devise crucial tests—tests which will necessarily debar some of the hypotheses from further consideration. The process of testing is then a process of elimination, at least until all but one of the hypotheses have been disproved.
> In the testing of hypotheses lies the prime difference between the investigator and the theorist. The one seeks diligently for the facts which may overthrow his tentative theory, the other closes his eyes to these and searches only for those which will sustain it. (Gilbert, 1886, p. 286)

This method of simultaneously confronting several hypotheses with the pertinent phenomena, both antecedent and deduced, goes back at least two centuries and perhaps, even further, back to Bacon. But it was much in the minds of both Gilbert and Chamberlin, whose much-quoted paper on the method of multiple working hypotheses was published ten years later.

Gilbert's method embodies four essential elements: (1) observing the phenomenon to be studied and systematically arranging the observational data, (2) inventing hypotheses regarding the antecedents of the phenomenon, (3) deducing expectable consequences of the hypothesis, and (4) testing these consequences against new observations.

Of the mental qualities involved, Gilbert ranked highest the ability to create hypotheses. Keen and pertinent observation in the gathering of data itself demands several hypotheses in order that the mind may be focused on significant features. Indeed, hypothesis is virtually implicit in judging what features of a phenomenon are really significant. An observer cannot observe everything. If enough possibilities do not occur to him as he is observing, he may fail entirely to recognize relations of the utmost significance. The bias arising from the inadequate observation will then vitiate all the logical processes to which the data may later be subjected.

Gilbert thus stressed highly the value of the creative imagination. He said,

> The great investigator is primarily and preeminently the man who is rich in hypotheses. In the plenitude of his wealth he can spare the weaklings without regret; and having many from which to select, his mind maintains a judicial attitude. The man who can produce but one, cherishes and champions that one as his own, and is blind to its faults. (1886, p. 287)

Gilbert tried to look into the nature of the scientific guess considered as a mental process. He once asked (1886, p. 286) whether it is possible by training to improve the guessing faculty, and, if so, how. His analysis of his own thinking led him to the conjecture that most, if not all, hypotheses arise from actual or fancied analogies. A newly recognized phenomenon reminds a person, consciously or unconsciously, of another more familiar one whose antecedents and consequents are thought to be understood. The mind swiftly constructs hypotheses in which the antecedents and consequences of the new phenomenon are similarly related to those of the analogue. This important analysis of mental processes had of course been suggested long before by Locke and Hume and had been much emphasized by John Stuart Mill.

Gilbert did not go on in this paper to expand explicitly upon how one is to develop the capacity to recognize abundant analogies among natural phenomena and thereby become fertile in hypotheses. But one may read between the lines of many of his papers and learn that diversified experience, both firsthand and vicarious, was an important catalyst in his own case. One may thus value the widest possible reading as an aid to the creation of hypotheses in the sciences of natural history. Reading furnishes experience, even though secondhand, of a wider range of natural phenomena with which to conjure analogies than could ever be acquired autonomously by a single person. It is impossible to reduce most natural relationships to the shorthand of mathematical equations. Perhaps this accounts for the fact that nearly all studies of scientific productivity show that geologists, botanists, and zoologists in general attain recognition later in life than do chemists, chemists later than physicists, and physicists later than mathematicians. The more complex the phenomena dealt with, the longer the apprenticeship that must be served before mastery. Certainly Gilbert's own growth as an investigator continued until his final illness.

Gilbert was no armchair theorist, but an intensely practical working geologist. He recognized that in our science we must always be satisfied with "as if." Although by implication he probably had the same attitude toward the more exact sciences, he expressed this outlook only with reference to the sciences of natural history. The impossibility of conducting experiments on a geologic scale demands that we must always be satisfied with hypotheses whose validity rests on the fact that they have not yet been proved wrong. Excluding directly observable processes, and even there within embarrassingly narrow limits, we can never assert that a given phenomenon could have arisen only in a single way, but merely that it might so have arisen.

If not influenced by personal motives, the mind naturally prefers the simplest among innumerable possible alternatives. This does not mean, however, that the simplest theory is necessarily correct. Occam's razor is a mental tool, not a touchstone. The simplest is only the momentarily preferred hypothesis and is lightly held pending exhaustive tests. The more numerous the tests that an hypothesis survives and the more abundant the uncontradicted deductions from it, the greater its credibility. Few hypotheses in geology remain simple, after analysis. But in the nature of geologic evidence, a geologic concept, even if it survives enough tests to have the rank of theory, can never be *proved*. On the other hand, a single definite negation is enough to disqualify it. How perilous the way of the geologic innovator!

If, then, the essential elements in Gilbert's philosophy were not new, what were his personal contributions that left so strong an impress on American geology? It seems to me that it was less his philosophical essays themselves than the philosophy he revealed by his superb geologic writings. His influence derived from his fertile imagination, from the logic and clarity with which he presented both his conclusions and the chain of reasoning by which he was led to them, and, not least, in the judicial and essentially undogmatic attitude he retained toward even his own most strongly fortified conclusions.

To detail the reasoning behind a conclusion seemed to him quite as important as the conclusion itself. In fact, one of his most influential papers presented no conclusion at all—it merely reviewed the lines along which the problem of the origin of Coon Butte (now Meteor Crater, Arizona) had been attacked (Gilbert, 1896). He repeatedly stated that review of methods is more valuable than the actual conclusion reached. An hypothesis that one researcher rejects as inadequate may suggest a useful application to another, either in the same problem or elsewhere.

It is thus through his many beautifully reasoned papers that Gilbert made so large an impact upon the science. He presented the facts unfavorable to a tentative thesis quite as prominently as he presented those favorable to it. He followed the logical implications of a phenomenon wherever they might lead, holding himself rigidly impartial.

Of innumerable examples in his work, none is more illustrative of his persistence in tracing the consequences of an hypothesis than the last paper published during his lifetime (1917). Starting with an analysis of the effect of the hydraulic mining debris from the Sierra Nevada on the regimen of the streams in the Sacramento Valley, he found that all of the sediment was trapped at least 50 miles northeast of the Golden Gate. Few geologists assigned to analyze such a problem would follow the subject beyond the point where the fate of all the debris had been determined. Not so with Gilbert. Other consequences were implied; he felt compelled to follow them out.

The several cubic miles of gravel carried to the upper bay were deposited below the level of high tide. They therefore filled several cubic miles of space that formerly had been filled at high tide by water. The tidal prism, the volume of water flowing out on the ebb, was diminished by a very notable fraction. The regimen of the offshore bar at the Golden Gate was therefore affected by the Sierran gravel, even though no gravel had come within 50 miles of the

Golden Gate! The bar had migrated inshore by nearly a mile in fifty years because of weakened tidal currents. Truly a plexus of antecedents and consequents pervades nature!

Through all his work, as his biographer, William Morris Davis (1926, p. 1) said, "It was his habit in presenting a conclusion to expose it as a ball might be placed on the outstretched hand—not gripped as if to prevent its fall, not grasped as if to hurl it at an objector, but poised on the open palm, free to roll off if any breath of disturbing evidence should displace it; yet there it would rest in satisfied stability. Not he, but the facts that he marshaled, clamored for the acceptance of the explanation that he had found for them." Here, in his example, rather than in the novelty of his philosophy, is the reason for the tremendous impact of G. K. Gilbert upon American and world geology.[2]

REFERENCES CITED

COHEN, I. B., 1959, Some reflections on the state of science in America during the Nineteenth Century: Natl. Acad. Sci., Pr., vol. 45, pp. 666–676.

DAVIS, W. M., 1926, Biographical memoir—Grove Karl Gilbert, 1843–1918: Natl. Acad. Sci. Biog. Mem., 5th Mem., vol. 21, 303 pp.

GILBERT, G. K., 1886, The inculcation of scientific method by example, with an illustration drawn from the Quaternary geology of Utah: Am. J. Sci., 3d ser., vol. 31 (whole no. 131), pp. 284–299.

———, 1896, The origin of hypotheses, illustrated by the discussion of a topographic problem: Science, n.s., vol. 3, pp. 1–13.

———, 1917, Hydraulic-mining débris in the Sierra Nevada: U.S. Geol. Survey, Prof. Paper 105, 154 pp.

---

[2] In preparing this discussion I have talked over Gilbert's work with many friends; in this way, I gained many of the ideas here included. Paul Averitt, W. H. Bradley, T. A. Hendricks, C. B. Hunt, W. T. Pecora, and G. D. Robinson have been especially helpful.

J. M. HARRISON
Geological Survey of Canada

Nature and Significance of Geological Maps

A geological map may be defined as one on which are shown the distribution and structural relations of rocks. As such it is the product of research undertaken in the geologists' principal laboratory, the earth itself. And because it describes and interprets the earth, the map must, in the last analysis, be the source of geological theory.

Many text-books and papers have been written on the technique of presenting geological data on maps, and the professional lives of many geologists are devoted to the preparation and interpretation of such maps. Nevertheless, the opinion is widely held that geological mapping is a routine procedure akin to an instrumental survey. Such a concept is extremely misleading. Unlike topographic maps, which record data that can be gathered largely by mechanical, instrumental, or routine methods, the geological map, although in part objective and a record of actual facts, is also to a very large degree subjective, because it also presents the geologist's *interpretation* of these facts and his observations. A good geological map is the result of research of a high order.

The first geological map is variously ascribed to Packe in 1743, to Guettard in 1746, to William Smith in 1801, and to several others, depending on the author's concept of what constitutes a geological map. The first person to study geology by making a map appears to have been Guettard, who, in presenting a paper to the Académie Royale Française in 1746, used a geological map to demonstrate that England and France were part of the same geological region (see Mather and Mason, 1939, pp. 77–78). According to Sir Archibald Geikie (1901, p. 22): "These maps, so far as I know, were the first ever constructed to express the superficial distribution of minerals and rocks. The gifted Frenchman who produced them is thus the father of all the national Geological Surveys . . ." Geikie also noted that, brilliant as were the deductions of Desmarest in 1771 concerning the volcanic origin of Auvergne, his geological map of the region must be considered his most memorable contribu-

225

tion to the progress of geology (p. 75). Most geologists agree, however, that William Smith's map of England and Wales, published in 1815, marked the real beginning of geological mapping. Tomkeieff (1948, p. 256) stated that prior to the publication of Hutton's "Theory of the Earth" in 1788, or to the appearance of William Smith's geological map, geology did not exist as an organized science. Since that day countless geological maps have been prepared and many areas have been surveyed several times, but great land areas of the world are still unmapped, and the geology of the sea floors is virtually unknown.

Any map of the surface of the earth can convey some information on the geology of the area. Air photographs, and the topographic maps derived from them, may show surface characteristics due to faults, folds, varying lithology, and other features, so that a good first approximation of the geology of the area can be obtained by an observer who is familiar with the interpretation of such features. Maps resulting from airborne magnetometer surveys may be useful as interim substitutes for geological maps in areas where geological observations are lacking, and, of course, they are widely used to supplement geological data. Similarly, soil maps and geochemical maps are useful guides to geology. All such maps disclose much about the geology of an area because, in most regions, it is the bedrock that controls the geochemical and geophysical characteristics.

To interpret geology from such maps, a geologist need not see a single rock or rock outcrop. His interpretation is made by applying his geological knowledge and experience to the study of chemical and physical data, topographic forms, colour variations, etc.; he deduces from these observations the physical cause of the observed phenomena. Although these maps are important to a geologist, they are not geological maps in the true sense because they do not portray the geology of the area—geological information is only incidental.

For most people, the geological map, with its scheme of contrasting colours, apparently unequivocal structural symbols, and sharply drawn contacts between rock units, creates the impression that it is, like most other types of maps, a factual and objective record of data derived from observations made on different classes of rocks clearly distinguishable from each other by well-defined physical characteristics. For most geological maps this impression is fallacious. A good geological map is much more than an objective presentation of the distribution of rock units, their structure and their relations; it is also a subjective presentation of interpretations based on a multitude of observations and, to a greater or less degree, based on theories and prejudices held at the time the map was made. This is true of the first maps made by Guettard, Lehmann, Packe, Smith and other pioneers, and it is true of the maps made today. We have accumulated much more knowledge since the days of the pioneers, and we hope we are producing maps more closely approximating the truth. But geological maps are not static or timeless; as the science evolves, so will the maps that portray our evolving concepts.

Consider the preparation of a modern geological map. We may assume the geologist has an accurate topographic map and air photographs, and that he will assemble all available geophysical, geochemical and other useful data pertaining to the area. From these he makes his first interpretative study and produces a rough outline of the geology. With it he plans critical traverses and selects sections for detailed study. Only then will he begin examination of the rocks and deposits themselves, including classification of the different rocks according to their physical characteristics *and his interpretation of their origin.* He must, in other words, decide on his classification before he can show it on the map. He must decide, for example, whether the rock is magmatic or migmatitic, whether it is volcanic or intrusive, whether two rocks represent different formations or different facies of the same formation, whether the rock was formed from a volcanic, marine, or continental sediment, whether it is metamorphic or metasomatic, and so on. The fact that the classification must be made in the field is probably unique in the scientific disciplines. It would indeed be a rash geologist who, in an area of even moderate complexity, would make a geological map based on a collection of hand specimens.

Not only is he concerned with the classification of the rocks, but also with the structural data—relative significance of unconformities, relationship of cleavage to folds and faults, relative movement on faults, age of structural deformation, age of igneous intrusions, and all the complexities of rock relationships. These data, together with those available from geophysics and geochemistry, borehole records, and other sources will be used to extend lithologic and structural units beneath the overburden. Even in areas where rocks are relatively well exposed, only a small part of the bedrock crops out, and these croppings, moreover, are usually not uniformly distributed.

The geologist always collects much more information than he can show on the map, so he must select the data he considers most significant. For example, he determines the mineral assemblages in scores of thin sections so that he may refine his classification of the rocks, or distinguish half a dozen metamorphic facies. These classifications, in turn, lead to conclusions concerning the geological history of the area. He may make a statistical analysis of hundreds of field observations to determine the shape of folds, the position of faults, directions of paleocurrents in ancient seas and rivers, or the significance of fossil assemblages. These investigations constitute the author's laboratory research, and he includes his interpretation of the results on his map along with his interpretations of geochemical analyses, geophysical measurements and isotope abundances.

Finally, the geologist must select the symbols and the scheme of presentation for all this information so that the map will best portray his selection of data

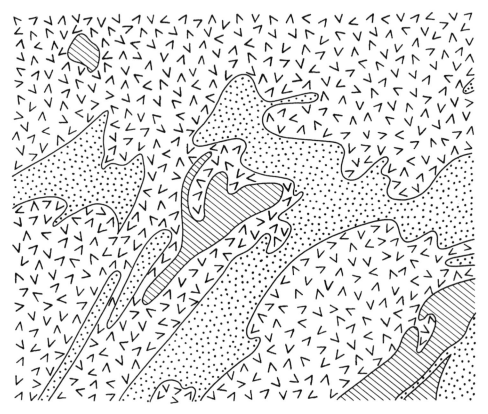

Geologically mapped 1928

 Batholithic intrusions;
granitic rocks, locally
numerous inclusions
of Grenville series

 Basic intrusions

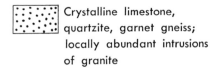 Crystalline limestone,
quartzite, garnet gneiss;
locally abundant intrusions
of granite

Scale of miles

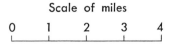

FIG. 1. Two geological maps of the same area in the Canadian Shield.

Geologically mapped 1958

 Granitic rocks

 Granitized rocks, migmatites, etc.; includes some granite

Basic rocks, mainly intrusions

Crystalline limestone, quartzite, paragneiss; includes some granitic and granitized rocks

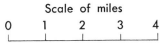

Scale of miles

0   1   2   3   4

FIG. 1 (*Continued*)

and interpretations. They must permit the user to look *into* the map, so that he may visualize the distribution and relationships of the rocks beneath the surface of the earth (Mackin, 1950, p. 55).

When all this material is synthesized, the final product is a lithographed geological map that looks as positive and incontrovertible as a colour photograph, at least to the layman and perhaps also to some geologists. Actually, it represents the sum of analyses made by an individual, using information that never can be complete. The results are conditioned by the "conventional wisdoms" of the day and to that extent the map represents the "geological knowledge at the time of its production" (North, 1928, p. 1). Moreover, in many instances, more than one interpretation can be made of the information presented on the map; another geologist may make interpretations quite different from those of the author and may even see more than the author realized was there.

In most regions, geologists of the same generation would produce similar maps, but if the origin of certain rock units were controversial, and the geologists were products of different schools of geological thought, their maps would be different. For example, the area of "granite" shown on a map of a metamorphic terrain could depend largely on whether the author belonged to a school believing that granites are, in the main, of magmatic origin, or to a school believing they are the product of ultrametamorphism or granitization. This may be an extreme example, but most geological maps to a greater or lesser degree reflect the background and prejudices of the author. Good maps also bring to light weaknesses in theory, or in the interpretation of experimental geology, or in classification. In other words, they lead to their own modification and eventual obsolescence. Certainly later generations of geologists will produce maps different from those of today.

The field geologist, besides providing basic information, is in a good position to appraise theories developed from laboratory work. Unhappily, many field investigators tend to accept the results of laboratory experiments with immoderate faith and to modify their mapping to bring it into accord with experiment and theory. The field man should not forget that the laboratory investigator, in his attempts to simulate geological processes, must extrapolate on a grand scale and thus may make unwarranted assumptions.

An example that comes to mind involves one of the great men of geological science, N. L. Bowen. About 1915 he began publishing the most outstanding petrological contributions of his generation, which culminated in his "The Evolution of the Igneous Rocks," published in 1928. His theories were based almost exclusively on brilliant laboratory research, and they dominated the thinking of nearly all geologists in North America for a generation or more. Too few geologists tested these concepts in the field; many geologists mapped according to them, overlooking all contradictory evidence. It was not until

1947 that enough heat was generated by field geologists to make a symposium on granites the major event at the Annual Meeting of the Geological Society of America in Ottawa (Geol. Soc. Am., Mem., 1948). Partly as an outcome of that meeting, the theory of granitization once more gained recognition among North American geologists, but only because the field evidence demanded its acceptance in opposition to prevailing theory.

For an example of how theory can control mapping see Fig. 1. The two maps, greatly simplified from the originals, are of the same area in the Canadian Shield. The older one was prepared when "magma" was at its apex in North America, the later one by a geologist who had accepted the field evidence for granitization. Part of the discrepancy is due to the more modern realization that some hornblende-rich and pyroxene-rich rocks have been derived from limy sediments. The basic difference, however, is due to the fact that the more recent author shows on the map his conclusions about the origin of the various rocks. Maps that more closely resembled the later edition of these two had been published for other areas by many geologists over a long period. It was the weight of their evidence that made it necessary to accept, in opposition to laboratory theory, the principle of large-scale granitization.

Similarly it was many years before field geologists and laboratory specialists resolved their differences on the temperatures of molten rocks. Laboratory investigations of silicate melts apparently demanded extremely high temperatures, but field geologists insisted that evidences of such temperatures could not be confirmed where magmatic material had invaded solid rocks. Eventually, it was found that addition of small amounts of "mineralizers," mainly water, reduced the temperatures of the melts to the point where they were in accord with the evidence from the earth itself.

To complete North's concept—"The geological map is an index of the extent and accuracy of geological knowledge at the time of its production, and is also the basis of future research. It is the vehicle by which men communicate to one another their discoveries relating to the nature and arrangement of the rocks of the earth's crust, [and it] makes possible the prosecution of further research concerning the distribution of rocks, their origin and the evidence of the life of the past which they may contain . . . The geological map may, therefore, be regarded as the dynamic force in geology." (North, 1928, p. 1)

REFERENCES CITED

Bowen, N. L., 1928, The evolution of the igneous rocks: Princeton, Princeton Univ. Press, 332 pp.

Geikie, *Sir* Archibald, 1901, The founders of geology, vol. 1 of Principles of geology: Baltimore, Johns Hopkins Press, 297 pp.

Geological Society of America, 1948, Origin of granite (James Gilluly, Chm.): Geol. Soc. Am., Mem. 28, 139 pp.

Greenly, Edward, and Williams, Howell, 1930, Methods in geological surveying: London, Thos. Murby, 420 pp.

Ireland, H. A., 1943, History of the development of geologic maps: Geol. Soc. Am., B., vol. 54, pp. 1227–1280.

Linton, D. L., 1948, The ideal geological map: Adv. Sci., vol. 5, no. 18, pp. 141–148.

Mackin, J. H., 1950, The down-structure method of viewing geologic maps: J. Geol., vol. 58, pp. 55–72.

Mather, K. F., and Mason, S. L., 1939, Source book in geology: New York, McGraw-Hill, 702 pp.

North, F. J., 1928, Geological maps, their history and development with special reference to Wales: Cardiff, Nat. Museum, Wales, 133 pp.

Pouba, Zdeněk, 1959, Geologické mapováni: Nakladateství, Československé Akad. Věd, 523 pp., 12 maps. (A complete account of the technique of geological mapping.)

Robertson, Thomas, 1956, Presentation of geological information in maps: Adv. Sci., vol. 13, no. 50, pp. 31–41.

Steiner, W. von, 1957, Zur Geschichte der geologischen Karte: Zs. Angew. Geol., nos. 8/9, pp. 417–424.

Tomkeieff, S. I., 1948, James Hutton and the philosophy of geology: Edinburgh Geol. Soc., Tr., vol. 14, pt. 2, pp. 253–276.

Wells, J. W., 1959, Earliest geological maps of the United States, 1756–1832: Washington Acad. Sci., J., vol. 49, pp. 198–204.

Woodward, H. B., 1911, History of geology: London, Watts, 154 pp.

ARTHUR F. HAGNER

University of Illinois

Philosophical Aspects of the Geological Sciences[1]

The geologic approach to nature raises some interesting philosophical questions, and at the same time exemplifies a point of view which should contribute to the thought and progress of other fields, if it can be clearly delineated. An attractive area of knowledge, still relatively unexplored, invites analysis and evaluation.

Intellectual Contributions of Geology

In the eighteenth and nineteenth centuries, geologists generated concepts that commanded universal attention. A venerable belief in an earth no older than a few thousand years, formed almost instantaneously by providential action, had long suppressed philosophic and scientific thought. Prior to the time of Hutton, moreover, it was generally believed that this brief past had been marked by extensive and violent changes, unlike any taking place today. Surface features of the earth were explained in terms of the Deluge. Erosion, the effects of glaciation in regions where today the climate is warm, and the presence of fossils on mountains were all attributed to Noah's flood. Geologic discoveries, and the resulting controversies in science and religion, led to a gradual abandonment of these beliefs.

Before James Hutton's "Theory of the Earth" appeared in 1788, natural philosophy was based more on speculation than observation. Hutton's uniformitarianism made it possible to explain earth features as a result of long-continued but ordinary processes, as opposed to extraordinary forces or cata-

[1] I would like to thank Dr. D. M. Henderson for carefully reading the manuscript and for offering suggestions that materially improved it. Dr. Norman Page contributed time and suggestions during the early stages of writing and preparation. A number of the authors of this volume have furnished helpful comments and criticism. I also wish to thank those graduate students in geology at the University of Illinois who took part in the informal and stimulating discussions on philosophy of science that were held during the academic year 1960–1961.

clysms. Speculations slowly gave way to careful observations, correlations, and substantiated interpretations. It was not, however, until the publication of Lyell's "Principles of Geology" in 1830–1833 that the revolution in this science became widespread and effective. By the middle of the nineteenth century "a satisfactory geological philosophy in the inorganic world had been attained and established on a solid foundation of observation, so far as the criteria of the times would allow. In the organic field the bomb-shell had not yet burst." (Gordon, 1951)

The idea of progressive change and development with time, as applied to physical science, has matured with the growth of modern geology. Previously historians had discussed the idea of progress, but only casually. When Hutton spoke of seeing no signs of a beginning or of an end, he realized that time was needed to produce many geologic phenomena—more time than scientists and philosophers were prepared to concede. The idea of *geologic time* enabled Darwin to construct his theory of evolution on a scientific foundation. "The principle of Uniformitarianism had to be clearly established, or else the history of life of the past could have a thousand interpretations based on physical conditions entirely dissimilar to those of the present." (Garrels, 1951) It was Lyell's *Principles*, then, that set the stage for Darwin and greatly influenced his ideas. "A long history of life on the earth, undisturbed by repeated world-wide catastrophies, no longer required successive creations of all living organisms . . . The possibility of the progressive development of life on the earth could no longer be dismissed." (Thomas, 1947) The idea of geologic time, perhaps the greatest contribution of geology to general thought, has been compared in importance with the astronomers' realization of the vastness of space and with the physicists' concept of the relationship between matter and energy. (Stokes, 1960, p. 5)

Geology thus made a major contribution to both science and philosophy by introducing the idea of history into science. Prior to the nineteenth century, science had been concerned largely with the present. Not until geologists introduced the concept that the earth *has* a history was it possible to develop a systematized knowledge of the remote past. Geology demonstrated that it is possible to study the past by scientific methods and that there "is a validity to history apart from and independent of physics and chemistry . . . The theory of evolution was a historical idea, not a law of nature. Its validity was to be tested by other criteria than those of mechanics." (Schneer, 1960, pp. 377–378)

Characteristic Features of Geologic Methodology and Reasoning

In discussing the nature of geology, Chamberlin (1904) observed that "Not a little consists of generalizations from incomplete data, of inferences hung on chains of uncertain logic, of interpretations not beyond question, of hypotheses not fully verified, and of speculations none too substantial. A part of the mass is true science, a part philosophy . . . a part is speculation, and a part is yet unorganized material." This remains true today, although the science is generally more quantitative and its generalizations and interpretations stand on a somewhat firmer basis of fact. Nevertheless many geologic theories rest on what Chamberlin (1904) referred to as "the working test" and Geikie (1905) called "a balance of probabilities." Often the geologist's explanation turns on his judgment in selecting the most likely working hypothesis and revising it as data accumulate. Consequently, as stressed by Bemmelen (1961), the personal capacity of the scientist is more important here than in sciences which rely mainly on instruments and do not use an historical approach to their problems. Geology has had to advance more by observation, description, and classification than by experiment and calculation.

The geologist has to work in an intellectual environment to which many other physical scientists are unaccustomed. In order to understand the nature of geologic problems and concepts, one must learn to live with uncertainty to a degree not imposed by problems involving closed systems, isolated variables, verifiable experiments, and the statistical treatment of large numbers of observable occurrences. Of the physical scientists, moreover, the geologist is most often confronted with the problem of working with *end products*, which result from the interplay of many complex variables. It is usually difficult to isolate the variables for realistic experimentation. Commonly there are more variables than the number of parameters needed to reach a solution, and these operate over extreme ranges of magnitude.

Geology differs from other sciences mainly in its concern with time. Processes and reactions that may take place so slowly as to be practically unobservable in the laboratory may be of great importance when given many millions of years of operation. Often the geologist must try to determine whether a phenomenon resulted from an intense process that acted through a short time, or whether the process operated at lower intensity over a longer period. Can he directly relate short-term laboratory experiments to natural phenomena that may have required an almost infinitely greater amount of time? Is he justified in speeding up the rate of an experiment in order to reduce the time factor? The geologist must rely not only on the soundness of his experiments, but also on the realization that, given enough time, many phenomena experimentally unreproducible at present *can* materialize in nature. A positive mental effort is always required to view problems in their proper temporal perspective.

Another major difference between the viewpoint of the geologist and that of other scientists is that the former commonly finds it necessary to "predict the past." Bubnoff (1959) believes that the principal difference between geology and other physical sciences "lies in the fact that geology not only must explain the contemporary situation by means of contemporary phenomena, but it must also observe and point out a genesis, a process which takes place in time and of which the different stages cannot be reached by us through immediate observation." Umbgrove (1947) has compared the geologist with the historian who reconstructs the past by using available data, and where these are incomplete, employs temporary constructs to bridge missing data. "Since many earth phenomena cannot be verified experimentally, and commonly the geologist cannot 'get at' the problem directly, it is necessary for him to use various indirect methods of analysis . . . These methods of reasoning and 'explaining' are necessary because the geologist deals with time and scale factors beyond human experience." (Hagner, 1961)

Physicists and chemists are accustomed to contemplate and manipulate exceedingly minute objects. While this is true to some extent of geologists, they must also attempt to conceive of the relative size and behavior of units of matter much larger than the observer. One may observe the tracks of atoms in a cloud chamber, but it will probably be some time yet before man can adequately observe a continent in motion. Scale in geology ranges from the submicroscopic to the planetary, from the structure of crystals to the structure of the earth.

In geology there is a rapidly growing trend toward quantification; nevertheless, geology differs from some of the other sciences in the lesser degree to which quantitative data are available. In this connection, many scientists seem to believe that qualitative data are wholly subjective, whereas quantitative data are objective. But, as Birch (1951) has said, "No one ever discovered a quality apart from a quantity nor a quantity apart from a quality. Why, then, are we so anxious to adopt the weird hypothesis that the quantitative is objective and real but the qualitative only subjective?" Geologists are deeply interested in this matter because they must deal with an "indispensible core of qualitative observation that forms the foundation of virtually every geological study . . ." (Krumbein, 1960)

As already stated, the physicists and chemists have been concerned largely with problems of the present and with a time scale closely related to that of the observer. It has been said that these sciences have been successful in the main because they have deliberately restricted their temporal scope, thus avoiding the kinds of problems that cannot be approached by experiment. The geologist, however, cannot escape such problems and, despite the complexity of earth phenomena and the incomplete record of earth history, he has succeeded largely by qualitative methods in establishing concepts which have withstood the test of time and which, in some cases, have been verified experimentally.

Perhaps the most important factor in the progress of geology has been the development of a "geologic frame of mind." This is acquired almost of necessity in the day-to-day effort of thinking about immense periods of time, very large units of matter, and the interplay of complex variables. Since it is impossible in geology to duplicate nature in the laboratory, natural phenomena are commonly studied as units. Where possible, factors are isolated for analysis, but since it is impossible to bring a mountain into the laboratory, experimentation plays a less important role than it does in physics and chemistry. The study of nature as a whole calls for the kind of reasoning in which *all* the variables are considered insofar as possible, even though this makes it necessary "to supplement in thought partially available facts." (Mach, 1903) The coordination of directly observable data with unobservable data by mental supplements has yielded models sufficiently useful to predict the location of subsurface oil, gas, and mineral occurrences.

Although interpretations of the evolution of mountains, basins, and the crust of the earth itself must be based on physical laws, there are many things connected with these and other gross features of the earth "that cannot be squeezed into a formula and can only be described." (Bertalanfly, 1952) As Bemmelen (1961, p. 458) has said,

> ... matter reacted upon matter in an infinite number of combinations in such a way that ultimately new possibilities and new factors originated, so-called 'emergent phenomena.' The latter cannot straight away be explained by the natural laws of the basic sciences ... the natural sciences tend to possess a certain type of hierarchy in which the rules and laws of the simpler stages are also valid for the higher organized ones, but not vice versa.

Because the earth does not behave like a stone, geologists have proceeded on the basis that, unless truly fundamental and pertinent physical laws are violated, geologic evidence must be accepted at face value. "In many instances, such as the controversies in the nineteenth century over the age of the earth and the thickness and rigidity of its crust, history has shown the geologists to have been more nearly correct than the other physical scientists." (Hagner, 1961)

Geologic concepts and theories differ greatly in the completeness and quantity of data or observations on which they are based, and consequently in their reliability and general acceptance. The theory of magmatic differentiation by crystal settling and crystal fractionation, for example, is well substantiated both by field observations and by experimental evidence. For any theory of mountain-building, however, there is no general agreement, because the data on which it rests are fragmentary. Consequently there are few rigorous laws applicable to large-scale earth phenomena.

Physics and chemistry deal largely with processes and the prediction of results from the action of these. For example, a basic assumption of thermodynamics is that it is necessary to know only the state of a system and the conditions imposed on it in order to predict the result—no knowledge of the "path" of the process is required. Geology deals with macroprocesses made up of many subsidiary dynamic processes. The observable end product is the sum of serial microprocesses that operated along a particular, often tortuous, path. The study of history in science is the diagnosis of pathways. Many lines of geologic evidence suggest that two different paths may lead to approximately the same kind of end product, e.g., the formation of granite by different processes. Such a possibility runs counter to a belief, perhaps intuitively held in some sciences, that distinctive end products generally form in only one way.

It is interesting to note that in the twentieth century, physicists have come to suspect that their reasoning and subject matter have been too restricted. The immensity of time, for example, has received much attention in the theory of relativity. Today the theoretical physicist must infer the unobservable. He is increasingly concerned with phenomena that cannot be transferred into actual sense perceptions and tested by direct experience. Like the geologist, he must "supplement in thought partially available facts." Major advances in physics and chemistry may well come as a result of concentrating on the whole rather than its smallest parts. This will call for reasoning more akin to that of the philosopher, historian, geologist, and biologist than is customary today among most physicists and chemists.

The Position of Geology Today

During the twentieth century a number of new concepts of general application and great fundamental importance have arisen both in physics and biology. These new ideas or principles pertain to all of science, not merely to one particular area of investigation. Although geology has advanced greatly during this period, it has produced little or nothing of similar significance. This is somewhat surprising, for many of the new ideas have long been implicit in some fields of geologic research and in many lines of geologic reasoning.

Recently emphasis has been placed by certain biologists (Bertalanffy, 1952) on a whole or organismic concept of nature—the organic idea of Whitehead— as opposed to an analytical point of view. This idea stresses the importance of the relations between the individual parts of an organism or system, and shows that a complete description of the organism must include the laws governing these relations as well as the laws governing the behavior of the component parts. Coupled with this idea is that of structure and form as temporary manifestations of the interaction of processes proceeding at different rates. It is the process that is fundamental, and nature so viewed is dynamic rather than static. At the same time the concept of open systems has been fitted into this general scheme, the organism being viewed as a locus of interacting processes maintaining itself in a steady state of minimal entropy by the constant dissipation of energy. Ideas of hierarchy of order have been formulated, each level with its own set of laws transcending those of the lower levels.

These concepts deal with more complex organizations of matter than are usually considered in physics, but they deny neither the basically statistical character of the laws of nature in the microphysical realm, nor the discontinuous nature of primary events. Physical concepts have been incorporated into modern biology, with necessary attention to the biological factors involved. Even Bohr's complementarity principle, the idea that sometimes nature cannot be described by one concept but rather by pairs of opposed and complementary concepts, has found an application in biology. Just as in physics both the wave and particle descriptions of matter apparently are equally necessary and valid, so in biology the organismic and physicochemical approaches appear to be required for understanding.

Geologists have dealt with these concepts in a qualitative manner and in varying degrees of explicitness, but apparently this has not been fully appreciated by scientists in other disciplines, or even by geologists themselves. Geology, too, is particularly concerned with the interaction of processes of different rates, and it has long been realized that a description of only one process operating in an area is incomplete and may be misleading unless its relations to other processes are known. In other words, the concept of the whole is reaffirmed. There has also been a continuing consideration among geologists of the relative importance of uniformity and catastrophism in nature. This is evident in such fields as tectonics, paleontology, and stratigraphy; in fact, when dealing with geologic periods of time, this consideration can rarely be avoided. In perhaps no other branch of science is the transitory nature of form and structure so clearly realized as in geology. Most geologic systems are "open" in that both matter and energy may move freely in and out of them, although there is a constant approach to temporary or local equilibrium. This approach to local equilibrium is a major unifying concept in geology.

Today, "Geology is in a period of unprecedented discovery . . . and traditional views concerning the physical and chemical processes that have produced and are now moulding the earth's crust are now being challenged . . . there is an atmosphere of fascinated suspense today such as has always marked the high points on the growth curve of a science." (Bucher, 1950) Major advances in geology can indeed be expected. Research methods and techniques are much more precise than those of the past; consequently it has become possible to analyze physical and chemical processes and phenomena more accurately than when these were amenable only to speculation or reasoning from inadequate qualitative information. Major contributions to our knowledge of continental growth and movement, the nature of the earth's interior, and the distribution and movement of material in the earth's crust are to be expected. Today the heredity principle is being applied to such diverse phenomena as tectonism, igneous processes, hydrothermal activity, and the inheritance of properties by successive mineral phases. Pospelov (1961) has discussed the concept of multistage geologic complexes as having validity on a global as well as regional scale. The concept of paragenesis has been enlarged and becomes "the basis of the theory of geologic formations, metallogenic complexes, etc. It pervades the entire problem of relationships between igneous activity and mineralization, between metamorphism and tectonics." Pospelov has also stated that "geology has come face to face with an understanding of the higher type of geologic form of motion, i.e., an understanding of the active self-development of the earth."

In spite of the marked progress of geology during the twentieth century, its relative position among the sciences has declined. This is partly a result of the spectacular findings in such fields as quantum physics and molecular biology. But other factors have contributed to this decline and some of these are attributable to disinterest and negligence on the part of geologists. Geology, perhaps more than other sciences, has suffered from a fragmentation into numerous semi-independent disciplines, so that geology is now essentially a group of sciences. Concurrently with fragmentation, the boundaries between geology and other sciences have been disappearing, and new names have been given to the interdisciplinary fields. The subject matter of some of these vigorous hybrids—geophysics, geochemistry, microcrystallography—has been defined so as to include the more concrete aspects of geology that can be studied by mathematical, physicochemical, and statistical methods. What is arbitrarily left under the label "geology" thus constitutes the less definite, more uncertain aspects of the science.

Need for Studies in the History and Philosophy of Geology

Geologists have accumulated vast amounts of data and are faced with much unorganized material requiring analysis and synthesis. Scientists in other disciplines are concerned with the possibility of achieving not only synthesis in their fields, but also a unification of all science. Because geology rests in part on physics, chemistry, and biology, in addition to being a science in its own right, the geologist is in an excellent position to appreciate attempts to unify science and to contribute to them. But geologists have published essentially nothing on this challenging subject. Is this field of knowledge also to be preempted by other scientists and philosophers to the exclusion of geologists?

Geology must elucidate its uniqueness of approach, demonstrate the ways it has contributed ideas of interest to all sciences, and formulate and name these ideas as specific principles or concepts. We must show wherein we deal with nature in general. We need to be more self-analytical in our processes of reasoning, as scientists in other disciplines have been. Recently a few studies have appeared on the problems of sampling, scale, time and measurement in the geosciences, but long overdue are searching analyses of the nature of geologic concepts, methods, reasoning, evidence, and interpretation. In other words, we should take inventory of the nature, subject matter, accomplishments, and directions of geology. There is an obvious need for fundamental thinking *about* geology.

Chamberlin (1904) has said "an appropriate atmosphere of philosophy . . . is necessary to the wholesome intellectual life of our science . . ." Study of the history and philosophy of science would add "perspective to the succession of facts as well as methods" and expose the "bond which holds scientific thought together." (Margenau, 1960) By history is meant the tracing of the development and interaction of ideas among different disciplines. The very nature of geology and its methods of study, in part historical and philosophical, should encourage the geologist to examine the evolution and substance of his ideas.

REFERENCES CITED

BEMMELEN, R. W. VAN, 1961, The scientific character of geology: J. Geol., vol. 69, pp. 453–461.

BERTALANFFY, L. VON, 1952, Problems of life, an evaluation of modern biological thought: London, Watts, 216 pp.

BIRCH, L. C., 1951, Concept of nature: Am. Scientist, vol. 39, pp. 294–302.

BUBNOFF, S. VON, 1959, Grundprobleme der Geologie: Berlin, Akademie-Verlag, 234 pp.

BUCHER, W. H., 1950, The crust of the earth: Sci. American, vol. 182, no. 5, pp. 32–41.

CHAMBERLIN, T. C., 1904, The methods of the earth-sciences: Popular Sci. Monthly, vol. 66, pp. 66–75.

GARRELS, R. M., 1951, A textbook of geology: New York, Harper, 511 pp.

GEIKIE, Sir ARCHIBALD, 1905, The founders of geology: London, Macmillan, 486 pp.

GORDON, W. T., 1951, Geology, *in*, H. Dingle, ed., A century of science: London, Hutchinson's Scientific and Technical Publ., pp. 98–113.

HAGNER, A. F., 1961, Geologic education and its influence on approaches to geologic problems: J. Geol. Educ., vol. 9, pp. 89–97.

KRUMBEIN, W. C., 1960, The "geological population" as a framework for analyzing numerical data in geology: Liverpool and Manchester Geol. J., vol. 2, pp. 341–368.

MACH, E., 1903, *quoted in* Schrödinger, Erwin, What is life? and other scientific essays: New York, Doubleday, 1956, 263 pp.

MARGENAU, H., 1960, Foreword to, The search for order, by C. J. Schneer: New York, Harper, xii pp.

POSPELOV, G. L., 1961, Geology as a science and its place in natural history: Izvestiya Acad. Sci., USSR, Geol. Ser., 1960, (trans. Nov., 1961), pp. 1–11.

SCHNEER, C. J., 1960, The search for order: New York, Harper, 398 pp.

STOKES, W. L., 1960, An introduction to historical geology: New Jersey, Prentice-Hall, 502 pp.

THOMAS, H. H., 1947, The rise of geology and its influence on contemporary thought: Ann. Sci., vol. 5, pp. 325–341.

UMBGROVE, J. H. F., 1947, The pulse of the earth: The Hague, Nijhoff, 358 pp.

ROBERT F. LEGGET

National Research Council of Canada

Geology in the Service of Man

From the dawn of history, the development of the human race has involved close contact with the earth. On the surface of the earth man has made his home, from the time of the earliest mud hut to the present day with its towering skyscrapers providing eyries for urban dwellers. From mines excavated within the upper few thousand feet of the earth's crust, man has obtained his fuels for heat and power, his precious metals for barter, his serviceable metals for use and decoration, and much of the material he has needed for building. Upon the ground he has developed his transportation routes, from the earliest paths between forest settlements to the great highways, railways, and airports of today, boring tunnels through the hills when necessary, bridging streams and valleys, making the crooked straight, and the rough places plain. And the foundations of all the structures ever built by man, from the simplest sacrificial altar of primitive man to launching sites for rockets aimed at the moon, depend for their essential stability upon their contact with the earth.

As man's mind developed and a sense of inquiry was generated into problems beyond that of daily subsistence, it was natural that the character of the ground on which he walked and lived and had his being should engage his lively interest. From such vague wonderings has developed the science of geology as it is known today. So intimate would appear to be the links between the study of the earth's crust and the daily activities of man that the inclusion of such a paper as this in a commemorative volume might at first sight appear to be superfluous. Geological studies might be thought always to be prosecuted in the service of man. Indirectly, this is probably true, but in the recent history of the science there appears to have been a tendency in some quarters to regard geological inquiry as the end in itself; its application to the activities of man as a slightly degrading use of pure scientific endeavour. A review of the way in which geology has developed through the ages, with special reference to its practical applications, may not therefore be out of place in this collection of papers prepared in recognition of the seventy-fifth anniversary of a society devoted to the promotion of geology in all its aspects. For the wheel appears to have turned full circle.

The beginnings of geology were rooted in the practical demands of early man; the early days of the modern science led to the flowering of pure geological study, much of it far removed from any thought of application; while today the practice of modern engineering in many of its branches is making such demands upon geology that there are now organized groups of petroleum and engineering geologists. The challenge of the next few decades gives promise of still wider use of geology in the service of man, concurrently with its advance and development as one of the truly great branches of natural science.

The fact that "earth" was one of Aristotle's four elements is a clear indication of the importance with which the Greeks regarded the study of the ground. Equally revealing are the frequent references to rock, stone, and soil in the "History" of Herodotus. He knew personally the great stone quarries near Memphis and "observed that there were shells upon the hills" during his stay in Egypt. Was he the first palaeontologist? He might equally have been the first to observe sulphate attack on structures, for he records that he saw "that salt exuded from the soil to such an extent as even to injure the pyramids." He certainly appreciated the engineering significance of geology, for he makes quite a few references to unusual excavation and river-diversion works carried out by warlike monarchs. Cyrus and his diversion of the Euphrates provide but one example. Two of the early queens of Babylon were similarly active, Semiramis who constructed massive flood-control embankments of soil, and the beautiful Nitrocris, who also diverted the Euphrates, but only temporarily, while its natural channel through the city was lined with bricks of burnt clay and a bridge of stone built over it "in the dry." (Herodotus, trans., 1910)

The contributions of Aristotle to early geological thought have often been quoted. Even though it seems probable that his own book on rocks and minerals was lost, it is pleasant to imagine that it was Aristotle who inspired Alexander to send out the special force that he directed to survey his empire, collecting information on the "natural history" of the districts in which they were at work, while maintaining the condition of the main roads. Anyone who has had the privilege of following Alexander's route down the Kabul River from what is now Afghanistan and then across the plains of Pakistan through Peshawar to Lahore can have no doubt that a lively appreciation of geology must have been yet another attribute of that commanding figure of history.

That these are not isolated cases from classical records of two thousand years ago can be shown by reference to Vitruvius, a Roman architect and engineer, of whom almost nothing is known except his famous "Ten Books on Architecture," believed to have been written in the first century B.C. Some of his comments on geological matters are almost uncanny in their modernity. He could well be the patron saint of the geobotanists, for he relates (Book I, Chapter V) that cattle on two sides of the river Pothereus, in Crete, were found to differ in their spleens. Physicians found the explanation in an herb which grew on one side of the river but not on the other. "From food and water, then, we may learn whether sites are naturally unhealthy or healthy" is his prophetic conclusion. (Vitruvius, trans., 1914)

His treatise includes a lengthy section on natural building materials; most of his Book II is devoted to this subject. One would expect to find descriptions of sand, lime, stone, and pozzolana, but who would expect to find—in a book written almost two thousand years ago—the suggestion that "since the stones are soft and porous, they are apt to suck the moisture out of the mortar and so to dry it up" (a lesson not yet learned by all modern builders)? Somewhat less scientific are the instructions that Vitruvius records for the construction of dining room floors, "filled in with charcoal compactly trodden down, a mortar mixed of gravel, lime, and ashes is spread on to a depth of half a foot (giving) the look of a black pavement. Hence, at dinner parties, whatever is poured out of cups, or spirted from the mouth, no sooner falls than it dries up, and the servants who wait there do not catch cold from that kind of floor, although they may go barefoot."

The "Ten Books" of Vitruvius not only reflected the high standard of Roman engineering at the time he wrote, but almost certainly exercised considerable influence upon its continued excellence. For several centuries after he wrote, the works of Roman engineers played their part in forming the Europe that is known today. Many miles of Roman roads and many examples of major Roman structures still stand and serve despite the passage of the centuries. The fact that there are no known examples of cyclopean or polygonal Roman masonry, all examples of Roman building extant being of rectangular blocks of stone set in regular courses, suggests that Roman engineers had a lively appreciation of the importance of the proper selection of building stone and its quarrying; their careful and selective use of travertine provides one specific example. Their discovery of the unusual properties of the volcanic ash in the vicinity of Naples, now called pozzolana but then *pulvis Puteolanus*, and especially the combination of this material with lime, opened up new prospects for Roman building and led to such masterpieces as the Pantheon. And although tunneling was not frequently an activity of the Romans, such tunnels as they are known to have constructed demonstrate fairly clearly an appreciation of the geology of the rocks penetrated. The use of vinegar poured over heated limestone as a means of excavation, barbaric in its effect upon slave workers but effective when used on the right type of rock, provides one unusual illustration.

It may be said that these examples are not of the applications of geology to the works of man, but merely incidents in the development of the ordinary practice of engineering; the name *geology* did not come into use for another thousand years. But may not the same comment be made about the early phases of all major branches of science and their applications? Chemistry and physics did not spring full blown into the experience of man but started haltingly through the probing inquiries of interested men; as a matter of fact, the general acceptance of the terms "physics" and "chemistry" and their recognition as distinct disciplines are relatively recent developments. One would imagine that geology acquired such a lead over those other branches of science, however, that it would have remained in the van of scientific development throughout the centuries. This was not to be. The grandeur of Rome departed. Human development entered its long centuries of delayed advance. Recent historical studies are showing that the so-called Dark Ages were not devoid of all progress, as is so often imagined, but the tempo of development was sadly slowed throughout the Western world. There were advances in other parts of the world, some of great significance, but for a thousand years or more Western man seemed to be content with the physical world as he knew it, and the minds that probed and the hands that experimented were few indeed. When one takes a general look at the growth of scientific thought during this long period, such as is so splendidly afforded by Charles Singer's eloquent volume, "A Short History of Scientific Thought to 1900," the retarded position of geological study in what little scientific advance did take place becomes all the more puzzling.

The Arab world, even though it contributed so notably to mathematical and astronomical knowledge, appears to have had very little interest in the study of the earth. It seems probable that the attitude of the Christian Church prior to the Reformation may have retarded geological studies. And yet as one stands in one of the great mediaeval abbey churches, still in use today as cathedrals in all their beauty, it is difficult to imagine that the learned monks who built them accepted without question the varied stones that were quarried for them and which they set in place with such obvious skill. To see in Wells Cathedral in the west of England, for example, the great inverted arches beneath the central tower, installed as a preventive measure in the fourteenth century, fills one with admiration not only for the skill in building they represent but also for the remarkable way in which the monks were able to obviate a catastrophic foundation failure which they must have envisaged as they developed their unique solution.

The records remain silent, however, and so the mystery of geological neglect must stand. Even the renaissance of learning in western Europe failed to change this strange stagnation of geological inquiry. Leonardo da Vinci quite naturally applied his unique genius to the study of the earth, as to so much else. His first observations on mountains were recorded in the year 1508 but, again as in other fields, his acute observations failed to lead to any general awakening of geological study. It was, indeed, not until the nineteenth century was well started that the first general stirrings of real interest in the earth's crust and in its constituents are to be found. And yet, by this time, Laplace had published his monumental "Celestial Mechanics," the most comprehensive survey of astronomical knowledge ever made and a work that can be studied with profit even today.

The contrast is indeed striking, so remarkable in fact that it demands an explanation. Could it be that, unlike the case with these other sciences, the awakening of modern geological study had to await the start of the industrial age and the practical demands of modern engineering for information about the earth's crust and the materials in it? At first sight, such a suggestion might appear to be verging on the absurd, so subservient have been the applications of geology to the prosecution of basic geological studies until comparatively recent years. When, however, the records of the great pioneers of geology are studied, some warrant for the suggestion becomes immediately apparent.

It is, for example, well known that the first of these modern "giants of geology" (as they have been happily called), Abraham Gottlob Werner, was appointed as an inspector of mines and instructor in mining and mineralogy at the Freiburg Academy in 1775 when he was only twenty-five years old. Here he conducted his famous classes for almost forty years until the disturbances in the wake of Napoleon's army of occupation made it impossible for him to continue. His skill as a teacher has never been questioned, even though some of the theories he taught became the centre of great controversy. His teaching, however, was specifically related to the application of geology in mining so that he was essentially an applied geologist. Even his antipathy to writing and his procrastination in relation to what little he did write fore-shadowed all too clearly what has (unfortunately) become almost a characteristic of those concerned with the application of the science of geology in the service of man. (Fenton, 1952)

It is, however, not so generally recognized that Werner's great Scottish antagonist, James Hutton, came to enjoy his interest in geology by way of a very practical route; his importance in the general picture of unfolding geological theory obscured his earlier interests in applied geology. After his early training in medicine and his disappointment at the prospects he saw in the medical profession, he turned to his friend James Davie and shared an interest with him in the production of sal ammoniac, while at the same time he farmed the small estate left to him by his father. To this latter task he applied his unusual scientific acumen, traveling extensively in Europe to study the most advanced farming methods he could find. His farm became a show place; and it is clear beyond all reasonable doubt that his farming activity introduced Hutton to the scientific study of the earth, for he certainly noticed the relation of soil properties to the character of the underlying rocks, as well as the insidious effects of soil erosion. When he rented his farm in 1768 and moved to Edinburgh to devote himself to his scientific studies, he was forty-two years old, with much valuable experience behind him and his geological interests fully awakened through his practical activities and particularly his scientific farming.

D'Aubuisson and von Buch, having been students of Werner, might be expected to have had interest in the applications of geology in mining. Von Buch actually spent a year as inspector of mines in Silesia before coming into the inheritance which gave him the freedom to pursue his scientific interests as he wished. It is well known that when, in 1818, Adam Sedgwick was elected to the chair of geology at Cambridge, he knew little of the science, his sound classical education having apparently won his election. But he was very soon learning his geology in the field, and he started in British lead mines, proceeding to study the copper mines of Staffordshire and then the great salt mines at Northwich in Cheshire. In his later years, even Sir Charles Lyell did not disdain to study accidents in mines, despite the many demands upon his time and his extensive travels.

Of even more significance is the fact that in his presidential address to the Geological Society of London in February 1836, Lyell, after announcing the award of the Wollaston Medal to Agassiz, went on to record his own part in the formation of the Geological Survey of England, the first national geological survey to be formed in the world:

> Early in the spring of last year application was made by the Master General and Board of Ordnance to Dr. Buckland and Mr. Sedgwick, as Professors of Geology in the Universities of Oxford and Cambridge, and to myself, as President of this Society, to offer our opinion as to the expediency of combining a geological examination of the English counties with the geographical survey now in progress. In compliance with this requisition we drew up a joint report, in which we endeavoured to state fully our opinion as to the great advantages which must accrue from such an undertaking not only as calculated to promote geological science, which would alone be a sufficient object, but also as a work of great practical utility, bearing on agriculture, mining, road-making, the formation of canals and railroads, and other branches of national industry. (Lyell, 1836, p. 358)

It is, perhaps, of even more significance to find a parallel development in the start of modern civil engineering. The great British pioneer in this field was originally a Yorkshire stone mason. John Smeaton (1724–1792) developed such skill in the design and construction of notable structures that he is widely regarded as the first civil engineer. His masterpiece was the first stone Eddystone Lighthouse, the remains of which may still be seen standing on Plymouth Hoe. His stone tower was built between 1756 and 1759. Many features of its construction are noteworthy, such as Smeaton's research into the Roman use of pozzolana and his use of the same material. Fortunately, Smeaton wrote an account of the entire project and the geological insights that this record contains are revealing indeed. His own training as a stone mason could be held to account for the detail in which he describes his search for the correct type of stone of which to build the lighthouse, but the way in which he examined the treacherous rock on which he had to build the structure goes far beyond what a mason might have been expected to do, especially in such an early and pioneer venture. Smeaton's own words are worthy of brief quotation:

> The congeries of rocks called Edystone appear to me to be all of the same kind of stone, and of a kind so peculiar that I have not seen any stone exactly like it in Cornwall or Devonshire . . . It differs from the Moorstone in this; instead of being composed of grains or small fragments, united by a strong cement, interspersed with a shining talky substance, as the Cornish moorstone appears to be; it is composed of the like matter formed into laminae commonly from one twentieth to one sixth part of an inch in thickness . . . as is nearly one foot dip to the westward, in two feet horizontal, that is, in an angle of about 26 degrees with the horizon. (Smeaton, 1791, p. 12)

These are the words of a practical civil engineer writing as early as 1791.

The nineteenth century had opened before engineering work really began to transform the physical face of Europe, but the appreciation of geology so well demonstrated by John Smeaton was shared by other leaders in the newly developing profession of civil engineering. Canal and road building created much building activity in Great Britain.

James Loudon McAdam was one of the towering practical road builders of these early days. He, too, published a record of his ideas on road building, a book that went through nine editions. A keenly developed sense of geological appreciation permeates the book, such as in this statement about road-building materials:

> Flint makes an excellent road, if due attention be paid to the size, but from want of attention, many of the flint roads are rough, loose and expensive. Limestone when properly prepared and applied makes a smooth solid road and becomes consolidated sooner than any other material; but from its nature it is not the most lasting. Whinstone is the most durable of all materials; and wherever it is well and judiciously applied, the roads are comparatively good and cheap. (McAdam, 1823, p. 20)

Thomas Telford, undoubtedly the greatest of these early British civil engineers, a man whose fame led to his being invited to undertake work in Sweden and other European countries, was a man of action rather than words. Fortunately, in addition to his own brief writings, we have records of his character and works from other writers, amongst them Robert Southey, the English poet. He accompanied Telford on an inspection tour, in 1819, through the Scottish Highlands, where Telford was responsible for many projects including the

Caledonian Canal. Southey kept a journal and this has been published privately by the Institution of Civil Engineers. To find regular geological references in a journal kept by the Poet Laureate of England suggests that they must have been a regular part of the conversation of the two friends as Telford, the engineer, explained to Southey, the poet, details of the many works they had examined together. Southey noted that a new pier at Bervie Harbour was being constructed of "pudding stone . . . of all stone it is the worst for working; but it is hard and durable, and when in place will do as well as if it were granite or marble." They saw a new bridge at Forres "built of granite of all colours . . . (near to which is) a bank of granite, in such a state of decomposition, or imperfect composition, that it crumbles at a touch." Southey tells how Telford advised a laird in Skye about developing a marble deposit, saving him from great expenditure by persuading him to make first an experimental shipment to London. And in a deposit of "marle" near Inverness they found it to be "full of very small shells, some resembling whelks, others like the fresh water muscle, but all very small." (Southey, 1929)

The position of William Smith (1769–1839) can now be seen to be no isolated phenomenon, as is sometimes suggested, but rather the supreme example of what was probably almost commonplace in the early years of civil engineering. For William Smith was a civil engineer; he so signed his name in documents still to be seen. It is almost amusing to note attempts in some geological writing to skirt around this basic fact, by such devices as referring to Smith as a surveyor or a land agent. Fortunately, the engineering work of the man who so well earned the title of "Father of British Geology" is well documented and it can be seen to be as thorough as were his geological studies, upon which his fame so firmly rests. His whole professional career was so intimate a blending of geology and its application to the practice of engineering that it is hardly necessary to do more than make this brief reference to it. But it may be useful to recall that his famous map appeared (in 1815) bearing a long title which began "A Delineation of the Strata of England and Wales, with part of Scotland, exhibiting the Collieries and Mines . . ." There was no doubt as to William Smith's appreciation of the value of applied geology, nor of the breadth of his vision as to how geology may be applied in the service of man, for (in his own words) his "New Geological Atlas of England and Wales," which followed the famous map between 1819 and 1824, was "calculated to elucidate the Agriculture of each County, and to show the Situation of the best material for Building, Making of Roads, the Construction of Canals, and pointing out those Places where Coal and other Valuable Materials are likely to be found." This must surely be one of the earliest charters of applied geology. (Phillips, 1844)

What of geology in the new world? Its indebtedness to the early geologists of Europe is well appreciated, but it may be asked whether the start of the scientific study of geology in North America had this same practical beginning. The answer is clear as soon as the records of early American geologists are consulted. William Maclure started his geological studies with the objective of assisting with the development of ores of iron, copper and zinc. His last years were taken up in part with the start of his school of agriculture because the scientific study of soil was one of his continuing interests. James Hall's early work in New York State resulted in a report (1843) that devoted much attention to mining matters as well as giving the first account of the geological sequence to be found in that state. (Fenton, 1952)

In early Canada, with its widely scattered and sparse population, the same picture is found, epitomized in another commanding founder of modern geology, Sir William Ernest Logan, first Director of the Geological Survey of Canada. Born in Montreal in 1798, Logan was sent to school in Edinburgh and then entered the business house of an uncle in London. In 1831 he moved to Wales to take charge of a copper smelter. He became interested in the local coal mining and prepared a geological map of the coal field, without any instruction. This led him to a detailed study of the underclays associated with coal, and he presented a paper about them to the Geological Society (of London) in 1840. He sailed for Halifax in 1841 and immediately upon landing started on those field studies of Canadian geology the record of which makes exciting reading even today, enlivened as it is by his quite brilliant pen and ink sketches.

His work soon attracted attention, with the result that in 1842 he was appointed director of a Geological Survey 15 years before the Dominion of Canada itself had been constituted. In supporting his candidature, Sir Henry de la Beche, Director of the British Survey, stated that "I would further observe that Mr. Logan is highly qualified as a miner and metallurgist to point out the applications of geology to the useful purposes of life, an object of the highest importance in a country like Canada, the mineral wealth of which is now so little known." From the time of his appointment until his eventual retirement in 1869 (he died in 1875), he seemed to do the work of several men, becoming almost a legendary figure throughout eastern Canada.

The practical aspect of his work was evident from the use to which his investigations were put by such great engineers as Thomas Keefer and George Stephenson (for the design of the piers of the Victoria Bridge, Montreal, piers that are still in use). He received many offers of other, and more gainful, employment. In writing about one such offer, he had this interesting observation to make.

When the British Government gave up the Michigan territory at the end of the last American war, with as little concern as if it had been so much bare granite, I dare say they were not aware that 12,000 square miles of a coal-field existed in the heart of it—larger than the largest in Britain, though the smallest of those belonging to the United States, which possess another of 55,000 square miles, and a third of 60,000 square miles ... Taking all this into consideration, notwithstanding I have requested my brother Edmond, of Edinburgh, who has a friend in the East India direction, to make some inquiry into the matter, I fancy you will see that the chances are that I am tied to Canada. (Harrington, 1883, pp. 235–236)

So germane to this study is Logan's whole philosophy that the temptation to quote from his own lucid writings is hard to resist. One more citation may perhaps be admitted, his own definition of the work of the Geological Survey of Canada.

> The object of the Survey is to ascertain the mineral resources of the country, and this is kept steadily in view. Whatever new scientific facts have resulted from it, have come out in the course of what I conceive to be economic researches carried on in a scientific way ... The analyses of new mineral species, while they directly regard a scientific result, must always have an economic bearing. You cannot tell whether a new substance is to be profitably available or not until you have ascertained its properties. The analyses of mineral species led to our knowledge of the limefeldspars, of so much agricultural importance to the Laurentian country. Thus economics lead to science, and science to economics. (Harrington, 1883, pp. 293–294)

Economics lead to science, and science to economics—and this from the man whose studies of the Precambrian have stood the test of a century of further study.

Words of Edmund Burke come vividly to mind as these glimpses at the early days of geological study are considered: "People will not look forward to posterity who never look backward to their ancestors." A seventy-fifth anniversary is not only a time for glancing backward, not alone a time for reviewing present achievements, but also a time for looking ahead to the challenges of the future. How is geology to serve mankind in the years ahead as it so surely did in the days of its beginnings?

The years between have a natural bearing upon the answer to be given, even though the record they present, certainly for the remainder of the nineteenth century, is not inspiring. Despite such auspicious beginnings, the divorce of geology from all its applications became very real as the century advanced, to such an extent that, in 1880, an eminent British geologist is reported to have said that the amount of money fruitlessly spent in Great Britain in a ridiculous search for coal, even within his own memory, would have paid the entire cost of the British Geological Survey. Early mining records are replete with examples of geological neglect, all supporting statements in this vein.

Developments in the application of geology in civil engineering followed a similar course. The fault almost certainly must be shared equally by geologists

and engineers, the mutual respect of early years giving way to differences that
were sometimes acrimonious. Another of the great pioneer British engineers
was involved in such divergences which, although now perhaps amusing, must
have had singularly unfortunate results at the time.

Isambard Kingdom Brunel was a young man of genius who gained his
experience from his distinguished father, Mark Isambard Brunel (born in
France), who was at one time Chief Engineer of the City of New York. In 1824
Mark Brunel was responsible for the start of work on the first subaqueous tunnel,
beneath the River Thames at Rotherhithe, just east of London. On the basis
of numerous trial borings, geologists assured the older Brunel that he would
find a stratum of strong blue clay and avoid the quicksand that had plagued
an earlier attempt at tunneling. The prediction proved to be quite wrong, and
although the tunnel was eventually finished by the elder Brunel, the extra cost,
incredible difficulties, and the hazards that had to be overcome must have left
an indelible imprint on the young man's mind.

When building the Great Western Railway, almost twenty years later, the
younger Brunel faced another major tunneling job in the construction of the
two-mile Box Tunnel between Chippenham and Bath. The tunnel penetrates
blue clay, blue marl, the Inferior Oolite and the Great Oolite, or Bath Stone.
After the tunnel had been completed and put into use the Reverend Doctor
William Buckland, then at Oxford, caused much trouble by declaring, even
though he had not visited the tunnel, that the unlined section was highly
dangerous and would certainly fall "owing to the concussion of the atmosphere
and the vibration caused by the trains." To this Isambard Brunel replied that
although he regretted his lack of scientific knowledge of geology, he had had
experience in excavating the rock in question and so considered it to be quite
safe. A Board of Trade inspector was called upon to report on the safety of
the tunnel and strongly supported Brunel. Some of the tunnel remains unlined
to this day, 120 years after its opening. (Rolt, 1961)

Pursuit of such arguments, disagreements, and outright mistakes, although
possibly of some human interest, is not profitable in a study such as this. The
schism was created, however, and persisted throughout the century. There
were naturally individual exceptions and occasional glimpses of the benefits
to be derived by cooperation, such as a series of articles by W. H. Penning
published in the British journal *The Engineer* in 1879, and reprinted a year
later in book form as "Engineering Geology." (Penning, 1880)

The academic isolation of the science almost certainly led eventually to its
neglect in the sphere of public interest, represented so unfortunately in its
almost complete absence from the curricula of schools, a neglect that persists
even today, and its general denigration until very recently in the activities of
natural history clubs and similar amateur scientific endeavours. This situation
is also in contrast with the position in earlier days. A rare book came recently

into the possession of the writer showing that almost a century ago no less a man than the Reverend Charles Kingsley, author of "The Water Babies" and other famous books for young people, was a popular lecturer on geology in addition to his many other activities. The book, "Town Geology," contains the text of lectures delivered in 1872 to the "young men of the city of Chester (England)," presumably at meetings sponsored by the Chester Natural History Society. In his introduction, Kingsley says:

> It does seem to me strange, to use the mildest word, that people whose destiny it is to live, even for a few short years, on this planet which we call the earth, and who do not at all intend to live on it as hermits . . . shall in general be so careless about the constitution of this same planet, and of the laws and facts on which depend, not merely their comfort and their wealth, but their health and their very lives, and the health and the lives of their children and descendants. (Kingsley, 1877, pp. xv–xvi)

In rolling, somewhat ponderous but still enjoyable Victorian prose, the author gives a lucid general picture of physical geology and then shows how it affects "The Soil of the Field," "The Pebbles in the Streets," "The Slates on the Roof," and similar very practical subjects. The science of geology, says Kingsley, "is (or ought to be), in popular parlance, the people's science—the science by studying which, the man ignorant of Latin, Greek . . . can yet become . . . a truly scientific man." And in urging his readers to use their eyes, even in their own town, he says: "Be sure, that wherever there is a river, even a drain; and a stone quarry, or even a roadside bank; much more where there is a sea, or a tidal aestuary, there is geology enough to be learnt, to explain the greater part of the making of all the continents on the globe." (Kingsley, 1877, pp. 4, 35)

These words written so long ago are still strangely relevant. After decades of popular neglect, geology is again beginning to win some degree of general recognition; its application at last is appreciated by the man in the street as something that affects him. University extension lectures are the modern equivalent of such popular lecture series as those of Charles Kingsley. To these have been added, however, the steady stream, flood it might almost be called, of cheap popular literature, and all that modern mass communication media can provide in purveying information. To see well-illustrated "paperbacks" on geology on even small bookstalls is now commonplace; the same cannot be said of other major scientific disciplines with the exception of meteorology. When radio and television are used as educational media, geology is not neglected. For example, the Canadian Broadcasting Corporation devoted one of its major nationwide evening "University" lecture series to an introduction to geology; later the lectures were reprinted in book form. (Baird, 1959) Slowly, geology is at last winning a place for itself in the curricula of some high schools, and some organizations, such as the Boy Scouts, are giving it increased recognition in their excellent training work. Once again, it is coming to be recognized as "the people's science."

What has prompted this awakening of the public interest? The reality of the change in attitude lends validity to the question. As in so many other social changes, the automobile would seem to hold the key to at least a partial answer. The potential mobility of the general public through the wide availability of private automobiles, when coupled with the unaccustomed leisure and extra wealth that the affluent society of North America is providing, has resulted in an amount of traveling for the ordinary citizen such as the world has never previously witnessed. And as the citizen travels, he must be conscious, to a degree, of the engineering of the roads on which he travels, especially when new highway construction interferes with his headlong high-speed touring. He can then see, as he waits impatiently to pass in single line through some construction project, that civil engineers have to excavate rock and soil for their cuttings and tunnels; some motorists at least must see that all rock is not the same. Even while traveling, the motorist will be at least conscious of the scenery through which he passes. Interest has been aroused to the degree that there are available today many route guides giving geological and historical information about unusually interesting routes. (W. Texas Geol. Soc., 1958)

Doubtless there are other causes of the regeneration of public interest in geology, but reflection suggests that it is the work of the civil engineer, as seen by the itinerant public, that is chiefly responsible. Few people have occasion to visit mines; fewer still probably give thought to the source of the gasoline they use so profligately; and, although adventures with mining stocks may make denizens of the stock market familiar with the names of mines, real and imaginary, this is no warranty of knowledge of geology—in fact, sober recitation of geological facts would remove much of the adventure from the bucket shops. As a prime example of the application of geology in the service of man, the practice of present day "engineering geology," as it has come to be called, will therefore be examined in brief review against the broader context of the unfolding science itself before a final glance is taken at what the future may hold. If, as William James once remarked, philosophy in the full sense is only man thinking, such a review might suggest a philosophy of applied geology.

Just as the work of William Smith epitomizes some of the earliest interrelations of geology and civil engineering, so the work of Charles P. Berkey marks a real turning point in the more recent history of the application of geology to civil engineering work. In 1905, he was retained in connection with the construction of the Catskill Aqueduct for the water supply of the City of New York. Thereafter for half a century, his services were in constant demand in association with many of the greatest civil engineering projects of North America. Dr. Berkey's outstanding contribution to the development of the Geological Society of America makes this reference to his work singularly appropriate. After serving as Secretary to the Society for eighteen years, he was elected President in 1941 and in the same year became an Honorary Member of the American Society of Civil Engineers, one of the many honours bestowed upon him which he always valued in a rather special way. In his presidential address Dr. Berkey had this to say about the assistance that geologists can render to civil engineers in the prosecution of:

> ... works marking the progress of material civilization and magnifying the limited competence of man's bare hands. They are literally fountains of power—perhaps in this present emergency the power that is to save the world. In a world seemingly bent on self-destruction, at least these adventurers face toward the future and stand out as if to promise better times in a more constructive world. So I claim a place of honor for these men who spent their lives in devising new ways of using their specialistic knowledge and experience and ingenuity for more effective public works and for the greater comfort and safety of men and women everywhere. (Berkey, 1942, p. 531)

These words were spoken twenty years ago; how relevant they are to the world of today.

It was in 1928, at the age of 61, that Berkey was retained by the U. S. Bureau of Reclamation just as the monumental Hoover Dam reached the final stages of planning. His assistance with the study of the foundation problems and the allied diversion tunnels associated with this great structure was recorded in a series of lucid reports that in no way minimize the details of the relevant geology but which make clear how the safety of the engineering structure depends ultimately and entirely upon the adequacy of the supporting rock strata. This point of view is now very generally accepted, to such an extent that the failure of a dam because of geological defects in its foundations is today almost unknown. The tragedy of the failure of the Malpasset Dam in 1959, and the exhaustive investigations into the cause of the disaster serve to confirm the foregoing suggestion in no uncertain manner.

All the tools and methods of geological investigation—geophysical methods, the use of large and small bore holes, exploratory shafts and tunnels all supplementary to detailed geological surveying—are now regularly used not only for the study of dam sites but also for determining the geological conditions to be anticipated along the routes of proposed tunnels. In studies for the long-discussed Channel Tunnel between England and France, comparative studies of microfossils (similar to the widely followed practice in petroleum engineering) were carried out in some detail in checking the assumed continuity of the Lower Chalk across the bed of the Strait of Dover. (Bruckshaw, *et al.*, 1961)

In all applications of geology to the works of the civil engineer there are reciprocal benefits of varying degree but the excavation of tunnels provides perhaps the most obvious examples. The civil engineer can be guided in his work by the preliminary predictions of the geologist; the geologist can obtain invaluable information if he is permitted to examine the rocks exposed as the tunnel advances. There is on record the particularly delightful incident which permitted Dr. Hans Cloos finally to solve the riddle of the Rhine Graben by his observations in the short tunnel beneath the Lorettoberg at Freiburg. (Cloos, 1954) New light was shed on some of the complexities of the geology of the Scottish Highlands by observations made as the great Lochaber water-power tunnel was excavated beneath the slopes of Ben Nevis. (Peach, 1930) And in more recent years, one of the most difficult tunnels ever driven, the Tecolote Tunnel in California, was put to good geological use before being placed in service; it was used for a detailed study of the trends in the Tertiary strata that it penetrates. (Bandy and Kolpack, 1962) The dewatering, by means of cofferdams, of dam sites provides correspondingly unique opportunities for the actual study of riverbed geology.

The construction of major bridges today always includes a detailed study of one or more river or lake crossings and the requisite test borings will sometimes reveal submarine geological features that were previously unsuspected. Discovery of a preglacial gorge in Mackinac Strait between lakes Michigan and Huron in the course of foundation studies for the great suspension bridge which now spans the Strait is a good and quite typical example. (Rosenau, 1958) Civil engineering structures built in the open sea necessitate unusually difficult site investigations which will always provide a dividend in the way of new information on submarine geology. Of unusual value has been the information on the deltaic deposits of the Mississippi River derived from soil mechanics studies of soil samples obtained in connection with site studies for offshore oil drilling platforms. (Fisk & McClelland, 1959)

Even more mundane engineering works such as the construction of roads and airports have their own contribution to make to the fund of geological knowledge, especially by the new sections revealed by major excavation work. At the same time, the wide areal coverage of such projects has led to developments in methods of field investigation which constitute advances in geological technique. Notable has been the use of geophysical methods (especially seismic) for the study of shallow deposits such as those in glaciated areas. Engineering use of geophysical methods for subsurface investigation has constituted a singularly useful link between geology and geophysics, a link that must be greatly strengthened in the years ahead as the concept of quantitative measurement becomes more widespread in geological practice.

Geological conditions on quite restricted building sites, such as those in central urban areas, are now engaging the attention of engineers to a degree

never experienced previously. The increasing complexity of foundation construction in crowded city areas, due to the proliferation of subsurface services,
makes knowledge of exact site conditions a virtual necessity. As geological
records of this very localized type are assembled and coordinated, valuable
information about the geology beneath city streets is developed. *Urban geology*
has therefore become a term of real significance and is not the mutually contradictory juxtaposition of words that it might at first sight appear to be.

There are some critical urban areas where a combination of steeply sloping
ground and unsatisfactory soil conditions gives rise to serious landslide hazards,
particularly after periods of heavy rain. Some of the suburbs around the city
of St. Louis, Missouri, are plagued by this danger, but the largest and most
notable area to have been developed in the face of this hazard is that constituted
by the city and county of Los Angeles. So serious has this local situation become
that legislation has been enacted requiring a report on any potentially unstable
site by an engineering geologist before development work can proceed. Here
indeed is a very obvious example of geology in the service of man. (Grove,
1957) This legal requirement has led to the establishment of a professional
society, the California Association of Engineering Geologists.

Antedating this group by more than a decade is the Division of Engineering
Geology of the Geological Society of America. The establishment of this division (in 1947) was public recognition, by the Society, of the importance of this
particular application of geology. Both of these organizations, however, are
fledglings in comparison with the geological divisions of several national insti-
tutions of mining engineers, whose continued work has long provided valuable
records of mining activity. Not much younger than the Geological Society
itself are two other North American societies serving the needs of applied
geology. Both are now international in scope, and their example has now been
followed at the local level by the establishment of more than a few local mining
or petroleum geological societies.

The formation of the Society of Economic Geologists in 1920 and of the
American Association of Petroleum Geologists in their more specialized field,
in 1917, provide further turning points in the applications of geology. It is
significant that alternatives considered to the name finally adopted for the
Society of Economic Geologists included the Society of Geological Engineers
and the Society of Applied Geology. Notable also is the fact that at the Society's
first meeting there was presented a paper on "The Relation of Economic
Geology to the General Principles of Geology" by President R. A. F. Penrose,
Jr. (1921).

It is not often that the official bulletin of a society antedates the society
itself, but this is the case with the distinguished journal, *Economic Geology*,
which is the bulletin of the Society of Economic Geologists. The first issue
appeared in October 1905, and the Fiftieth Anniversary Volume in 1955. The

two parts of this notable compilation, containing 1130 pages, present a comprehensive survey of all main aspects of the geology of ore deposits, to which the journal itself has been generally devoted, but review papers dealing with engineering geology, soil mechanics, and ground water are also included. It is impossible to make even a cursory examination of this significant collection of papers without appreciating how much the application of geology in the search for ores and fuel has contributed to significant advances in the science of geology itself.

The start of exploration for petroleum in Oklahoma about 1913 led to great interest in this area in the application of geology to the discovery and winning of oil. At a dinner in Tulsa, Oklahoma, on October 2, 1915, it was decided to form an association of geologists interested in this relatively new aspect of applied geology. The Southwestern Association of Petroleum Geologists was organized on February 19, 1917, also in Tulsa, but the name was changed in the following year to the American Association of Petroleum Geologists. The Association now has a worldwide membership of more than 15,000—a number that is clearly indicative of the importance of this branch of applied geology. Through its Bulletin, associated specialized journals, and its more than thirty special volumes, the Association has made significant contributions to the literature of geology. As is the case with *Economic Geology*, the *Bulletin* of A.A.P.G. includes many papers that may properly be described as theoretical, some seemingly far removed from the search for petroleum.

The search for minerals and fuels will long continue. Exploration for new reserves of petroleum is today being pursued throughout the world on an unprecedented scale, to such an extent that it undoubtedly represents at present the most extensive application of geology in the service of man. Inevitably, however, it must be a transitory application even in comparison with the corresponding search for minerals. All who are familiar with the Paley report— and what geologist is not?—will know the challenge that even now exists in the mineral field. And all such exploratory work will involve the most assiduous application of the principles and techniques of geology and geophysics, if indeed the two need to be separated; it will involve deep probings beneath the surface of the earth and the bottom of the sea; and in this and many other ways, it will add to the store of geological knowledge and doubtless make its own special contributions to the advance of geological theory and principles. Economics will long lean on science, and science upon economics.

As the future becomes the present, and the present the past, who can tell what advances will be seen in this unceasing hunt for the treasures of the earth? It is when one considers carefully the surface of the earth that the most important of all the possible applications of geology in the service of man comes into view. The population of the world is now exploding, and the rate of increase still shows no significant signs of slackening. Even assuming that some of the

worldwide measures for population control that can now be seen to be impera-
tive are introduced before it is too late, it is safe to say that by the year 2000 A.D.
—a crucial point in time that will be seen by most readers of this volume—the
population of the world will be almost double what it is today. To maintain
these more than 6 billion lives, the use of almost all available arable land will
be necessary as will also supplies of water that will make public water-supply
systems of the present day appear almost parsimonious in comparison. Conservation of the renewable resources of the earth, notably soil and water, is
therefore a public responsibility of immediate urgency.

Some may be tempted to say—what has this to do with geology? Just this,
that in the conservation of the renewable resources of the earth for man's
future use, and especially water, civil engineering works will be called for on a
scale surpassing anything yet seen, except in certain carefully developed river
valleys. And in all these works the aid of the geologist will be essential, particularly in all considerations of subsurface water and of soil-erosion control.
These projects will be in addition to the works and buildings required for the
ordinary service of communities and areas, in the execution of which close
collaboration of engineer and geologist will be vitally necessary. In all this
work the engineer must have essential geological information for the stability
and safety of his structures, and the geologist will gain new insights into sub-
surface conditions as these are revealed by the excavations of the engineer.
In this way the bounds of geological knowledge will steadily increase.

What, then, is the conclusion of the matter? Even in such a pedestrian review
as this, it has not been possible even to mention all the main applications of
geology in the service of man. Military geology, for example, is now a well-
accepted branch of applied geology upon which many comments could have
been made. Much more could have been said about the new techniques that
even now can be seen to have great value in all such engineering projects. It
is exceedingly clear, however, that geology will be applied in the works of the
engineer in steadily increasing measure as far into the future as the mind can
foresee.

It has been well said that merely boring holes in the ground is not geology.
But if, in the location of test bore holes, geological advice is always sought and
in the interpretation of test bores geological significance is always considered,
the needs of the engineer can be better met while new information will thus
become available for the use of the geologist. It is clear that there is no special
philosophy of applied geology. How could there be in the application of the
science to the art of engineering? If, however, the geologist brings to bear in
his part of such cooperative endeavour a lively appreciation of the philosophical
aspects of his work, he will be the more appreciative of the philosophical background of all true engineering. And with such a meeting of the minds in the
prosecution of what must always be essentially detailed and utilitarian work,

what potential is presented for advancing the boundaries of knowledge while serving the needs of man!

Some must have thought it a hard saying as they were reading these words of the late Mr. Justice Holmes: "Science teaches us a great deal about things that are not really important, philosophy a very little about those that are supremely so." This Olympian view might have been expected from the eminent jurist. To the geologist at work in the field or in the laboratory, as to the engineer engaged in the design or the construction of some vitally needed public project, the words will seem to be almost heresy. And yet, as one sets the acknowledged wonders of geological investigation or the applications of geology in even the greatest of engineering works against the backdrop of human history and as one glimpses ahead into ages yet unborn, the words persist in their challenge, reminding one of the dominance of the mind of man in all such studies, of the human core of all understanding. This is no new thought, for down through almost four centuries of time come words with which this essay may most fitly close, words of a philosopher-scientist whose prescience so frequently surprises his modern readers. It must have been with thoughts such as those now ventured that Sir Francis Bacon recorded his great concern "To make the mind of man, by help of art, a match for the nature of things."

REFERENCES CITED

BAIRD, D. M., 1959, An introduction to geology: Toronto, Canadian Broadcasting Corp., 111 pp.

BANDY, O. L., and KOLPACK, R. L., 1962, Formaniferal and sedimentological trends in the Tertiary section of Tecolote Tunnel, California: Geol. Soc. Am., Abs., Ann. Mtg., Houston, p. 8A.

BERKEY, C. P., 1942, The geologist in public works: Geol. Soc. Am., B., vol. 53, pp. 513–532.

BRUCKSHAW, J. M., GOGUEL, J., HARDING, H. J. B., and MALCOR, R., 1961, The work of the Channel Tunnel Group 1958–1960: Inst. Civil Eng., Pr., vol. 18, pp. 149–178; *See* also discussion in vol. 21, pp. 611–628.

CLOOS, H., 1954, Conversation with the earth (trans. by E. B. Garside): London, Routledge and Kegan Paul, 402 pp.

FENTON, C. L. and M. A., 1952, Giants of geology: Garden City, N. Y., Doubleday, 333 pp.

FISK, H. N., and McCLELLAND, B., 1959, Geology of continental shelf off Louisiana; its influence on offshore foundation design: Geol. Soc. Am., B., vol. 70, pp. 1369–1394.

GROVE, D. E., 1957, A geologic challenge: GeoTimes (Am. Geol. Inst.), vol. 2, no. 5, p. 8.

HARRINGTON, B. J., 1883, Life of Sir William E. Logan, Kt.: Montreal, Dawson Bros., 432 pp.

Herodotus, 1910, The History of Herodotus (trans. by G. Rawlinson), 2 vols.: London, J. M. Dent and Sons, Ltd., 719 pp.

Kingsley, C., 1877, Town geology: London, Daldy, Isbister and Co., 239 pp.

Lyell, Charles, 1836, Geol. Soc. London, Pr., vol. 2, no. 44, pp. 357–361.

McAdam, J. L., 1827, Remarks on the present system of road making, 9th ed.: London, Longman, Hurst, Rees, Orme, and Brown, 236 pp.

Peach, B. N., 1930, The Lochaber water power scheme and its geological aspects: Water and Water Eng. (London), vol. 32, p. 71.

Penning, W. H., 1880, Engineering geology: London, Balliére, Tindall and Cox, 164 pp.

Penrose, R. A. F., Jr., 1921, The relations of economic geology to the general principles of geology: Econ. Geol., vol. 16, pp. 48–51.

Phillips, J., 1844, Memoirs of William Smith, LL.D.: London, John Murray, 150 pp.

Rolt, L. T. C., 1961, Isambard Kingdom Brunel: London, Arrow Books, 383 pp.

Rosenau, J. C., 1958, Geology of the Mackinac Bridge site, Michigan: Geol. Soc. Am., Abs., vol. 69, Ann. Mtg., St. Louis, p. 1636.

Singer, C., 1959, A short history of scientific ideas to 1900: Oxford, Clarendon Press, 525 pp.

Smeaton, J., 1791, A narrative of the building and a description of the construction of the Edystone lighthouse with stone . . .: London, H. Hughs, sold by G. Nicol, 198 pp.

Southey, R., 1929, Journal of a tour in Scotland in 1819: London, John Murray, 276 pp.

Vitruvius, 1914, The Ten Books of Architecture (trans. by M. H. Morgan): Cambridge, Harvard University Press, 331 pp.

West Texas Geological Society, 1958, Geological road log, Del Rio to El Paso: Midland, West Texas Geol. Soc., 48 pp.

CLAUDE C. ALBRITTON, JR.

Southern Methodist University

Philosophy of Geology: A Selected Bibliography and Index[1]

This bibliography contains references to some four hundred writings which reflect upon the scope, methods, and contributions of the geological sciences. The collection is not comprehensive; neither are its selections evenly balanced with regard to their professional origins, geographic distribution, or years of publication.

Because the main effort here is to identify live rather than fossil problems, I have drawn more than half the items from works published since 1949. A geographical weighting in favor of American publications—a little more than half the entire list—is unintentional. With more time, and with continued access to competent translators of eastern European and Scandinavian languages, a better geographical balance could have been attained. I have made a special effort to learn how geology is viewed by persons who are not geologists. Consequently, a fourth of the references are to the works of historians, philosophers, mathematicians, physicists, astrophysicists, biologists, bibliographers, and linguists.

The index at the end of this paper tells something about degrees of interest in different problems and subjects. As might be expected, three areas of spirited discussion center around the concepts of time, change, and the classification of natural phenomena.

Hutton, as one admiring author claims, *discovered* time. In any event, the science he founded has seemed to differ from others by its concern with the changes that have occurred over vast stretches of time. Because history is also concerned with temporal sequences of events, geology has come to be known as

---

[1] Prepared with the aid of National Science Foundation Grant G–23887.

an historical science. This leads one to ask whether historians and historical geologists use the same basic methods. No, say those historiographers who insist that the only proper history is human history, and that in order to write it, one must relive in the imagination the things that actually happened to human beings in the past. Yes, say those philosophers who maintain that the explanation of whatever has happened, immediately or remotely in the past, requires the formulation and use of laws. However this particular issue may be resolved, it would appear that historical geologists are called upon to explain their explanations and to show what use, if any, they make of laws.

"The present is the key to the past," we say. The principle of uniformity, to which this adage refers, is held by many to be the foundation stone of geology. With regard to the validity of the principle, however, the range of opinion is amazing. Most modern historians of science seem to agree that Lyell's famous principle was an a-historic device, which was discarded after evolutionism became popular in the nineteenth century. Most modern philosophers of science seem to feel either that the principle is too vague to be useful, or that it is an unwarranted and unnecessary assumption. Geologists and other scientists have such varied opinions on the matter that it would be impossible, without a vote, to say which view prevails. Surely the principle of uniformity needs the critical attention of geologists. Is it no more than a prescription for analogical reasoning? Will it reduce to the principle of simplicity, as applied to the agencies of geological change? And if so, with which of the many varieties of simplicity is it to be equated?

As Simpson has said, all theoretical science is ordering. Many of the papers cited in the bibliography deal with the classification and ordering of natural phenomena. Admittedly, the things studied by geologists and paleontologists are hard to classify. Minerals, rocks, and natural fluids rarely occur in any pure or ideal state. The surface of the earth is so irregular, both morphologically and tectonically, that it is hard to devise classifications of land forms or geological structures that will apply to all terranes. Stratigraphic units are rarely clear cut, and it is difficult to name and group them in ways that will disclose both their relationships in space and their sequences in time. In classifying fossils, the paleontologist must contend with the imperfections of the fossil record, as well as the variable influences of environmental change and evolutionary development.

The greater part of this bibliography was assembled during the summer of 1962, which will explain why certain publications of more recent date are not included. The search for titles began with a scanning of the indexes for all issues of the "Bibliography and Index of North American Geology" (1732–1959), and of the "Bibliography and Index of Geology Exclusive of North America" (1933–1960). The search was continued through the files of "Philosophy of Science," the "British Journal for the Philosophy of Science," and the

"Zentralblatt für Geologie und Paläontologie." "Isis," with its annual bibliographies for the history of science, yielded additional material. The bibliographic card service of the *Service d'Information Géologique du Bureau de Recherches Géologiques et Minières* led to many articles published in Russian journals since 1960.

I should like to thank the agency which made this work possible and the individuals who helped bring it to an end. A grant from the National Science Foundation permitted me to give three months of concentrated effort to the project. Mrs. Robert R. Wheeler did much of the searching for titles and assembled the index. Mrs. Natalie Voshinin also helped with the searching, and she translated the Russian articles. To Mrs. Nadine George, Reference Librarian of the Science Information Center in Dallas, I am much indebted for her patient and fruitful efforts at locating out-of-the-way materials.

Many friends have called my attention to pertinent references they had run across in their own reading. Dr. Arthur F. Hagner graciously sent me a lengthy bibliography of the philosophy of geology, which he had prepared for his advanced students at the University of Illinois. Miss Marie Siegrist has called my attention to references which are to appear in future issues of the "Bibliography of Geology Exclusive of North America." Mr. Charles Gotschalk, Chief of the Stack and Reader Division of the Library of Congress, provided a private room for my use during a month of study in Washington. Mrs. Jacquelyn Newbury typed the manuscript and helped with the proofreading. Although I am deeply grateful to all these persons, I must say, for their protection, that I am solely responsible for the selection and annotation of titles, the design of the index, and for any errors.

Bibliography

American Commission on Stratigraphic Nomenclature, 1961, Code of stratigraphic nomenclature: Am. Assoc. Petroleum Geol., B., vol. 45, no. 5, pp. 645–665. Defines and differentiates rock-stratigraphic, soil-stratigraphic, bio-stratigraphic, time-stratigraphic, geologic-time, and geologic-climate units.

AMSTUTZ, GERHARDT CHRISTIAN, 1960, Some basic concepts and thoughts on the space-time analysis of rocks and mineral deposits in orogenic belts: Geol. Rundschau, vol. 50, pp. 165–189. "The discovery, proof, and acceptance of evolution of life was only one victory of the principle of endogenesis over 'higher superstition' which clung . . . to exogenesis. The gradual departure of science from alchemistic concepts is essentially a development from exo- toward endo-genesis, and of epi- toward syn-genesis . . ."

ANDERSON, CHARLES ALFRED, 1951, Older Precambrian structure in Arizona: Geol. Soc. Am., B., vol. 62, no. 11, pp. 1331–1346. An explicit application of the principle of simplicity to tectonic history is found on p. 1346. "Until more precise correlations of the older Precambrian rocks in Arizona can be made . . . the simplest explanation is that only one period of orogeny . . . has occurred in Arizona during early Precambrian time."

ANDRÉE, KARL ERICH, 1938, Rezente und fossile Sedimente; Erdgeschichte mit oder ohne Aktualitätslehre?: Geol. Rundschau, vol. 29, no. 3–5, pp. 147–167. "Die Erdgeschichte . . . die auch für den Aktualitätsanhänger . . . den Kern geologischer Forschung bildet, vermag der Aktualitätslehre nicht zu entraten, ohne überhaupt den Boden unter den Füssen zu verlieren, auf dem sie aufbaut."

ANDREWS, ERNEST CLAYTON, 1936, Some major problems in structural geology: Linnean Soc. New South Wales, Pr., vol. 63, pts. 1–2, no. 275–276, pp. iv–xl. "The student of the Newton and Darwin type seeks a simple explanation of natural phenomena; he knows that there are many ways in which, conceivably, a form such as a mountain range may have been caused, whereas, in reality, it was produced in only one way . . ."

APRODOV, V. A., 1961, Osnovnyje cherty filosofskago materializma v geologicheskikh rabotakh M. V. Lomonosova (Basic features of philosophical materialism in the geologic works of M. V. Lomonosov): Sovet. Geol., no. 12, pp. 3–13. Lomonosov's formulation of a materialistic method of scientific investigation was as follows: through observations, form a theory; through theory, check observations.

ARKELL, WILLIAM JOSCELYN, 1956, Species and species: Systematics Assoc., London, Pub. no. 2, pp. 97–99. As conceived by paleontologists, species and genera are "purely artificial and subjective categories . . . Thus the only logical criterion for the size and definition of the taxon in paleontology is its usefulness."

2——1956, Comments on stratigraphic procedure and terminology: Am. J. Sci., vol. 254, no. 8, pp. 457–467. "In stratigraphic procedure, it is not what terms an author uses that matters, but whether he knows what he is talking about. If he does, he will be unambiguous however few and simple the terms he employs, but if he does not, the more technical terms he uses, and the more technical those terms are, the greater will be the danger of confusion and misapprehension."

BACKLUND, HELGE G., 1941, Zum Aktualitätsprinzip: Geol. Rundschau, vol. 32, no. 3, pp. 394–397.

BAKER, HOWARD BIGELOW, 1938, Inductive logic and Lyellian uniformitarianism: Michigan Acad. Sci., Sect. Geol. and Miner., pp. 1–5. "In the inductive process the more hypotheses the better . . . Contrary to this essential . . . the doctrine of uniformitarianism leads to poverty where riches are desired."

BARGHOORN, ELSO STERRENBERG, JR., 1953, Evidence of climatic change in the geologic record of plant life, Chapter 20, pp. 235–248 in Harlow Shapley, ed., Climatic change; evidence, causes, and effects: Cambridge, Harvard Univ. Press, ix and 318 pp. "There are two basic assumptions for the paleobotanical interpretation of climatic history. The first of these is that plant groups of the past had environmental requirements similar to those which they possess today . . . The second . . . is that an environmental complex of definable climatic and other physical conditions supports a biotic population which is in general equilibrium with these conditions . . ."

BARKER, STEPHEN F., 1961, The role of simplicity in explanation, pp. 265–274 in Herbert Feigl and Grover Maxwell, eds., Current issues in the philosophy of science: New York, Holt, Rinehart, and Winston, 484 pp. The logical-empiricist view of explanation, "exaggerates the correlation between prediction and explanation, . . . exaggerates the contrast between theoretical and observational terms in science, and . . . by neglecting the factor of simplicity it gives no real account of what it is for one explanation to be a better explanation than another."

2——1961, On simplicity in empirical hypotheses: Philosophy of Science, vol. 28, no. 2, pp. 162–171. ". . . the hypothesis that . . . fossils really are remains of primeval organisms is a better hypothesis than is the hypothesis that they are not and were created only recently. The former hypothesis is better than the latter, not because it fits more facts or enables more predictions to be elicited; it is better because it is a simpler hypothesis."

BARRELL, JOSEPH, 1917, Rhythms and the measurement of geologic time: Geol. Soc. Am., B., vol. 28, pp. 745–904. "The doctrine of uniformitarianism has ignored the presence of age-long rhythms, and where they were obtrusive has sought to smooth them out; but in so doing it has minimized the differences between the present and the past, and the constant variations within that past. This doctrine should be looked on only as supplying a beginning for investigation."

BARTH, THOMAS FREDRIK WEIBY, 1952, Theoretical petrology: New York, John Wiley; London, Chapman and Hall, Ltd., viii and 387 pp. "Now that experimental methods have led to the synthesis of minerals and rocks and the determination of their thermodynamical constants, petrology has become physico-chemistry applied to the crust of the earth."

BAULIG, HENRI, 1938, Questions de terminologie. I.—Conséquent, subséquent, obséquent; ou cataclinal, monoclinal, anaclinal?: J. Geomorphology, vol. 1, no. 3, pp. 224–229. ". . . one should never lose sight of the fact that theoretical schemes imply hypotheses, and that the appropriate genetic terminology is applicable only to the extent that these hypotheses are demonstrated to be correct, or else are explicitly admitted as a basis of discussion. Otherwise it is better to employ purely descriptive terms."
2——1949, Causalité et finalité en géomorphologie: Geog. Ann., Stockholm, vol. 31, no. 1–4, pp. 321–324. Geomorphic explanations are commonly colored by anthropomorphism—a tacit ascription of motives and aspirations to the mechanical agencies of erosion and deposition.
3——1950, William Morris Davis: master of method: Assoc. Am. Geographers, Annals, vol. 40, no. 3, pp. 188–195. "Davis's general method, as, in fact, all geological inferences from the present to the past, suffers from a sort of congenital weakness: for one term of the analogist argument, i.e., the present, can not be taken to represent the 'normal' condition of the Earth."

BECKER, CARL LOTUS, 1932, The heavenly city of the eighteenth-century philosophers: New Haven, Yale Univ. Press, Yale Paperbound Y-5, 168 pp. "Much of what is called science is properly history, the history of biological or physical phenomena. The geologist gives us the history of the earth; the botanist relates the life history of plants . . . We cannot properly know

things as they are unless we know 'how they came to be what they are' . . .
Historical mindedness is so much a preconception of modern thought that
we can identify a particular thing only by pointing to the various things it
successively was before it became that thing which it will presently cease
to be."

BECKNER, MORTON, 1959, The biological way of thought: New York, Columbia
Univ. Press, viii and 200 pp. "Scientists are most likely to have recourse
to historical explanation . . . when present phenomena seem explicable in
terms of a temporal sequence of past events."

BELL, WILLIAM CHARLES, 1959, Uniformitarianism—or uniformity: Am. Assoc.
Petroleum Geol., B., vol. 43, no. 12, pp. 2862–2865. "Paradoxically,
although we give lip-service to an awareness of isochronous but different
facies when we write theoretically, in practice most of our arguments are
peripheral to an almost axiomatic declaration that similarity implies
isochroneity—and the greater the similarity the more probable the identity
in age."

BELOUSOV, V. V., 1938, "Teoriya zemli" Dzhemsa Gettona (James Hutton's
"Theory of the Earth"); Istoriya i Filosofiya Estestvoznaniya, no. 7–8,
pp. 156–162. Hutton stated two general propositions which are important
to the philosophy of geology: (1) in reconstructing the past we can see and
foresee the results of changes but neither the beginning nor the end of the
processes which caused them, and (2) geologic time is vastly long in terms
of ordinary human perspectives.

BEMMELEN, REINOUT WILLEM VAN, 1959, Die Methode in der Geologie: Geol.
Ges. Wien, Mitt., vol. 53, pp. 35–52. "Unser irdisches System geochem-
ischer Prozesse ist nicht eine endlose Verflechtung wiederkehrender Kreis-
läufe . . . Es ist ein Teil einer kosmichen Evolution mit gerichtetem
Ablauf . . ."
2—1961, The scientific character of geology: J. Geol., vol. 69, no. 4, pp. 453–
463. Geology, essentially an historical science, differs from physics, chemistry, and biology in that the possibilities for experiment are limited. The
principle of uniformity and the method of comparative ontology are
examples of rules followed in geological practice, but the premises inherent
in these are not so firmly grounded as are the natural laws of physics and
chemistry. Thus the geologist must resort to the method of multiple working hypotheses to test the greatest number of presuppositions.

BERINGER, CARL CHRISTOPH, 1954, Geschichte der Geologie und des geologischen Weltbildes: Stuttgart, Ferdinand Enke, 158 pp.

BERKEY, CHARLES PETER, 1933, Recent development of geology as an applied
science: Am. Phil. Soc., Pr., vol. 72, no. 1, pp. 25–37.

BERRY, EDWARD WILBER, 1925, On correlation: Geol. Soc. Am., B., vol. 36, no. 1, pp. 263–277. "After all that can be said for them, it remains true that classifications are conveniences for reference and mediums of exchange, and chronologic boundaries are quite as artificial as most political boundaries and far more subjective."

2——1929, Shall we return to cataclysmal geology?: Am. J. Sci., 5th ser., vol. 17, pp. 1–12. "So much nonsense has been written on various so-called ultimate criteria for correlation that many have the faith or the wish to believe that the interior soul of our earth governs its surface history with a periodicity like that of the clock of doom, and when the fated hour strikes strata are folded and raised into mountains, epicontinental seas retreat, the continents slide about, the denizens of the land and sea become dead and buried, and a new era is inaugurated."

BÉTHUNE, Pierre de, 1953, Le cycle d'érosion: Rev. Questions Sci., an. 66, vol. 124 (s. 5, vol. 14) f. 3, pp. 321–346. ". . . la théorie si féconde des cycles d'érosion ne constitue qu'une première approximation, et . . . seules de patientes recherches comparatives permettront d'édifier la théorie générale . . ."

2——1957, Un demi-siècle de géomorphologie davisienne: Rev. Questions Sci., an. 69, vol. 128 (s. 5, vol. 18) f. 1, pp. 100–111. "La faiblesse congénitale du davisianisme est dans cette méthode a priori, 'deductive,' de son raisonnement. Nonobstant tout ce que les davisiens ont pu écrire à ce sujet, la vraie méthode de la géomorphologie . . . est l'induction."

BEURLEN, KARL, 1935, Der Aktualismus in der Geologie, eine Klarstellung-Zbl. Miner., 1935, Abt. B., no. 12, pp. 520–525. "Der stärkste und nach haltigste Verstoss gegen den Dogmatismus in der Geologie war die Einführung der aktualistischen Methode. . . . Wenn diese Methode dann allerdings zu einem Forschungsprinzip gemacht wurde . . . so war das allerdings eine unzulässige Verallgemeinerung und Umwertung der Methode zu einem Dogma . . . Dadurch machte sich der Aktualismus selbst dessen schuldig, was er zunächst bekämpfte."

2——1935—1936, Zur Kritik des Aktualismus; I. Bedeutung und Aufgabe geologischer Forschung; II. Das Klima des Diluviums; III. (with S. Thiele) Das Experiment in der Tektonik und seine Bedeutung in der Geologie: Zs. gesamte Naturw., vol. 1, pp. 23–36, 209–220; vol. 2, pp. 49–61.

BILLINGS, MARLAND PRATT, 1950, Stratigraphy and the study of metamorphic rocks: Geol. Soc. Am., B., vol. 61, no. 5, pp. 435–448. In attacking field problems, including those involving many metamorphic terranes, stratigraphy and structure must be solved simultaneously.

BLACKWELDER, ELIOT, 1909, The valuation of unconformities: J. Geol., vol. 17, pp. 289–299. "The entire geological record . . . is not to be conceived

of as a pile of strata, but as a dovetailed column of wedges, the unconformities and rock systems being combined in varying proportions. The
former predominate in some places and periods, while the latter prevail in
others."

BLAKE, RALPH M., DUCASSE, CURT J., and MADDEN, EDWARD H., 1960,
Theories of scientific method; the Renaissance through the nineteenth
century: Seattle, University of Washington Press, iv and 346 pp. Critiques
of the principle of uniformity of nature as treated in the writings of Newton,
Hume, Herschel, Mill, and Jevons.

BLANC, ALBERTO CARLO, 1951, Cosmolyse et épistémologie non-cartésienne, in
Sciences de la terre, XXI Cong. Internat. Phil. Sci., Paris, 1949: Paris,
Hermann, pp. 105–122. Distinctive floras and faunas (including the specialized human races of so-called 'primitive cultures'), as the simplified
derivatives of originally more complex entities, are analogous to the hydrogen atom, which, according to the views of modern physics, is a simplified
end-product in the evolution of cosmic matter.

BLISS, HENRY EVELYN, 1952, A bibliographic classification: New York, H. W.
Wilson, 2 vols. Astronomy, geology, geography, and meteorology are
special natural sciences combining concrete and descriptive subject matters
with theoretical components derived from and dependent upon both
physics and chemistry.

BONDI, HERMANN, 1959, Science and structure of the universe: Manchester Lit.
and Phil. Soc., Mem. and Proc., vol. 101 (1958–1959), pp. 58–71. "I have a
suspicion (although I would not put it higher than that) that the statement
of uniformity makes sense in just such a universe as I think we have got,
which, though it is infinite in extent, yet is effectively finite owing to the
recessional velocities . . . The assumption [of uniformity] is by no means
clear in its meaning but empirically it seems by far the most fertile we can
make."
2——1961, Cosmology: Cambridge Monographs on Physics, Cambridge Univ.
Press, 182 pp. ". . . in all our physics we have presupposed a certain uniformity of space and time; we have assumed that we live in a world that
is homogeneous at least as far as the laws of nature are concerned. Hence
the underlying axiom of our physics makes certain demands on the structure of the universe; it requires a cosmological uniformity."

BRADLEY, WILMOT HYDE, 1948, Limnology and the Eocene lakes of the Rocky
Mountain region: Geol. Soc. Am., B., vol. 59, no. 7, pp. 635–648. "But
what is the central theme peculiar to the science of geology—that core
which is not derived from any of the sister disciplines? Perhaps you will
agree that it is the history and constitution of the earth."

Bretsky, Peter William, Jr., 1962, Barker on simplicity in historical geology: Dallas, Southern Methodist Univ. Press, J. Graduate Research Center, vol. 30, no. 1, pp. 45–47. "If Lyellian uniformitarianism . . . be a kind of notational simplicity, does it not then become trivial?"

Bridgman, Percy Williams, 1959, The way things are: Cambridge, Harvard Univ. Press, x and 333 pp. Occam's Razor "appeals to me as a cardinal intellectual principle . . . I do not know what logical justification can be offered for the principle. To me it seems to satisfy a deep seated instinct for intellectual good workmanship. Perhaps one of the most compelling reasons for adopting it is that thereby one has given as few hostages to the future as possible and retained the maximum flexibility for dealing with unanticipated facts or ideas."

Broggi, Jorge Alberto, 1935, Los dominios de la geología: Bol. Minas, Ind. y Constr. (Lima, Peru) s. 3, vol. 7, pp. 13–18. "El tiempo actual en historia, es un elemento de su constitución futura; en geología es la base de las investigaciones sobre el pasado."

Broom, Robert, 1932, Evolution as the palaeontologist sees it: South African J. Sci., vol. 29, pp. 54–71. "As evolution has practically finished and cannot be repeated unless all higher life is wiped off from the earth and a new start made from the very beginning, we may perhaps conclude that man is the end to which some power has guided evolution."

Brouwer, Aart, 1957, On the principles of Pleistocene chronology: Geol. en Mijnbouw (n.s.) vol. 19, pp. 62–68. "What is it that has induced geologists to adopt paleontology as the base of geochronology? Certainly not its reliability."

Brown, Bahngrell Walter, 1959, Preliminary study of stochastic terms used in geology: Geol. Soc. Am., B., vol. 70, no. 5, pp. 651–654. Precision would be gained in geological writing if definite ranges of probability values were assigned to the following words expressing likelihood: impossibly, improbably, equally likely, probably, undoubtedly, and possibly. 2——1961, Stochastic variables of geologic search and decision: Geol. Soc. Am., B., vol. 72, no. 11, pp. 1675–1685. Demonstrates that certain problems of geologic search and decision can be treated stochastically.

Bryan, Kirk, 1950, The place of geomorphology in the geographic sciences: Assoc. Am. Geographers Annals, vol. 40, no. 3, pp. 196–208. "The first and most natural application of geomorphic study is to the history of the earth."

Bubnoff, Serge von, 1937, Die historische Betrachtungsweise in der Geologie: Geistige Arbeit, Berlin, vol. 4, no. 13, pp. 1–3. "Aktualismus bedeutet nicht, dass alles immer ebenso war wie heute, sondern dass Reaktionen (physikalische und biologische) derselben Grössenordnung von Raum und Zeit unter gleichen Voraussetzungen gleich verlaufen."

2——(Hans Cloos and Georg Wagner), 1943, Warum Geologie?: Beitr. Geol. Thüringen, vol. 7, no. 4–5, pp. 191–204. "Diese Verknüpfung naturwissenschaftlicher und historischer Denkungs- und Untersuchungsart und diese Lebensnähe und 'Bodenständigkeit' lassen die Geologie für die Schule daher besonders wichtig und notwendig erscheinen . . ."

3——1954, Grundprobleme der Geologie, 3rd ed.: Berlin, Akademie-Verlag, vii and 234 pp. "Die Grundfragen, welche dazu formuliert werden müssen, wären etwa: Was ist unsere Wissenschaft, welche Wege verfolgt sie, welche Fehler sind in ihrem methodischen Aufbau möglich, was sind ihre Endziele?"

BUCHER, WALTER HERMANN, 1936, The concept of natural law in geology: Ohio J. Sci., vol. 36, no. 4, pp. 183–194. "Geology is peculiarly dual in its aims: on the one hand it is concerned with what happened *once* at a *certain place*, in individual mines, mountains, regions. Interest that centers on individuals is *history*, not science. As a *science*, geology is concerned with the *typical* that finds expressions in *generalizations*, whether they be called laws or something else."

2——1941, The nature of geological inquiry and the training required for it: Am. Inst. Min. Met. Eng., Tech. Pub. 1377, 6 pp. "The typical 'geological' processes cannot be studied directly by laboratory methods but only indirectly by their results; that is, by the methods of the historical sciences. . . . the greater part of all geological work is not primarily concerned with 'timeless' knowledge but with concrete, 'time-bound' reality. It deals not with ore bodies, but with this ore body; not with valleys in general, but with that valley."

3——1957, The deformation of the earth's crust; an inductive approach to the problems of diastrophism: New York, Hafner, xii and 518 pp. Forty-six laws relating to diastrophism are formulated.

BÜLOW, KURD VON, 1943, Geschichte und Zukunft der Formationstabelle: Neues Jb. Miner., Geol., u. Paläont., 1943, Abt. B., no. 5, pp. 116–130. "So entstand die Tabelle nicht eigentlich als Gliederung, Einteilung eines Ganzen, sondern dieses Ganze wurde erst durch die stratigraphische Kleinarbeit gefügt."

2——1960, Der Weg des Aktualismus in England, Frankreich und Deutschland: Geol. Ges. Deut. Dem. Rep., Ber., vol. 5, no. 3, pp. 160–174. Actualism has been interpreted in two different ways: as a presupposition concerning the steady course of nature, and as a method for applying the experience of the present to the reconstruction of the past. The present tendency among geologists is to accept actualism as a useful method rather than as an article of faith.

BUNGE, MARIO AUGUSTO, 1961, The weight of simplicity in the construction and assaying of scientific theories: Philosophy of Science, vol. 28, no. 2, pp. 120–149. "Historical theories—such as those of geology, evolution and human society—have a high explanatory power but a small predictive power, even counting retrodictions."

CAILLEUX, ANDRÉ, and TRICART, JEAN, 1961, Idéalisme, matérialisme et accélération: Rev. Géomorph. Dynamique, vol. 12, no. 1, pp. 1–2. A defense of materialism, in the sense of an empirical approach to geological problems.

CAMP, CHARLES LEWIS, 1952, Geological boundaries in relation to faunal changes and diastrophism: J. Paleont., vol. 26, no. 3, pp. 353–358. "Nothing much can happen to our facts, but fitting these facts together to erect . . . systems of biological classification and geological age-dating is an unending struggle. Awaiting possible refinements in absolute age-dating, we are often constrained to fit the facts together, and let the devil take the age boundaries of the geological time scale—the facts and the boundaries don't always coincide."

CANNON, WALTER F., 1960, The uniformitarian-catastrophist debate: Isis, vol. 51, pt. 1, no. 163, pp. 38–55. ". . . if Darwin was deeply indebted to Charles Lyell for the method of accounting for large changes by summing up small changes over immense periods of time, nevertheless he did not accept the general Uniformitarian account of the history of nature. Evolution by means of natural selection involves the acceptance of the idea that some sort of cumulative development is demonstrated by geological and biological evidence—and it is just this idea that Uniformitarianism consistently denied."
2——1960, The problem of miracles in the 1830's: Victorian Studies, vol. 4, no. 1, pp. 5–32. "With their stubborn insistence on the historical nature of the cosmos . . . the Catastrophists forced speculation away from Lyell's unprogressive position and kept a developmental view of the world alive, so that today we popularly describe the history of the world as Whewell saw it (but without his miracles), not as Lyell saw it."
3——1961, John Herschel and the idea of science: J. History of Ideas, vol. 22, no. 2, pp. 215–239. "It might seem to a modern man that geology is necessarily a 'historical' science, but Uniformitarianism attempted to make it as 'unhistorical,' that is to say, as much without development, as possible. Lyell's *Principles of Geology* was the last great codification of a non-developmental cosmography."
4——1961, The impact of uniformitarianism; two letters from John Herschel to Charles Lyell, 1836–1837: Am. Phil. Soc., Pr., vol. 105, no. 3, pp. 301–314. Herschel's belief that the Uniformitarian-Catastrophist debate was at base inconsequential was incorrect, "since the Uniformitarian antidevelop-

mental view of the world was quite antithetic to the Catastrophist insistence on a world developing geologically from a primitive chaos."

CARNAP, RUDOLF, 1955, Logical foundations of the unity of science: Chicago, Univ. Chicago Press, Int. Encyc. Unified Sci., vol. 1, pts. 1–5, pp. 42–62. "Let us take 'physics' as a common name for the non-biological field of science, comprehending both systematic and historical investigations within this field, thus including chemistry, mineralogy, astronomy, geology (which is historical), meteorology, etc."

CASSIRER, ERNST, 1953, An essay on man; an introduction to a philosophy of human culture: Garden City, N. Y., Doubleday, 294 pp. The same logical structure characterizes the historical thought of the historian, geologist, and paleontologist, but the historian has the unique task of interpreting the symbolic content of human documents and monuments. (See Chapter 10, *History*.)

CAYEUX, LUCIEN, 1941, Causes anciennes et causes actuelles en géologie: Paris, Masson, 79 pp. "Il est nécessaire de réserver une place à des Causes anciennes, à côté des Causes actuelles, dans l'étude des formations sédimentaires de l'écorce terrestre, si l'on veut faire appel à toutes les lumières, susceptibles de nous en donner l'intelligence."

CHAMBERLIN, THOMAS CHROWDER, 1897, The method of multiple working hypotheses: J. Geol., vol. 5, pp. 837–848. 'In developing the multiple hypotheses, the effort is to bring up into view every rational explanation of the phenomenon in hand and to develop every tenable hypothesis relative to its nature, cause or origin, and to give to all of these as impartially as possible a working form and a due place in the investigation."

2——1898, The ulterior basis of time divisions and the classification of geologic history: J. Geol., vol. 6, pp. 449–462. "The most vital problem before the general geologist today is the question whether the earth's history is naturally divided into periodic phases of world-wide prevalence, or whether it is but an aggregation of local events dependent upon local conditions uncontrolled by overmastering agencies of universal dominance."

3——1904, The methods of the earth sciences: Pop. Sci. Monthly, vol. 66, pp. 66–75. "In some sense the earth sciences must come to comprehend the essentials of all the sciences. At least as much as any other scientists we are interested in the fundamental assumptions of all the sciences and in their consistent application."

4——1907, Editorial: J. Geol., vol. 15, pp. 817–819. "The cheapest device for making the largest show of quasi-results in technical garb with the least investment of scientific capital known to our profession is found in giving new names to known formations."

CHORLEY, RICHARD J., 1957, Illustrating the laws of morphometry: Geol. Mag., vol. 94, no. 2, pp. 140–150. "The laws of morphometry are here illustrated from three regions of maturely dissected sandstone terrain, lacking in differential gross structural control, and it is discovered that uniform, dimensionless ratios hold for their geometry."

CLARKE, JOHN MASON, 1917, The philosophy of geology and the order of the state: Geol. Soc. Am., B., vol. 28, pp. 235–248. "Nature makes for the individual . . . The ants are nature's . . . highest performance in communistic effort and in cooperative achievement."

CLEMENTS, FREDERIC EDWARD, and SHELFORD, VICTOR E., 1939, Bio-ecology: New York, John Wiley, vii and 425 pp. ". . . the key to the past is fashioned by the present, to use these terms in their everyday significance. On the other hand, the present is the sole heir to the past, and no adequate understanding of it is possible without tracing the continuity of developmental processes from the one to the other."

CLEUGH, MARY FRANCES, 1937, Time and its importance in modern thought: London, Methuen, viii and 308 pp. "'The Past' is a curious entity. Although changeless . . . it yet has a peculiar habit of growing. The possible, the general, the abstract: all these are subject to logical determinations— but . . . when we pass from possibility to actuality, when we come to events happening in time, we have left that ideal realm of logic, and have introduced a radical contingency into the universe."

CLOUD, PRESTON ERCELLE, JR., 1959, Paleoecology—retrospect and prospect: J. Paleont., vol. 33, no. 5, pp. 926–962. A review of fundamental concepts and problems, with an extensive bibliography.

COLBERT, EDWIN HARRIS, 1953, The record of climatic changes as revealed by vertebrate paleoecology, Chapter 21, pp. 249–271, in Harlow Shapley, ed., Climatic change; evidence, causes, and effects: Cambridge, Harvard Univ. Press, ix and 318 pp. "We assume that ecological conditions (and by extension, climatic conditions as well) were thus and so because of the presence of certain animals in the sediments. This assumption rests upon a basic precept that must be accepted at the outset, if our interpretation of past climates upon the evidence of vertebrate paleoecology is to have order and validity. The precept is that within wide limits the past is to be interpreted in terms of the present."

COLLINGWOOD, ROBIN GEORGE, 1956, The idea of history: New York, Oxford Univ. Press, xxvi and 339 pp. ". . . whereas science lives in a world of abstract universals, which are in one sense everywhere and in another nowhere, in one sense at all times and in another at no time, the things about which the historian reasons are not abstract but concrete, not universal but individual, not indifferent to space and time but having a where and a when of their own, though the where need not be here and the when cannot be now."

2——1960, The idea of nature: New York, Oxford Univ. Press, viii and 183 pp. "I conclude that natural science as a form of thought exists and always has existed in a context of history, and depends on historical thought for its existence. From this I venture to infer that no one can understand natural science unless he understands history: and that no one can answer the question what nature is unless he knows what history is. This is a question which Alexander and Whitehead have not asked. And that is why I answer the question, 'Where do we go from here?' by saying, 'We go from the idea of nature to the idea of history.'"

COOMBS, D. S., 1957, The growth of the geological sciences; an inaugural lecture delivered before the University of Otago on 5 July, 1956: Dunedin, New Zealand, Univ. Otago, 19 pp.

COOPER, GUSTAV ARTHUR, 1958, The science of paleontology: J. Paleont., vol. 32, no. 5, pp. 1010–1018. Paleontology is essentially a biological science embracing six disciplines: morphology, taxonomy, evolution, distribution of fossils in space, paleoecology, and correlation.

COTTA, BERNHARD VON, 1874, Die Geologie der Gegenwart: Leipzig, J. J. Weber, xii and 450 pp. "Die Mannigfaltigkeit der Erscheinungsformen ist eine nothwendige Folge der Summierung von Resultaten aller Einzelvorgänge, die nacheinander eingetreten sind . . ."

CRICKMAY, COLIN HAYTER, 1959, A preliminary inquiry into the formulation and applicability of the geological principle of uniformity: Calgary, Alberta, privately printed, iii and 50 pp. "Uniformity as a principle was originally conceived as a rupture with the older notion of geomorphic immutability, and was therefore in essence a theory of uniformity of change . . . The law of uniformity of the essence of things geologic must include, in order to be general, the possibility of wider variation of causes and effects than any so far assigned."

DALY, REGINALD ALDWORTH, 1910, Some chemical conditions in the pre-Cambrian ocean: 11th Internat. Geol. Cong., Stockholm, C. R., vol. 1, pp. 503–509. ". . . a strictly uniformitarian view of the ocean's history must be in error; . . . its evolution has, on the whole, meant progress from a relatively fresh condition to the present saline condition . . ."

2——1945, Biographical memoir of William Morris Davis: Nat. Acad. Sci. Biog. Mem., vol. 23, 11th Mem., pp. 263–303. "Valuable as it is, the scheme of the erosion cycle is not so important for research in earth science as the underlying philosophy, which makes deduction no whit inferior to induction in the tool-chest of the naturalist."

DAVIS, WILLIAM MORRIS, 1895, Bearing of physiography on uniformitarianism (Abs.): Geol. Soc. Am., B., vol. 7, pp. 8–11. "Uniformitarianism, reasonably understood, is not a rigid limitation of past processes to the rates of present processes, but a rational association of observed effects with competent causes. Events may have progressed both faster and slower in the past than during the brief interval which we call the present, but the past and present events differ in degree and not in kind."

2——1904, The relations of the earth sciences in view of their progress in the nineteenth century: J. Geol., vol. 12, pp. 669–687. "Geology objectively considered is not merely one of the earth's sciences; it is the whole of them: it is the universal history of the earth."

3——1926, The value of outrageous geological hypotheses: Science, n.s., vol. 63, pp. 463–468. "The very foundation of our science is only an inference; for the whole of it rests on the unprovable assumption that, all through the inferred lapse of time which the inferred performance of inferred geological processes involves, they have been going on in a manner consistent with the laws of nature as we know them now."

4——1926, Biographical memoir—Grove Karl Gilbert, 1843–1918: Nat. Acad. Sci. Biog. Mem., vol. 21, 5th Mem., v and 303 pp. Gilbert's laws of erosion are discussed on pp. 49–50, and his views of scientific method on pp. 145–148.

5——1954, Geographical essays (edited by Douglas Wilson Johnson): New York, Dover Publications, vi and 777 pp.

DAWSON, Sir JOHN WILLIAM, 1894, Some recent discussions in geology: Geol. Soc. Am., B., vol. 5, pp. 101–116. "Dead materialistic uniformitarianism, should it ever become the universal doctrine of science, would provoke a reaction in the human mind which would be itself a cataclysm."

DEER, WILLIAM ALEXANDER, 1953, Trends in petrology: Manchester Lit. and Phil. Soc., Mem. and Pr., vol. 94 (1952–1953) pp. 63–92. The petrologist "is presented with end products that have attained their present state after many changes both in space and time. The basic problem is to unravel this complex and ever-changing time-space pattern. Although this is the essence of all science, it is much more the everyday province of geology than of the other sciences. Most sciences start with the raw material; the geologist is presented with the finished product and, unlike the biologist, his material is not alive but dead. It is his job to make it live."

DEEVEY, EDWARD SMITH, JR., 1944, Pollen analysis and Mexican archeology: an attempt to apply the method: Am. Antiquity, vol. 10, no. 2, pp. 134–149. "On the whole, then, Occam's principle of economy of hypotheses compels us to hold in abeyance, for the moment, so detailed an application of the 'climatic factor' in human history, but this would not destroy the usefulness of slight changes of vegetation or climate as chronological markers in a pollen sequence."

2——1953, Paleolimnology and climate, Chapter 22, pp. 273–318 *in* Harlow Shapley, ed., Climatic change; evidence, causes, and effects: Cambridge, Harvard Univ. Press., ix and 318 pp. "In the study of lakes, which are the eco-systems that lend themselves most readily to the kind of analysis that does not lose sight of their essential wholeness, the geologist and the ecologist can collaborate most happily. One knows that the present is the key to the past, the other knows that the past is the key to the present, and each can think of the other as the captive expert."

DE GOLYER, EVERETTE LEE, 1948, Science—a method, not a field: Norman, Univ. of Oklahoma Press, 15 pp. ". . . we may be somewhat pragmatical and accept as truth that which is conformable with fact within our present understanding."

DEMAY, ANDRÉ, 1951, Observation, interprétation et théorie en géologie, *in* Sciences de la terre, XXI Cong. Internat. Phil. Sci., Paris, 1949: Paris, Hermann, pp. 41–54. In geology, where the more difficult problems are those of genesis or evolution, a theory generally attempts to reconstruct a sequence of phenomena and to disclose in these phenomena the workings of mechanical, physical, or chemical laws.

DINGLE, HERBERT, 1955, Philosophical aspects of cosmology, *in* Arthur Beer, ed., Vistas in astronomy: Oxford, Pergamon Press, vol. 1, pp. 162–166. ". . . we cannot grant the inaccessible past freedom to sow its wild oats as it pleases . . .; it must to some extent conform to the pattern on which we organize the present behavior of the universe."

DYLIK, JAN, 1953, Caractères du développement de la géomorphologie moderne: Soc. Sci. et Lettres Łódź, Cl. III, B., vol. 4, no. 3, 40 pp.

EBERT, HEINZ, 1953, Petrologie im kristallinen Praekambrium, genetisch oder historisch?: 19th Internat. Geol. Cong., Algiers, 1952, C.R., sec. 1, fasc. 1, pp. 81–87. "With respect to the 'precambrian shields' certain petrological mistakes remain hidden because of the widely spread misunderstanding that the genetical viewpoint of petrologists is [the] equivalent of the historical one of geologists. . . . Instead of attributing a genetical 'explanation' to rocks, one must consider them as products of a long and complicated evolution . . ."

EISLEY, LOREN COREY, 1958, Darwin's century; evolution and the men who discovered it: Garden City, N. Y., Doubleday, xvii and 378 pp. "If there is one mind that deserves to rank between the great astronomical geniuses of the seventeenth century and Charles Darwin in the nineteenth, it is James Hutton . . . He discovered an intangible thing against which the human mind had long armored itself. He discovered, in other words, time—time boundless and without end, the time of the ancient Easterners —but in this case demonstrated by the very stones of the world . . ."

EMMONS, EBENEZER, 1855, American geology, containing a statement of the principles of the science with full illustrations of the characteristic American fossils, with an atlas and a geological map of the United States, vol. 1, pt. 1: Albany, N. Y., Sprague, J. Munsell, xvi and 194 pp. "Each period then is a fragment; but the present is a greater fragment than all the past put together."

ENGELS, FRIEDRICH, 1940, Dialectics of nature; Translated and edited by Clemens Dutt, with a preface and notes by J. B. S. Haldane: New York, International Publishers, xvi and 383 pp. "The defect of Lyell's view— at least in its first form—lay in conceiving the forces at work on the earth as constant, both in quality and quantity. The cooling of the earth does not exist for him; the earth does not develop in a definite direction but merely changes in an inconsequent fortuitous manner."

FAIRCHILD, HERMAN LE ROY, 1904, Geology under the planetesimal hypothesis of earth origin (with discussion): Geol. Soc. Am., B., vol. 15, pp. 243–266. "Geologists have been too generous in allowing other people to make their philosophy for them."

FEIGL, HERBERT, 1943, Logical empiricism, pp. 373–416 in Dagobert David Runes, ed., Twentieth Century Philosophy: New York, Philosophical Library, 571 pp. "If all a priori knowledge is analytic, then we cannot deduce a synthetic assertion, like the principle of the uniformity of nature, from a priori premises. And if we try to validate induction on the basis of its certainly eminent success in the past, we are simply making an induction about induction and thus presuppose the very principle we set out to prove."

FEUER, LEWIS SAMUEL, 1957, The principle of simplicity: Philosophy of Science, vol. 34, pp. 109–122. The metascientific and methodologic principles of simplicity are independent concepts, the latter being no more than a special case of the principle of verifiability.
2——1959, Rejoinder on the principle of simplicity: Philosophy of Science, vol. 26, pp. 43–45. ". . . if we are going to make scientific statements concerning the distant past or future, the only way we can do so is by an extrapolative use of the known laws of nature. As applied to the past, this is precisely what historical geology does."

FISHER, *Sir* RONALD AYLMER, 1954, The expansion of statistics: Am. Scientist, vol. 42, no. 2, pp. 275–282, 293. Some of the greatest advances of the nineteenth century were accomplished by the application of statistical ideas. A case in point is Lyell's subdivision of the Tertiary sequence according to the percentage of fossil species with living descendants. But the statistical argument "by which this revolution in geological science was effected was almost immediately forgotten . . . It had served its purpose; the ladder by which the height had been scaled could be kicked down."

FLETT, *Sir* JOHN SMITH, 1940, Pioneers of British geology: Roy. Soc. New South Wales, J. Pr., 1939, vol. 73, pt. 2, pp. 41–66. ". . . though it is recognised that there are limitations to its application, the general principle holds good that the explanation of the past history of the earth must first be sought in the processes that we see going on around us at the present day."

FRANKEL, CHARLES, 1957, Explanation and interpretation in history: Philosophy of Science, vol. 24, pp. 137–155. ". . . it seems to be the case sometimes that when we ask for an explanation of a given phenomenon, what we want, and are satisfied to get, is an account of the stages of a process, the last stage of which is the phenomenon in the shape in which it exhibits those traits about which we have asked our question. This is one of the stable and accepted meanings of 'explanation' in ordinary usage."

FREYBERG, BRUNO VON, *et al.*, 1938, Fragen der geologischen Ausbildung: Deut. Geol. Ges., Zs., vol. 90, no. 3, pp. 148–166. "Für jede Ausbildung muss leitend sein, dass es *Erdgeschichte* ist, was wir treiben, keine *Erdbeschreibung*."

FU, C. Y., 1948, Methods and problems of geophysics: Chinese Geophys. Soc., J., vol. 1, no. 1, pp. 1–15. "There are . . . scientists who believe that natural laws tend to be simple and natural phenomena . . . inherently uniform. It is perhaps wise to aim at simplicity, but there is no *a priori* reason why nature should be so characterized. The fact is that simplicity and complexity alternate as science progresses . . ."

GALBRAITH, F. W., ed., 1961, What is geology?: Univ. Arizona, Studies in Geology, vol. 1, 36 pp. Contains eleven articles on the scope of geology and the interrelationship of the principal geological specialties.

GALLIE, WALTER BRYCE, 1955, Explanations in history and the genetic sciences: Mind, vol. 64, pp. 160–180. ". . . a characteristically genetic explanation emphasizes the one-way passage of time—what came earlier explains, in the genetic sense, what came later, and not *vice versa*. In other words the prior event is not taken, in conjunction with certain universal laws, to constitute both a sufficient and a necessary condition of the occurrence of the subsequent event."

GEIKIE, *Sir* ARCHIBALD, 1893, Geological change, and time: Smithsonian Inst., Ann. Rept., 1892, pp. 111–131. "Lord Kelvin is willing, I believe, to grant us some twenty millions of years, but Professor Tait would have us content with less than ten millions . . . After careful reflection on the subject, I affirm that the geological record furnishes a mass of evidence which no arguments drawn from other departments of nature can explain away, and which, it seems to me, can not be satisfactorily interpreted save with an allowance of time much beyond the narrow limits which recent physical speculation would concede."
2——1897, The founders of geology: London, Macmillan, x and 297 pp. Traces the evolution of geological thought from 1750 to 1820.

GIGNOUX, MAURICE, 1951, Le rôle joué par les sciences de la terre dans nos répresentations de la matière, *in* Sciences de la terre, XXI Cong. Internat. Phil. Sci., Paris, 1949: Paris, Hermann, pp. 123–129. The physical and dynamical properties which determine the mechanics of the deformation which a given substance will exhibit vary according to the scale of time employed by the investigator.

GILBERT, GROVE KARL, 1886, The inculcation of scientific method by example, with an illustration drawn from the Quaternary geology of Utah: Am. J. Sci., 3d ser., vol. 31 (whole no. 131), pp. 284–299. A natural phenomenon generally has multiple antecedents and consequents, the linear chains of which are plexiform. To discover the antecedents of phenomena, hypotheses are invented and tested. The reasoning involved in devising and testing hypotheses is analogical.
2——1896, The origin of hypotheses, illustrated by the discussion of a topographic problem: Science, n.s., vol. 3, pp. 1–13. ". . . hypotheses are always suggested through analogy. The unexplained phenomenon on which the student fixes his attention resembles in some of its features another phenomenon of which the explanation is known."

GILLISPIE, CHARLES COULSTON, 1951, Genesis and geology, a study in the relations of scientific thought, natural theology and social opinion in Great Britain, 1790–1850: Cambridge, Harvard Univ. Press, xiii and 315 pp. "Geology . . . was the first science to be concerned with the history of nature rather than its order . . . That its historical character made geology a different sort of science was appreciated from the beginning of its development. Doubts were sometimes expressed as to whether it could properly be called a science at all. Since the geologist, like the historian, had to rely largely on ancient relics and monuments of change, his conclusions were thought to be debatable in a way that those of the physicist, for example, were not."

GILLULY, JAMES, 1949, Distribution of mountain building in geologic time: Geol. Soc. Am., B., vol. 60, no. 4, pp. 561–590. ". . . I can see no grounds whatever for assuming any increased tempo for diastrophism during post-Lipalian time. The uniformitarianism of Lyell seems not yet to require any of the amendments that have been suggested."

GOGUEL, JEAN, 1948, La place de la géophysique parmi les disciplines géologiques: Géol. Appliquée et Prosp. Min., no. 2, pp. 123–135. "Certes dans l'ère de la géophysique nous faisons des mesures, mais ce que nous mesurons, ce n'est pas, ce n'est jamais ce que nous voudrions deviner."
2——1951, La géologie, science naturelle ou science physique?, in Sciences de la terre, XXI Cong. Internat. Phil. Sci., Paris, 1949: Paris, Hermann, pp. 7–15. From the physical sciences, geology is distinguished by its historical method. The historical reconstructions of geology must, however, be in accord with the physical, chemical, and mechanical laws, which are presumed to be permanent.

GOLD, THOMAS, 1956, Cosmology, in Arthur Beer, ed., Vistas in astronomy: London and New York, Pergamon Press, vol. 2, pp. 1721–1726. "The postulate of simplicity is sometimes so firmly in our minds that it is hard to recognize; but it is quite certain that it is a postulate of the greatest importance and that without it scientific progress, through the generalization of known facts, would be impossible."

GOODCHILD, JOHN GEORGE, 1896, Some geological evidence regarding the age of the earth: Roy. Phys. Soc. Edinburgh, Pr., vol. 13 (1896–1897), pp. 259–308. ". . . the fundamental idea which a geologist steadily keeps in mind is that all changes, physical and biological, which the records of the rocks inform us have taken place on the Earth in the Past, can only be understood and properly interpreted by reference to changes of the same nature which are known to be in progress during the Present. This, of course, does not imply absolute uniformitarianism (as this is commonly understood) but allows for catastrophism in certain exceptional cases, along with normal uniformity of action in the rest."

GOODMAN, NELSON, 1943, On the simplicity of ideas: J. Symbolic Logic, vol. 8, no. 4, pp. 107–121. "The most economical idea, like the most economical engine, is the one that accomplishes most by using least."
2——1955, Fact, fiction and forecast: Cambridge, Harvard Univ. Press., 126 pp. "The typical writer begins by insisting that some way of justifying predictions must be found; proceeds to argue that for this purpose we need some resounding universal law of the Uniformity of Nature, and then inquires

how this universal principle itself can be justified . . . Such an invention . . . seldom satisfies anyone else; and the easier course of accepting an unsubstantiated and even dubious assumption much more sweeping than any actual predictions we make seems an odd and expensive way of justifying them."

3——1958, The test of simplicity: Science, vol. 128, no. 3331, pp. 1064–1069. "Nothing could be more mistaken than the traditional idea that we first seek a true system and then, for the sake of elegance alone, seek a simple one. We are inevitably concerned with simplicity as soon as we are concerned with system at all; for system is achieved just to the extent that the basic vocabulary and set of first principles used in dealing with the given subject matter are simplified."

GORDEEV, D. I., 1960, Znachenije filosofskikh trudov V. I. Lenina dlya geologii (The meaning of V. I. Lenin's philosophical works for geology): Moscow Univ., Vest., ser. 4, Geol., no. 4, pp. 3–7. Geology, more than any other science, deals with cyclic phenomena; but this same periodicity, if not approached from Lenin's viewpoint, will acquire a metaphysical and anti-historical character, as can be seen in certain foreign writings.

2——1961, Stikhiinaya materialisticheskaya dialektika v geologicheskikh sochineniyakh M. V. Lomonosova (Dialectical materialism in the works of M. V. Lomonosov): Moscow Univ., Vest., Geol., no. 5, pp. 7–26. In 1763, Lomonosov introduced the principle of actualism in geology. Because he perceived that the earth is evolving in a definite direction, his uniformitarianism was more substantial than Lyell's.

GORDON, WILLIAM THOMAS, 1934, Plant life and the philosophy of geology: British Assoc. Adv. Sci., Rept., 1934, pp. 49–82. "Taking everything we know into consideration, the general consensus of opinion is that plants *do* afford an index of climatic changes, and that these changes have been very considerable in past time."

GOUDGE, THOMAS ANDERSON, 1958, Causal explanations in natural history: British J. Phil. Sci., vol. 9, no. 35, pp. 194–202. ". . . the model of a hierarchical deductive system, so often presented as the ideal to which the theoretical part of *every* science should approximate, is not relevant to the sciences concerned with natural history, however much it is relevant to non-historical sciences."

2——1961, The genetic fallacy: Synthese, vol. 13, no. 1, pp. 41–48. Geology, paleontology and other studies with a concern for historical development regularly and justifiably make use of genetic explanations. Fallacies are introduced in such explanations when temporal order is confused with logical order, when it is assumed that a genetic explanation says all there is to say about the phenomenon in question, when it is assumed that the phenomenon to be explained is simply the summation rather than the outcome of its antecedent stages, and when a trivial but necessary condition of a highly developed state is treated as if it were a sufficient condition of that state.

3——1961, The ascent of life; a philosophical study of the theory of evolution: Toronto, Univ. Toronto Press, 263 pp. ". . . the doctrine of evolution would fail to be intelligible unless the uniformitarian principle describes what is the case."

GOULD, R. P., 1957, The place of historical statements in biology: British J. Phil. Sci., vol. 8, pp. 192–210. "Retrodictions are obviously not as convincing as predictions as confirmation or falsification of an explanatory hypothesis because a Statement about the Past (which is largely hypothetical) is being used as though it were an observation record."

GRABAU, WARREN EDWARD, 1960, Geology as an historical tool: Gulf Coast Assoc. Geol. Societies, Tr., vol. 10, pp. 87–91. As a reconstructive art, geology is potentially applicable to any field of human effort concerned with the reconstruction of the past. Examples are given of historical events in the Civil War which are explicated in terms of geological evidence.

GREENE, JOHN COLTON, 1959, The death of Adam; evolution and its impact on Western thought: Ames, Iowa, Iowa State Univ. Press, 338 pp. ". . . the explanation of terrestrial phenomena must be sought in the everyday workings of nature, not in cataclysmic events. This was the basic principle of *uniformitarianism*, the foundation stone of modern geology . . ."

GRENE, MARJORIE, 1958, Two evolutionary theories: British J. Phil. Sci., vol. 9, no. 34, pp. 110–127; no. 35, pp. 185–193. ". . . instead of Ockham's razor we might adopt as a test of theories of evolution the opposite principle: that entities, or more generally perhaps aspects of reality . . . should not be *subtracted* beyond what is honest. In the light of this principle, we should ask of any theory of evolution, does it pretend to do without concepts which in fact it does not do without."

GRESSLY, AMANZ, 1838, Observations géologiques sur le Jura soleurois: Allgem. Schweiz. Ges. f. d. gesammten Naturwiss., Neue Denkschr., vol. 2, 349 pp. "Et d'abord il est deux faits principaux, qui charactérisent partout les ensembles de modifications que j'appelle *facies* ou *aspects de terrain:* l'un consiste en ce que *tel ou tel aspect pétrographique d'un terrain quelconque suppose nécessairement, partout où il se rencontre, le même ensemble paléontologique;* l'autre, en ce que *tel ou tel ensemble paléontologique exclut rigoureusement des genres et des espèces de fossiles fréquents dans d'autres facies.*"

GRIFFITHS, JOHN CEDRIC, 1960, Aspects of measurement in the geosciences: Mineral Industries, vol. 29, no. 4, pp. 1, 4–5, 8. "The natural sciences lie somewhere between the 'precise' sciences and the 'imprecise' sciences and possess some of the advantages and disadvantages of both; indeed, because of this transitional position, the procedures utilized in the natural sciences may benefit from an analysis using logical procedures from both 'hard' and 'soft' sciences."

GUNTER, GORDON, 1953, The development of ecology and its relationship to paleontology: Texas J. Sci., vol. 5, no. 2, pp. 137–147. ". . . all paleo-ecology is based upon the fundamental assumption that any given group of organisms lived in the past in an environment essentially similar to that in which they or their counterparts live today. The validity of this assumption is borne out by the fact that students of entirely different groups of organisms check each other in their paleoecological interpretations."

GUTENBERG, BENO, 1937, Geophysics as a science: Geophysics, vol. 2, no. 3, pp. 185–187.

HAARMANN, ERICH, 1935, Um das geologische Weltbild, *malleo et mente:* Stuttgart, Ferdinand Enke, xi and 108 pp. "Diese *universale Bedeutung der Geologie* muss uns nicht nur anspornen, eifrig an der Lösung der vielen geologischen Probleme weiterzuarbeiten, sondern auch veranlassen, unsere *Forschungsergebnisse in einer verständlichen und klaren Sprache mitzuteilen, die jeder Gebildete verstehen kann.* Nur so ist es möglich, dass die Geologie der Menschheit dort dient, wo sie ihr unentbehrlich ist: *als Grundstein für das gesamte Weltbild der Menschheit.*"

HABER, FRANCIS COLIN, 1959, The age of the world: Moses to Darwin: Baltimore, Johns Hopkins Press, xi and 303 pp. "It seems to me that the constant pressure of the Christian view of historical process on views of natural process helped to preserve a genetic outlook in terms of concrete, actualistic time. It was largely a matter of conditioning and prejudice during the sixteenth, seventeenth and eighteenth centuries, but it held the potential in readiness until the geologists discovered the real chronology of the earth in fossil strata . . ."

HACK, JOHN TILTON, 1960, Interpretation of erosional topography in humid temperate regions: Am. J. Sci., vol. 258-A (Bradley Volume), pp. 80–97. "The theory of dynamic equilibrium explains topographic forms and the difference between them in a manner that may be said to be independent of time."

HALDANE, JOHN BURDON SANDERSON, 1944, Radioactivity and the origin of life in Milne's cosmology: Nature, vol. 153, no. 3888, p. 555. Milne's cosmological theory permits description of events in terms of two different time scales, which have different implications for geologic history. Use of a time scale based on a finite past and Euclidean space implies that the rate at which energy has been liberated through subatomic or chemical change has been constant. Use of a scale based on hyperbolic space implies, conversely, that in the geological past chemical change was less efficient as a source of mechanical energy than it is now or will be in the future.

2——1949, Human evolution: past and future, Chapter 22, pp. 405–418, *in* Glenn L. Jepsen, Ernst Mayr, and George Gaylord Simpson, eds., Genetics, paleontology, and evolution: Princeton, Princeton Univ. Press, xiv and 474 pp. "We are polymorphic not only in our aesthetic but in our intellectual abilities. Ways of describing the world as different as analytical and projective geometry may be equally true, even if at present one human mind cannot accept more than one of them at a time."

3——1956, Can a species concept be justified?: Systematics Assoc., London, Pub. no. 2, pp. 95–96. A species is a name given to a group of organisms as a matter of convenience and necessity. ". . . the concept of a species is a concession to our linguistic habits and neurological mechanisms."

HALL, JAMES, 1883, Contributions to the geological history of the American continent: Am. Assoc. Adv. Sci., Pr., 1882, vol. 31, pp. 29–69. "The grand problem of geology is the entire history, chemical, physical, zoological and botanical, of the groups of strata constituting the formations of the globe."

HAMEISTER, ERNST, 1935, Übersichtstabelle der Methoden der angewandten Geophysik in der praktischen Geologie: Zs. prakt. Geol., vol. 43, no. 2, pp. 26–29. Shows in tabular form how different geophysical methods— electrical, seismic, magnetic, and gravimetric—may be used to investigate various geological phenomena.

HARRASSOWITZ, HERMANN, 1936, Die Grenzen geologischer Erkenntnis: Forsch. u. Fortschr., Berlin, vol. 12, no. 28, pp. 355–357. "Bei dieser ontologischen Methode oder der Anwendung des Grundsatzes des Aktualismus ist natürlich nie der Beweis zu erbringen, dass in der geologischen Vergangenheit Gesteine nicht auch unter anderen Umständen entstanden sind."

2——1936, Die Grenzen geologischer Erkenntnis in ihrer Bedeutung für Geologie und Bergbau: Metall u. Erz, vol. 33, no. 16, pp. 425–431. "Geologische Schlüsse geschichtlicher Art bleiben immer nur Annahmen, die niemals als Tatsachen erweisbar sind."

HARRINGTON, JOHN WILBUR, and HAZLEWOOD, E. L., 1962, Comparison of Bahaman land forms with depositional topography of Nena Lucia dune-reef-knoll, Nolan County, Texas: study in uniformitarianism: Am. Assoc. Petroleum Geol., B., vol. 46, no. 3, pp. 354–373. The development of present land forms in the Bahamas is taken as a basis for explaining the growth of a reef-knoll in the sub-surface Pennsylvanian of the Midland Basin in Texas.

HAUGHTON, SIDNEY HENRY, 1957, The geophysicist and some geological problems: Roy. Soc. S. Africa, Tr., vol. 35, pt. 2, pp. 59–69. "Observations are still the backbone of the science of geology: but to those made by the eye in the field or in the petrological, mineralogical, and palaeontological laboratories we now add the observations made by the varied types of instrument that the physicist has placed at our disposal."

HAWKES, LEONARD, 1957–1958, Some aspects of the progress of geology in the last fifty years; I: Geol. Soc. London, Quart. J., vol. 113, pp. 309–321, 1957; II: *ibid.*, vol. 114, pp. 395–410, 1958. Uniformitarians, in the Lyellian sense, are back again in force, although it is not yet clear how atmospheric oxygen or Precambrian jaspillite banded ironstone can be explained according to the dictum that the present is the key to the past.

HAWKINS, HERBERT LEADER, 1936, Palaeontology and humanity: British Assoc. Adv. Sci., Rept., 1936, pp. 57–80. "Just as a net has been described as a set of holes held together with string, so a series of strata must often represent a succession of non-sequences separated by films of sediment."
2——1938, Humanity in geological perspective: British Assoc. Adv. Sci., Rept., 1938, pp. 546–556. "The hoary imposture of the accuracy of the 'exact' sciences still deludes mankind, through the wildly illogical belief that a rigidly logical argument must reach a correct result whatever errors may have existed in the premises on which it is based."

HEDBERG, HOLLIS DOW, 1948, Time-stratigraphic classification of sedimentary rocks: Geol. Soc. Am., B., vol. 59, no. 5, pp. 447–462. ". . . man's . . . need to apply an arbitrary and strictly delimited classificatory system to what in Nature is frequently a continuous process or gradual change in characters results from the clamoring of the human mind for steps on which to rest as a relief from the more precarious footing of the continuous slope which often more correctly represents these natural relations."
2——1959, Towards harmony in stratigraphic classification: Am. J. Sci., vol. 257, no. 10, pp. 674–683. "Stratigraphic classification is the systematic zonation of the strata of the earth's crust with reference to any of the properties or attributes which rock strata may possess."

HEMPEL, CARL GUSTAV, 1942, The function of general laws in history: J. Phil., vol. 39, no. 1, pp. 35–48. "In history as anywhere else in empirical science, the explanation of a phenomenon consists in subsuming it under general empirical laws; and the criterion of its soundness is not whether it appeals to our imagination, whether it is presented in suggestive analogies, or is otherwise made to appear plausible . . . but exclusively whether it rests on empirically well confirmed assumptions concerning initial conditions and general laws."

2——1958, The theoretician's dilemma, a study in the logic of theory construction; *in* H. Feigl, M. Scriven and G. Maxwell, eds., Minnesota Studies in the Philosophy of Science, vol. 2: Minneapolis, Univ. Minnesota Press, pp. 37–98. "Scientific explanation, prediction, and postdiction all have the same logical character: they show that the fact under consideration can be inferred from certain other facts by means of specified general laws."

HENBEST, LLOYD GEORGE, 1952, Significance of evolutionary explosions for diastrophic division of earth history (Introduction to a symposium on the distribution of evolutionary explosions in geologic time): J. Paleont., vol. 26, pp. 299–318. "Without intending to deny that rhythm or vibration is a common characteristic of natural processes, it is evident that the theorizing on rhythm in nature has outrun the facts and possibly its actual importance."

HERSCHEL, *Sir* JOHN FREDERICK WILLIAM, 1831, A preliminary discourse on the study of natural philosophy, *in* The cabinet of natural philosophy conducted by the Rev. Dionysius Lardner: Philadelphia, Carey and Lea, 279 pp. ". . . geologists have no longer recourse, as formerly, to causes purely hypothetical . . . ; but rather endeavor to confine themselves to a consideration of causes evidently in action at present, with a view to ascertain how far they, in the first instance, are capable of accounting for the facts observed, and thus legitimately bringing into view, as residual phenomena, those effects which cannot be so accounted for."

2——1841, Whewell on inductive sciences: Quart. Rev. (London), vol. 68, pp. 177–238. "The most strenuous advocate for the exclusion of paroxysmal epochs will not contend for *perfect* uniformity so long as earthquakes are not of daily occurrence . . . : and the question as to what is and what is not paroxysm, to what extent the excursion from repose or gentle oscillation may go without incurring the epithet of a catastrophe, is one of mere degree, and of no scientific importance whatsoever."

HÖLDER, HELMUT, 1950, Geologie und Paläontologie in Texten und ihre Geschichte: Munich, Karl Alber Freiburg, xviii and 566 pp. A source book for geology and paleontology. Part 1, the last three sections of part 3, and part 4 are given largely to philosophical citations. Lengthy bibliography.

HOFF, KARL ERNST ADOLF VON, 1822–1841, Geschichte der durch Überlieferung nachgewiesenen natürlichen Veränderungen der Erdoberfläche: Gotha, Justus Perthes (vols. 1–3), H. Berghaus (vols. 4–5). ". . . überwiegende

Gründe erlauben nicht nur, sondern fordern sogar, dass man die Veränderungen, die man auf der Erdoberfläche wahrgenommen hat, und noch
wahrnimmt, nicht nur als auf einzelne Theile und Gegenden derselben
beschränkt betrachten muss, sondern auch dass man sie keinen ausserordentlichen Naturwirkungen, welche aufgehört haben, sondern allein der
Wirkung derjenigen Kräfte zuschreiben darf, durch die man noch jetzt
alle und jede Naturerscheinungen hervorgebracht sieht; und dass die für
uns unermessliche Grösse der Zeiträume, in welchen diese Kräfte allmählich und immerfort gewirkt haben, genügt, die Veränderungen durch eben
diese Kräfte hervorbringen zu lassen." (v. 3, pp. 252, 1834)

HOOYKAAS, REIJER, 1956, The principle of uniformity in geology, biology and
    theology: Victoria Inst., J. of Tr., vol. 88, pp. 101–116. "Strict uniformitarianism may often be a guarantee against pseudo-scientific phantasies
    and loose conjectures, but it makes one easily forget that uniformity is not
    a law, not a rule established after comparison of facts, but a methodological
    principle, preceding the observation of facts. It is the logical principle of
    parsimony of causes and of economy of scientific notions."
2——1959, Natural law and divine miracle: a historical-critical study of the
    principle of uniformity in geology, biology and theology: Leiden, E. J.
    Brill, 237 pp. "A less strict maintenance of uniformitarianism would
    perhaps give freer play to fantasy, but it might also open new vistas. The
    uniformitarian position, at its worst, forces past phenomena into a preconceived frame built upon events occurring in our time."

HORBERG, CARL LELAND, 1952, Interrelations of geomorphology, glacial geology, and Pleistocene geology: J. Geol., vol. 60, no. 2, pp. 187–190. ". . . a
    central aspect of geomorphology is its application to the task of deciphering
    Pleistocene history."

HORTON, ROBERT ELMER, 1945, Erosional development of streams and their
    drainage basins, hydrophysical approach to quantitative morphology:
    Geol. Soc. Am., B., vol. 56, no. 3, pp. 275–370. Develops laws of drainage
    composition, law of stream slopes, and law of overland flow.

HUBBERT, MARION KING, 1937, Theory of scale models as applied to the study
    of geologic structures: Geol. Soc. Am., B., vol. 48, no. 10, pp. 1459–1520.
    A general theory of the similarity between a model and its original, for
    purely mechanical systems, is derived and then applied to illustrative
    geologic problems.
2——1938, The place of geophysics in a department of geology: Am. Inst. Min.
    Met. Eng., Tech. Pub. 945, 19 pp. Ranked according to degree of dependence on other sciences for fundamental concepts, geology is a third-
    order discipline subordinate to physics, chemistry, and astronomy. Geophysics and geochemistry are not sciences, properly speaking, but are

rather the vehicles by which a more dependent science incorporates the data and techniques of a less dependent science.

3——(Hendricks, Thomas Andrews and Thiel, George Alfred, Chm.), 1949 Report of the Committee on Geologic Education of the Geological Society of America: Geol. Soc. Am., Int. Pr., 1949, pt. 2, pp. 17–21. ". . . your Committee recommend *that at all instructional levels from the most elementary to the most advanced, only those inferences be presented to students for which the essential observational data and the logical steps leading to the inference have also been presented.* The satisfaction of this criterion will compel a badly needed critical reexamination from the ground up of the logical structure of geological science."

HUNT, CHARLES B., 1956, A skeptic's view of radiocarbon dates: Univ. of Utah, Anthropological Papers, no. 26, pp. 35–46. "Consistency of results, including consistency in a series of radiocarbon dates, may be evidence of precision, but it is *not* evidence of accuracy although it commonly is cited as such."

HUTTON, JAMES, 1788, Theory of the earth; or an investigation of the laws observable in the composition, dissolution, and restoration of land upon the globe: Roy. Soc. Edinburgh, Tr., vol. 1, pp. 209–304. "In examining things present, we have data from which to reason with regard to what has been; and from what has actually been, we have data for concluding with regard to that which is to happen hereafter. Therefore upon the supposition that the operations of nature are equable and steady, we find, in natural appearances, means for concluding a certain portion of time to have necessarily elapsed, in the production of those events of which we see the effects."

HUXLEY, THOMAS HENRY, 1862, The anniversary address to the Geological Society: Geol. Soc. London, Quart. J., vol. 18, pp. xl–liv. "Allied with geology, palaeontology has established two laws of inestimable importance: the first, that one and the same area of the earth's surface has been successively occupied by very different kinds of living beings; the second, that the order of succession established in one locality holds good, approximately, in all."

2——1881, The rise and progress of palaeontology: Nature, vol. 24, pp. 452–455. "The whole fabric of palaeontology is based upon two propositions: the first is, that fossils are the remains of animals and plants; and the second is, that the stratified rocks in which they are found are sedimentary deposits; and each of these propositions is founded upon the same axiom that like effects imply like causes."

Interdepartmental Stratigraphic Committee, USSR, 1956, Stratigraphic classification and terminology (Translated from the Russian by John Rodgers.): Int. Geol. Rev., vol. 1, Feb. 1959, pp. 22–38. A scheme of classification is developed on the premises that stratigraphic subdivisions exist objectively in Nature, rather than subjectively in the mind of the investigator, and that these subdivisions reveal the actual course of geologic history.

JACOBS, JOHN ARTHUR, and ALLAN, D. W., 1956, The thermal history of the earth: Nature, vol. 177, no. 4500, pp. 155–157. Studies of earth models suggest that the crust of the earth, down to about 100 km, may have been remelted during the first billion or so years of earth history, that the rate of cooling of the earth was greater in the past than now, and thus that orogenic activity may have decreased with time.

JAMES, HAROLD LLOYD, 1960, Problems of stratigraphy and correlation of Precambrian rocks with particular reference to the Lake Superior region: Am. J. Sci., vol. 258-A (Bradley Volume), pp. 104–114. "The most basic geologic law is that of superposition. Though the principle itself can be called obvious, its application to highly deformed rocks is rarely easy."

JELETZKY, JURIJ ALEXANDER, 1956, Paleontology, basis of practical geochronology: Am. Assoc. Petroleum Geol., B., vol. 40, no. 4, pp. 679–706.
2——1962, The allegedly Danian dinosaur-bearing rocks of the globe and the problem of the Mesozoic-Cenozoic boundary: J. Paleont., vol. 36, no. 5, pp. 1005–1018. "This obviously geologically contemporary extinction of the terrestrial and marine Mesozoic animals at the Maestrichtian-Danian boundary must reflect some kind of radical, world-wide change in the physical regime of our planet. This event can be quite properly referred to as a 'catastrophe' or 'revolution' . . ."

JENNINGS, HERBERT SPENCER, 1933, The universe and life: New Haven, Yale Univ. Press, 94 pp. "The universe would be so much easier to deal with if the laws of its action were simple and uniform. Let us assume therefore that they are simple and uniform! The doctrine is a marked case of wishful thinking."

JEPSEN, GLENN LOWELL, 1949, Selection, "orthogenesis" and the fossil record: Am. Phil. Soc., Pr., vol. 93, no. 6, pp. 479–500. "Orthogenesis was frequently expressed as a 'law' at a time when there was an eager search for biological phenomena or principles which could be called laws, after the model of the eponymic laws of physics and chemistry."

JOHNSON, DOUGLAS WILSON, 1933, The rôle of analysis in scientific investigation: Geol. Soc. Am., B., vol. 44, no. 3, pp. 461–494. "Multiple working hypotheses as a method, employed in connection with critical analysis as an instrument of precision, offer us . . . the best guarantee of success in scientific research."

2——1938–1942, Studies in scientific method: J. Geomorphology, vol. 1, pp. 64–66, 147–152; vol. 2, pp. 366–372; vol. 3, pp. 59–64, 156–162, 256–262, 353–355; vol. 4, pp. 145–149, 328–332; vol. 5, pp. 73–77, 171–173. "Hence the golden rule of scientific exposition: *Never discuss an unknown in terms of an unknown.*"

JOHNSON, MARTIN, 1951, The meanings of time and space in philosophies of science: Am. Scientist, vol. 39, no. 3, pp. 412–421. "Crudely stated, it may be said that physical science is interested in the changing or the flux of the world, not in any static picture, and is in fact a study of a sequence of events whose basic pattern is a time-order."

JORALEMON, IRA BEAMAN, 1952, Age cannot wither, or varieties of geological experience: Econ. Geol., vol. 47, no. 3, pp. 243–259. ". . . we have not sufficient reliable evidence . . . for hard-and-fast generalizations or laws of ore occurrence."

JOYSEY, KENNETH A., 1952, Fossil lineages and environmental change: Geol. Mag., vol. 89, no. 5, pp. 357–360. "An essential key to the interpretation of fossil communities lies in the study of living animals on the present day time-plane. Equally, the process of evolution can only be seen in perspective when the zoological picture is projected along the dimension of geological time."

JUDSON, SHELDON, 1958, Geomorphology and geology: New York Acad. Sci., Tr., ser. 2, vol. 20, no. 4, pp. 305–315. "Geology is history. Perhaps more than any other single characteristic, the time factor distinguishes geology from the other sciences."

2——1960, William Morris Davis—an appraisal: Zs. Geomorph., vol. 4, no. 3–4, pp. 193–201. "The cycle of erosion had an almost immediate acceptance not only because of its skilful presentation but also because the geologic profession was ready for such a synthesis. Uniformitarianism, a major element in the development of the cycle, was by then almost universally accepted by geologists. Furthermore, the orderly development of landforms through successive stages represented a type of non-organic evolution . . . in harmony with the exciting new ideas in organic evolution then sweeping the scientific world."

3——1961, Archaeology and the natural sciences: Am. Scientist, vol. 49, no. 3, pp. 410–414. "The archaeologist reconstructs history largely from objects recovered from the ground . . . Such reconstructions are generally classed under the heading of 'pre-history', a term that has always bothered me a bit because the inference exists that events of the pre-literate period do not combine to constitute history, a particularly unacceptable inference to a geologist."

KAISER, ERICH, 1931, Der Grundsatz des Aktualismus in der Geologie: Deut. Geol. Ges., Zs., vol. 83, pp. 389–407. "Aber ganz abwegig ist es, wenn man jetzt mehr und mehr von einem *Gesetz des Aktualismus* liest, trotzdem doch die Begründer und Verfechter des Aktualismus nur von einer aktualistischen (ontogenetischen) Methode redeten."

KALKOWSKY, ERNST, 1910, Geologie und Phantasie: Naturw. Ges. Isis, Dresden, Sitzungsber. u. Abh., Jan-June, 1910, pp. 10–19. "Nie hat jemand eine ganze Schicht gesehen, immer nur Stückchen davon hat er vor Augen gehabt, und das Ganze ist in jedem einzelnen Falle nichts als ein Phantasiegebilde. Der Begriff der Schicht, meine ich, steht somit etwa auf derselben Stufe, wie der des Atoms . . ."

KELVIN, WILLIAM THOMSON, *Baron*, 1864, On the secular cooling of the earth: Roy. Soc. Edinburgh, Tr., vol. 23, pt. 1 (1861–1862), pp. 157–169. "It must be admitted that many geological writers of the 'Uniformitarian' school, who in other respects have taken a profoundly philosophical view of their subject, have argued in a most fallacious manner against hypotheses of violent action in past ages. If they had contented themselves with showing that many existing appearances, though suggestive of extreme violence and sudden change, may have been brought about by long-continued action, or by paroxysms not more intense than some of which we have experience . . . their position might have been unassailable . . ."
2——1871, On geological time: Geol. Soc. Glasgow, Tr., vol. 3, pt. 1, pp. 1–28. "It would be just as reasonable to take a hot water jar, such as is used in carriages, and say that that bottle has been as it is for ever—as it was for Playfair to assert that the earth could have been for ever as it is now, and that it shows no traces of a beginning, no progress towards an end."

KEMENY, JOHN GEORGE, 1959, A philosopher looks at science: Princeton, D. Van Nostrand, xii and 273 pp. The scientist's assumption of the "uniformity of nature" simply asserts that human capacities and the complexity of nature are such that it is possible for scientists to learn something about nature in a reasonably short time. See pp. 59–64 for a discussion of the principle of uniformity.

KERMACK, K. A., 1956, Species and mutations: Systematics Assoc., London, Pub. no. 2, pp. 101–103. "Our justification for creating species, mutations, etc., in paleontology is solely one of practical convenience: the categories themselves are man-made and artificial."

KHAIN, VIKTOR EFIMOVICH, 1958, Nekotorye filosofskiye voprosy sovremennoy geologii (Some philosophic questions of modern geology): Nauchnye Doklady Vysshei Shkoly, Filosofskiye Nauki, vol. 2; Moskva, pp. 148–161. Soviet scientists approach each theoretical question from the standpoint of dialectic materialism; each geological concept in the Soviet science follows the idea of a directed and irreversible development.

2——1961, Lomonosov i sovremennaya geologiya (Lomonosov and modern geology): Sovet. Geol., vol. 12, pp. 14–28. Since the end of World War II, geology has tended to change from a descriptive to an explanatory science whose aim is to discover the basic laws of the development of the planet Earth, and of the earth's crust in particular.

KING, CLARENCE, 1877, Catastrophism and evolution: Am. Naturalist, vol. 11, pp. 449–470. "Men are born either catastrophists or uniformitarians. You may divide the race into imaginative people who believe in all sorts of impending crises—physical, social, political—and others who anchor their very souls *in status quo*."

KING, LESTER CHARLES, 1953, Canons of landscape evolution: Geol. Soc. Am., B., vol. 64, no. 7, pp. 721–752. "There is a general homology between all epigene landscapes."

2——1957, The uniformitarian nature of hillslopes: Edinburgh Geol. Soc., Tr., vol. 17, pt. 1, pp. 81–101. ". . . the manner of hillslope evolution is essentially uniformitarian in all climatic realms outside the frigid zones and the erg deserts."

KITTS, DAVID B., 1963, Historical explanation in geology: J. Geol., vol. 71, pp. 297–313.

KOBAYASHI, TEIICHI, 1944, Concept of time in geology: Imp. Acad. Tokyo, Pr., vol. 20, no. 7, pp. 475–478 (On the major classification of the geologis cal age.); no. 10, pp. 742–750 (An instant in the Phanerozoic Eon and it-bearing on geology and biology.); pts. 1 and 3 in a series of articles. "Time . . . may be classed into two major kinds, one with and the other without historical contents. Time of the latter kind is abstract, absolute, objective and physical; that of the former kind, concrete, relative, subjective and historical. *Geological age* belongs to the former while *chronology* is of the latter kind . . ."

KOBER, LEOPOLD, 1946, Geo-Logismus: Geog. Ges. Wien, Mitt. vol. 89, no. 1–6, pp. 3–7. "Absolute kosmo-geo-logische Wahrheit aller Evolution der Erde ist der Geo-Logismus: die Vergeistigung der Natur in Menschen. Der Mensch ist das Mittel der Natur, sich selbst zu erkennen."

KOCH, LEO E., 1949, Tetraktys; the system of the categories of natural science and its application to the geological sciences: Australian J. Sci., vol. 11, no. 4, suppl., 31 pp. "This method of application of the Tetraktys coincides with Aristotle's doctrine . . . that a system of categories of a very elementary nature is the necessary basis of *any* scientific definition."

KRUMBEIN, WILLIAM CHRISTIAN, 1960, The "geological population" as a framework for analysing numerical data in geology: Liverpool and Manchester Geol. J., vol. 2, pt. 3, pp. 341–368. Statistical analysis may be applied to classes and aggregates of geological objects and events, toward the ends of deriving inferences and making predictions. (With annotated bibliography.)

2——1962, The computer in geology; quantification and the advent of the computer open new vistas in a science traditionally qualitative: Science, vol. 136, no. 3522, pp. 1087–1092. "The present dominantly empirical aspect of much data analysis in geology is not disturbing in a science where much effort . . . must still be directed toward a search for controls and responses in a web of intricately interlocked data."

KRYNINE, PAUL DIMITRI, 1951, A critique of geotectonic elements: Am. Geophys. Union, Tr., vol. 32, no. 5, pp. 743–748. ". . . it seems that the classical principle of the description and classification of landforms as introduced by W. M. Davis—the concepts of describing landforms in terms of *structure*, *process*, and *stage*—could be fruitfully applied to the classification of geotectonic elements. This powerful generalization of the immortal Davis is indeed the great 'universal solvent' of geology, and no subject in the Earth sciences contains problems that would not yield to this method, providing that adequate data can be gathered."

KUENEN, PHILIP HENRY, 1958, Experiments in geology: Geol. Soc. Glasgow, Tr., vol. 23, pp. 1–28. "In a certain sense present day processes show an experimental relation to historical geology and the investigation of ancient rocks . . . Hence . . . the 'Present as key to the Past' is an experimentally tainted maxim."

KULP, JOHN LAURENCE, 1961, Geologic time scale; Isotopic age determinations on rocks of known stratigraphic age define an absolute time scale for earth history: Science, vol. 133, no. 3459, pp. 1105–1114.

KUMMEROW, EGMONT, 1932, Die aktualistische Methode in der Geologie: Deut. Geol. Ges., Zs., vol. 84, pp. 563–565. "Der Grundsatz des Aktualismus besitzt keine uneingeschränkte Gültigkeit. Er lässt sich auf periodische Vorgänge im allgemeinen nicht anwenden. Die Gegenwart ist um so weniger geeignet, für alle Kräfte und Vorgänge der Vergangenheit Beispiele zu liefern, als sie keine normale Warmzeit, sondern eine glaziale Ausnahmezeit darstellt."

LADD, HARRY STEPHEN, 1957, Introduction, and Paleoecological evidence, Chapters 1 and 2, pp. 1–66, *in* Treatise on marine ecology and paleoecology, vol. 2, Paleoecology (H. S. Ladd, ed.): Geol. Soc. Am., Mem. 67. Describes the nature of the paleontological record, and explains how ancient marine environments are reconstructed on the basis of paleonto-logical and lithological evidence.

LAHEE, FREDERIC HENRY, 1909, Theory and hypothesis in geology: Science, n.s., vol. 30, pp. 562–563. "The misconception of the need for unity of cause may be an outgrowth from the doctrine of uniformity. But uni-formity is not synonymous with simplicity, any more than complexity is synonymous with chaos."

LAIRD, JOHN, 1919, The law of parsimony: Monist, vol. 19, no. 3, pp. 321–344. "The complexity of the universe can never be simplified out of existence . . . It is conceivable, therefore, that the law of economy is neither more nor less than a rule of direction stating that we should always select the simplest of any general propositions which may be true and ascertainable, since it is these truths only that are likely to aid the mind in making further dis-coveries. This rule shows the path of wisdom in view of the limited powers and scope of the mind."

LAKE, PHILIP, 1930, The centenary of Lyell's Principles of Geology: Geol. Mag., vol. 67, pp. 433–436. "Each attitude of mind has its own dangers, and the chief danger of the uniformitarian attitude is that the mind may be closed to new ideas . . . There is little need now, however, to dwell on the dangers of the uniformitarian attitude. There is nothing uniformitarian about post-war geological theories, and there are so many of them that it is difficult not to keep an open mind. Meanwhile geology progresses in spite of theories."

LAMONT, ARCHIE, 1944–1945, Geology in literature: Quarry Managers' J., vol. 27, pp. 555–560, 567; vol. 28, pp. 28–31, 77–79, 121–127, 194–202, 287–291, 365–369, 405–407, 439–441, 495–499, 551–554. Illustrates, with many quotations, the impact of geological ideas on literature. "Geology is *par excellence* the science which deals with the repetition of the same events in widely separated epochs."

LANE, ALFRED CHURCH, 1906, The geologic day: J. Geol., vol. 14, pp. 425–429. "Time is measured by change, and change . . . must progress from point to point . . . there is always a rate of progress which is measurable, and any interval of time must be marked by a certain stage in the change, and so begin differently at different points."

LASKY, SAMUEL GROSSMAN, 1947, The search for concealed deposits—a re-orientation of philosophy: Am. Inst. Min. Met. Eng., Tech. Pub. 2146, Mining Tech., vol. 11, no. 3, 8 pp. "Instead of looking for information indicating that ore is likely to be present, we ought . . . to balance and fit together the observed facts so as to discover whether [it] could be present. In other words, the geology need be only permissive instead of definitely indicative."

LAUNAY, LOUIS DE, 1922, La science géologique, ses méthodes, ses résultats, ses problèmes, son histoire: Paris, Armand Colin, 3d. ed., viii and 775 pp. A survey of geological methodology and the evolution of geological ideas.

LAUTERBACH, ROBERT, 1957, Paläogeophysik, *in* Geol. u. Geophys. (Karl-Marx-Univ., Geol. u. Pal. Inst.), pp. 57–66.

LECLERQ, RENÉ, 1960, Histoire et avenir de la méthode expérimentale: Paris, Masson, 138 pp. "La recherche des puits de pétrole par l'examen géologique du sol est devenue courante. Ce n'est qu'un cas particulier de la méthode qui consiste à prévoir une allure de stratification ou une couche déterminée à un endroit précis à partir de la connaissance de la géologie d'une region. On émet une hypothèse en se fondant sur des observations et on la vérifie par une autre observation."

LE CONTE, JOSEPH, 1900, A century of geology: Pop. Sci. Monthly, vol. 56, pp. 431–443, 546–556. "The fundamental idea underlying geological thought is the history of the earth."

LE GRAND, HARRY E., 1962, Perspective on problems of hydrogeology: Geol. Soc. Am., B., vol. 73, pp. 1147–1152. "Mathematical research relating to synthesis of the elements of hydrogeology is showing some promise, but it tends to wilt when faced with a kaleidoscope of hydrologic conditions caused by heterogeneities of geology."

LENZEN, VICTOR F., 1955, Procedures of empirical science: Int. Encyc. Unified Sci., vol. 1, pt. 1, Chicago, Univ. Chicago Press, pp. 280–339. "A stage in the investigations of correlations of events is the determination of temporal sequences. The history of political events, historical geology, and paleontology are arrangements of events in temporal order. Science in the form of history systematizes observations of events by fitting them into schemes of development of the cosmos, life and society."

LEOPOLD, LUNA B., and LANGBEIN, WALTER B., 1962, The concept of entropy in landscape evolution: U. S. Geol. Survey, Prof. Paper 500-A, 20 pp. ". . . we believe that the concept of entropy and the most probable state provides a basic mathematical conception which does deal with relations of time and space. Its elaboration may provide a tool by which the various philosophic premises still characterizing geomorphology may be subjected to critical test."

LINTON, DAVID LESLIE, 1948, The ideal geological map: Adv. Sci., vol. 5, no. 17, pp. 141–149. The symbols of geological cartography will require standardization on an international scale before all geological maps will be intelligible to all geologists. Choices of color symbols have been variously determined by the "principle of the distinctive horizon" (bold colors for index formations), by the association of ideas (fiery red for volcanic rocks), by the "principle of associative colouring" (e.g., red for the Old Red sandstone), and by reference to a spectrum arbitrarily selected to indicate relative ages of rocks. Even greater diversity and confusion exist in the array of index letters and numbers—variously sequential, nonsequential, or hybrid—used to designate map units.

LOEWINSON-LESSING, FRANTS YULEVICH, 1954, A historical survey of petrology (Translated from the Russian by S. I. Tomkeieff): London, Oliver and Boyd, vi and 112 pp. "There is one fundamental and leading principle which lies at the base of petrological science. This principle was dimly perceived at the dawn of modern geology and petrology and since that time its conception has been steadily growing and expanding. The principle is that of development—the evolution or gradual change to which every rock is subjected from the very moment of its formation."

LOSSKIY, NIKOLAI ONUFRIEVICH, 1956, Organicheskii aktualizm Bergsona (Organic actualism of Bergson) in An introduction to philosophy, Chapter XX, pp. 190–198: Frankfurt a. M., Possev. Actualism is a philosophic concept according to which the whole world consists of events and processes which appear and disappear in time.

LUCIUS, MICHEL, 1957, Les principes fondamentaux de travail et de recherche en géologie: Soc. Nat. Luxembourg, B., n.s., vol. 49, no. 60, pp. 141–143. "Mais le principe d'actualisme n'est pas toujours apparent. Nous ne voyons pas se former aujourd'hui du granite, des schistes cristallins. Dans la nature, les deux états extrêmes d'un même phénomène peuvent être si différents, qu'il n'apparait, à première vue, aucune connexion entre eux. Mais si on trouve une suite d'états intermédiaires entre les deux extrèmes, on peut admettre un état original identique. C'est le principe des états intermédiaires."

LYELL, CHARLES, 1830, Principles of geology, being an attempt to explain the former changes of the earth's surface, by reference to causes now in operation, vol. 1: London, John Murray, 511 pp. "Our estimate . . . of the value of all geological evidence . . . must depend entirely on the degree of confidence which we feel in regard to the permanency of the laws of nature. Their immutable constancy alone can enable us to reason from analogy, by the strict rules of induction, respecting the events of former ages."

MACGREGOR, ALEXANDER MIERS, 1951, Some milestones in the Precambrian of Southern Rhodesia: Geol. Soc. S. Africa, Pr., vol. 54, pp. xxvii-lxvi. "In dealing with rocks formed when the world was less than half of its present age, a strict adherence to the doctrine of uniformitarianism is considered unjustified . . . the [older Precambrian] sedimentary rocks were closer in their mineral composition to igneous rocks and were therefore more amenable to granitization. The geothermal gradient was probably steeper . . . The crust of the earth may have been less rigid . . . Volcanism was more active than it is now . . . The earth's rotation was more rapid and tidal forces may have been greater."

McLACHLAN, DAN, JR., 1961, A guess as to what is science: Physics Today, vol. 14, no. 6, pp. 22–27. "When one science swallows another . . . the general attitude among scientists is that the new science has built a firm foundation under the old science. The physicists and chemists would like to do this for geology . . ."

McLAREN, DIGBY JOHNS, 1959, The role of fossils in defining rock units, with examples from the Devonian of western and Arctic Canada: Am. J. Sci., vol. 257, no. 10, pp. 734–751. "All geology depends on one basic principle—that it is possible to interpret the history of the earth by examining the positional relationships of rock and mineral bodies. Stratigraphy relies primarily on a special case of this principle—the positional relationships of stratified rock bodies, from which derives the law of superposition.

MANLEY, GORDON, 1953, Climatic variation: Roy. Meteorological Soc., Quart. J., vol. 79, pp. 185–209. (Reviews of modern meteorology No. 9) "The forecaster on a November day who considers whether a low moving up the Baltic will occlude more or less rapidly on account of a newly established snow cover in Lithuania is probably touching on the whole problem of the alimentation of the Pleistocene ice caps. But the time scale is very different. Yet it is the present writer's conviction that in the present can be sought the key to the past; the day-to-day synoptican will do well to integrate some of his findings into a greater pattern."

MARSH, OTHNIEL CHARLES, 1879, The history and methods of palaeontological discovery: Am. Assoc. Adv. Sci., Pr., vol. 28, no. 1880, pp. 1–42. "If I may venture . . . to characterize the present period in all departments of science, its main feature would be a *belief in universal laws.*"

MASON, STEPHEN FINNEY, 1953, Main currents of scientific thought: New York, Henry Schuman, viii and 520 pp.

MAYR, ERNST, 1951, Bearing of some biological data on geology: Geol. Soc. Am., B., vol. 62, no. 5, pp. 537–546. "As far as paleontology is concerned, there has been a rather futile argument in recent years as to whether it is a branch of geology or of biology. The answer, of course, is that it is either both or neither."

2——1957, Species concepts and definitions, *in* The species problem. A symposium presented at the Atlanta meeting of the American Association of the Advancement of Science, Dec. 28–29, 1955: Washington, D. C., Am. Assoc. Adv. Sci., Pub. 50, pp. 1–22. ". . . the analysis of the species problem would be considerably advanced, if we could penetrate through such empirical terms as phenotypic, morphological, genetic, phylogenetic, or biological, to the underlying philosophical concepts. A deep, and perhaps widening gulf has existed in recent decades between philosophy and empirical biology. It seems that the species problem is a topic where productive collaboration between the two fields is possible."

MELTON, MARK ALDRIDGE, 1958, Correlation structure of morphometric properties of drainage systems and their controlling agents: J. Geol., vol. 66, no. 4, pp. 442–460. "The variability in any natural environment is the product of the happenings in many geologic periods . . . To argue that this variability could ever be entirely explained is absurd. Geology differs from physics and other exact sciences in the kind of variability encountered, as well as the amount . . . the concept of the universe applicable to geology and physics is accordingly quite different; . . . there is not just a single scientific 'world view', but two or perhaps many."

MERRIAM, JOHN CAMPBELL, 1921, The earth sciences as the background of history: Sci. Monthly, vol. 12, no. 1, pp. 5–7. "Our greatest scientific contributions to the study of history and of origins have come through geological and biological investigations. Geology is the greatest of historical sciences."

MILLER, BENJAMIN LEROY, 1941, Geology and the allied sciences: Pennsylvania Acad. Sci., Pr., vol. 15, pp. 82–89. ". . . the principal reasons for geological investigation should be economic."

MILLER, HUGH, 1939, History and science; a study of the relation of historical and theoretical knowledge: Berkeley, Univ. of California Press, x and 201 pp. "Thus nature is still conceived as pure history, in human history, and as pure structure, in physicochemical theory; and biology and geology remain alone in the synthesis of historical and theoretical principles. While everyone speaks of universal evolution, the presence of evolutionary character is really admitted only in some branches of biological and geological science; and even here the dominant intention is often a reduction of historical change to structural law, just as if Darwin had never lived and taught."

MILLER, JOHN PRESTON, 1959, Geomorphology in North America: Przeglad Geograficzny, Warsaw, vol. 31, no. 3–4, pp. 567–587. "Like all the other phases of historical geology, geomorphic history is based ultimately on the Principle of Uniformitarianism. This view that 'the present is the key to the past' implies only that physical and chemical mechanisms have been constant in kind, but it recognizes that their magnitudes and rates may have varied. In any case, interpretation of history assumes an adequate knowledge of the present. Contrary to the belief of Davis and his followers that process was known or could be inferred, current opinion holds that our knowledge of present processes and their products is so meager that inferences about geomorphic history rest too heavily on untested assumptions."

MILLHAUSER, MILTON, 1954, The scriptural geologists, an episode in the history of opinion: Osiris, vol. 11, pp. 65–86. "Stratigraphy and paleontology not only established the preconditions for a biological theory like Darwin's; in their day they were nearly as revolutionary in their impact on the popular mind."

MILNE, EDWARD ARTHUR, 1935, Some points in the philosophy of physics: time, evolution and creation: Smithsonian Inst., Ann. Rept., 1933, pp. 219–238. "The world is thus a continuing system; each particle or nebula has an evolutionary experience behind it and in front of it, with ultimate decay as its goal, yet the world as a whole cannot be said to decay. It is not the same in an observer's today as in the observer's yesterday, but it is the same forever."

MISES, RICHARD VON, 1951, Positivism, a study in human understanding: Cambridge, Harvard Univ. Press, vi and 404 pp. ". . . the various sciences are distinguished by the *objects* they deal with . . . If we examine a little more closely what the individual scientists make concrete statements about, we find that the objects of the various sciences can be summarized under a common expression: every proposition of a positive science refers to actions of men and observed by men (Bridgman) . . . The purely descriptive natural sciences do not constitute an exception . . . even the geologist can only say what happens if one examines rocks by means of hammer and drill."

MITCHELL, RAOUL C., 1955, Changement de cadence des phénomènes géologiques: Cahiers Géol., Seyssel, no. 33, pp. 331–334. The principle of uniformity must be emended to allow for variations in the rate at which geologic processes have acted during the past.

MOORE, RAYMOND CECIL, 1948, Stratigraphical paleontology: Geol. Soc. Am., B., vol. 59, no. 4, pp. 301–326. ". . . stratigraphical paleontology is synonomous with paleontology itself, viewed with the eyes of a geologist, whereas so-called systematic paleontology comprises a purely biological approach, without reference to geology except for arrangement of fossils in order of time succession."

2——1949, Meaning of facies: Geol. Soc. Am., Mem. 39, pp. 1–34. ". . . many features of geological history can never be learned, because they never became incorporated in the rock record. These also are actual parts of earth history, which happen not to have left a trace . . . it is obvious that geological history is circumscribed in no way by what we think we know about it."

3——1955, Invertebrates and geologic time scale, pp. 547–574 *in* Arie Poldervaart, ed. Crust of the earth (a symposium),: Geol. Soc. Am., Spec. Paper 62, viii and 762 pp. "The elementary but fundamental Law of Superposition, on which every geologist depends for indispensable evidence of the relative age of sedimentary deposits laid down bed on bed, could be formulated by reasoning, without studies made first in the field. On the other hand, the nature of fossil assemblages in any given layer is not subject to prediction, at least not without much accumulated experience."

MORRISON, R. B., GILLULY, JAMES, RICHMOND, G. M., and HUNT, C. B., 1957, In behalf of the Recent: Am. J. Sci., vol. 255, pp. 385–393. ". . . geologic . . . time is subdivided on a purely arbitrary, subjective basis, largely for convenience in classification of formations and depending upon the amount of detail recognized in the rock-stratigraphic record. Duration has never been a determining factor in defining time units, just as thickness has not been in defining formations or other rock-stratigraphic units."

MOULTON, FOREST RAY, 1929, Thomas Chrowder Chamberlin as a philosopher: J. Geol., vol. 37, pp. 368–379. "The methods of science, like styles in dress, appear to come and go in cycles. At one period it is the fashion to emphasize the accumulation of observational data and to disparage attempts at their interpretation . . . The opposite extreme is the fashion of hastily constructing theories, one after another, for explaining each new phenomenon that is observed . . . the fashion during periods of frenzied research when priority is more highly prized than soundness and permanence."

MÜLLER, ARNO HERMANN, 1951, Grundlagen der Biostratonomie: Deut. Akad. der Wiss., Berlin, Abh., Kl. Math. u. allgem. Naturwiss., Jg. 1950, Nr. 3, 147 pp. In seeking to reconstruct the sequences of events which have led to the preservation of organic remains as fossils, biostratonomy employs the principle of actualism.

MUNITZ, MILTON KARL, 1957, Space, time and creation, philosophical aspects of scientific cosmology: Glencoe, Ill., The Free Press and The Falcon's Wing Press, x and 182 pp. ". . . the Perfect Cosmological Principle, like

the Principle of the Uniformity of Nature, functions not as a factual statement at all, capable of serving as a premise in an argument, but as a definition that functions as a criterion or rule of what in the language of science
is to be regarded as a law."

MURCHISON, RODERICK IMPEY, 1839, The Silurian System, pt. 1: London,
   John Murray, 576 pp. ". . . while I rejoice in what I would call the
   'Lyellian method' of testing geological phenomena by modern analogies,
   I do not believe in the doctrine, that the dislocations of the present day are
   produced by causes of the same degree of *intensity* as those of which geology
   affords the proof. I must always be of opinion that, although they may
   belong to the same class, the geological catastrophe (such as the *overturning
   of a mountain chain*) and modern earthquake cannot be placed side by side
   without our exclaiming '*sic parvis componere magna.*'"

NAGEL, ERNEST, 1952, Some issues in the logic of historical analysis: Sci.
   Monthly, vol. 74, pp. 162–169. "The distinction between history and
   theoretical science is . . . analogous to the difference between medical
   diagnosis and physiology, or between geology and physics. A geologist
   seeks to ascertain, for example, the sequential order of geologic formations,
   and he is able to do so by applying various physical laws to the materials
   he encounters; it is not the geologist's task, *qua* geologist, to establish the
   laws of mechanics or of radioactive disintegration that he may employ."

NEWELL, NORMAN DENNIS, 1956, Catastrophism and the fossil record: Evolution, vol. 10, no. 1, pp. 97–101.
2——1959, The nature of the fossil record: Am. Phil. Soc., Pr., vol. 103, no. 2,
   pp. 264–285. "Paleontological exploration of the past is a sampling procedure in which provisional estimates of the whole are made from small,
   frequently biased, samples."
3——1959, Adequacy of the fossil record: J. Paleont., vol. 33, no. 3, pp. 488–499.
   ". . . the limitations of the fossil record are not so much a matter of poor
   preservation or insufficient quantity but rather insufficient collecting and
   inefficient methods of preparing fossils."
4——1962, Paleontological gaps and geochronology: J. Paleont., vol. 36, no. 3,
   pp. 592–610. ". . . the geologic systems, series and stages are all, in the last
   analysis, world-wide units that are defined and identified by means of
   their fossils. The time scale that is based on them is in no sense subjective
   or arbitrary."

NICHOLSON, HENRY ALLEYNE, 1872, Contemporaneity of strata and the doctrine of geological continuity: Canadian J., n.s., vol. 13, pp. 269–281.
   ". . . in so far as we can judge from the known facts of the present distribution of living beings, the recurrence of exactly the same fossils in beds far
   removed from one another is *prima facie* evidence that the strata are *not*

exactly contemporaneous; but that they succeeded one another in point of time, though by no long interval geologically speaking."

NIGGLI, PAUL, 1949, Probleme der Naturwissenschaften, erläutert am Begriff der Mineralart: Basel, Birkhäuser, Wissensch. u. Kultur, vol. 5, xii and 240 pp. "Die Natur ist also nach gewissen Grundprinzipien *gestaltet*, und es ist diese *Gestaltung* und *Gliederung*, die trotz der offensichtlichen 'Unerschöpflichkeit' den Versuch der Naturerkenntnis zu keinem hoffnungslosen Beginnen stempelt."

NÖLKE, FRIEDRICH, 1937, Astronomie und Geologie: Deut. Geol. Ges., Zs., vol. 89, no. 3, pp. 167–175. Astronomical hypotheses, such as those related to the secular decline in solar radiation and to the migration of the moon's orbit away from the earth, have important implications for geologic history, e.g., warmer climates and stronger tides in the geological past.

NOLAN, THOMAS B., 1962, Role of the geologist in the national economy: Geol. Soc. Am., B., vol. 73, no. 3, pp. 273–278. To problems involving the welfare of nations, geologists might usefully apply the habits of thought ingrained by the practice of their science. These include the tendency to think in three dimensions, an almost instinctive use of the fourth dimension of time, an appreciation of the inevitability of change, and an acceptance of the variety of natural materials which lie below the surface of the earth.

NORTH, FREDERICK JOHN, 1933, From Giraldus Cambrensis to the geologic map, the evolution of a science: Cardiff Naturalists' Soc., Rept. and Tr., vol. 64, pp. 20–97. "The spirit of caution that was evident in Kidd's lectures was also shared by those who founded the Geological Society of London, for their chief aim was to observe and to record; they discouraged further attempts at solving problems that could not be solved until more information was available, and they would have nothing to do with hypotheses like those in which the previous century had been so prolific. This attitude profoundly affected the course of geologic investigation, which for many years consisted solely in the collection and classification of specimens and facts."

2——1934, From the geological map to the Geological Survey, Glamorgan and the pioneers of geology: Cardiff Naturalists' Soc., Rept. and Tr., vol. 65, pp. 41–115. "Geology cannot be regarded as an exact science, for, from the nature of things, the unknown must always be greater in extent than the known. We can never hope to examine more than an exceedingly small proportion of the rocks of the earth's crust, and all the fossils we can ever hope to unearth will represent but an infinitesimally small part of the whole pageant of life."

ÖPIK, ERNST JULIUS, 1954, The time scale of our universe: Irish Astron. J., vol. 3, no. 4, pp. 89–108. "We will be guided by the principle of minimum hypothesis, or economy of thought, which requires that new laws of nature must not be used for the explanation of phenomena which can be accounted for by known laws."

ORCEL, JEAN, 1954, Essai sur le concept d'espèce et les classifications en minéralogie et pétrographie: Soc. Franç. Minér. Crist., B., vol. 77, pp. 397–432. The evolution of the concept of mineral species reflects an interaction of discoveries and ideas developed in crystallography, chemistry, and mineralogy. According to the present concept, mineral species are differentiated primarily on the basis of two criteria: crystalline structure, as determined by the refraction of x-rays, and chemical composition.

OSBORN, HENRY FAIRFIELD, 1904, The present problems of paleontology: Pop. Sci. Monthly, vol. 66, pp. 226–242. "Just as the uniformitarian method of Lyell transformed geology, so the uniformitarian method is penetrating paleontology and making observations of animal and plant life as it is today the basis of the understanding of animal and plant life as it was from the beginning."

PAGE, DAVID, 1863, The philosophy of geology; a brief review of the aim, scope and character of geological inquiry: Edinburgh, William Blackwood and Sons, ix and 160 pp. "The philosophy of our science is thus to believe in the fixity and uniformity of nature's operations, and under this belief to regulate all our methods and arrange our results."

PARKS, WILLIAM ARTHUR, 1925, Cultural aspects in geology: Nature, vol. 116, no. 2916, pp. 432–435. ". . . uniformitarianism is being questioned seriously from both the inorganic and the organic points of view. We are swinging back to a conception of a milder catastrophism variously expressed as rhythm, diastrophism, and so on."
2——1928, Some reflections on paleontology: Geol. Soc. Am., B., vol. 39, pp. 387–402. ". . . the modern tendency is to regard the time factor as the *motif* of geology—that is, to regard geology, in the first instance, as history. We speak . . . more and more of the sequence of events in time."

PASSENDORFER, EDWARD, 1950, O zasadzie aktualizmu w geologii (na marginesie książki L. Cayeux, "Causes anciennes et causes actuelles en géologie"): Wiadomósci Muz. Ziemi (Polish Geol. Mag.), vol. 5, no. 1, pp. 63–70. ". . . les phénomènes géologiques anciens sont dus aux mêmes causes, agissant selon les mêmes lois qu'aujourd'hui. Les mêmes causes dans les mêmes conditions donnent les mêmes effets."

PENCK, WALTHER, 1953, Morphological analysis of land forms (Translated from the German by Hella Czech and Katherine Cumming Boswell):

London, Macmillan, xiv and 429 pp. "This state of affairs forms the substance of the fundamental law of morphology: the modelling of the earth's surface is determined by the ratio of the intensity of the endogenetic to that of the exogenetic displacement of material."

PIATNITZKY, P. P., 1939, Sur les défauts de la terminologie du Précambrien: Int. Geol. Cong., 17th., U.S.S.R., Rept., vol. 2, pp. 15–24. Many of the names given to geological systems below the base of the Cambrian are ambiguous, illogical, subjective or otherwise unscientific.

PLAYFAIR, JOHN, 1802, Illustrations of the Huttonian theory of the earth: Edinburgh, Cadell and Davies, and William Creech (Facsimile reprint with an introduction by George W. White, Urbana, Univ. of Illinois Press, 1956, xix, xx and 528 pp.). "Every river appears to consist of a main trunk, fed from a variety of branches, each running in a valley proportioned to its size, and all of them together forming a system of vallies, communicating with one another, and having such a nice adjustment of their declivities, that none of them join the principal valley, either on too high or too low a level; a circumstance which would be infinitely improbable, if each of these vallies were not the work of the stream that flows in it."

POINCARÉ, HENRI, 1913, The foundations of science (Translated by George Bruce Halsted) in Science and Education, a series of volumes for the promotion of scientific research and educational progress, J. McKeen Cattell, ed., v. 1: New York, Science Press, 553 pp. "It is often said: Who knows whether the laws do not evolve and whether we shall not one day discover that they were not at the Carboniferous epoch what they are to-day? What are we to understand by that? What we think we know about the past state of our globe, we deduce from its present state. And how is this deduction made? It is by means of laws supposed known . . . So that if the laws of nature were not the same in the Carboniferous age as at the present epoch, we shall never be able to know it, since we can know nothing of this age, only what we deduce from the hypothesis of the permanence of these laws."

POPOV, VLADĪMĪR IVANOVĪCH, 1940, Protiv morfologicheskikh ustanovok v geologii (Against morphological tendencies in geology): Sovet. Geol., no. 5–6, (May-June), pp. 167–172. The view that geology is basically a morphologic science, devoted to a study of external structural features and their relationships, not only inhibits the development of the science but is contrary to Engels' dialectic principle of 'struggle of the opposites.'

POPPER, KARL RAIMUND, 1957, The poverty of historicism: London, Routledge and Kegan Paul, xiv and 165 pp. ". . . while the theoretical sciences are mainly interested in finding and testing universal laws, the historical

sciences take all kinds of universal laws for granted and are mainly interested in finding and testing singular statements."

2——1959, The logic of scientific discovery: London, Hutchinson, 479 pp.
"Thus we are led back, by our concept of simplicity . . . to that rule or
principle which restrains us from indulgence in *ad hoc* hypotheses and aux-
iliary hypotheses: to the principle of parsimony in the use of hypotheses."

POTONIÉ, ROBERT, 1957, Vom Wesen der Geschichte der Geologie: Germany,
Geol. Landesanst., Geol. Jb., vol. 74, pp. 17–30. "Wir wollen in den
Schriften der Geologen und Forscher blättern, welch sich in einem höheren
Sinne um die Geschichte unserer Wissenschaft bemüht haben; nicht nur
registrierend, sondern nach allgemeineren Erkenntnissen strebend, zu
höheren Schluszfolgerungen."

PRUVOST, PIERRE, 1951, Les refuges de l'hypothèse en géologie, *in* Sciences de
la terre, XXI Cong. Internat. Phil. Sci., Paris, 1949: Paris, Hermann,
pp. 3–39. Scientific hypotheses, though born to die, have ways of living
on, perpetuated in handbooks, embedded in popular opinion, upheld by
scientific authority, or concealed by jargon. Geologic hypotheses, in particular, may seek refuge at the bottom of the ocean, in the depths of the
earth, or in the abyss of time.

RAGUIN, EUGÈNE, 1951, Méthodes d'études des formations géologiques anciennes, *in* Sciences de la terre, XXI Cong. Internat. Phil. Sci., Paris, 1949:
Paris, Hermann, pp. 17–28. The principle of actualism is insufficient for
the reconstruction of Precambrian history. For explication of the older
terranes, studies of the spatial distribution of metamorphic zones, structural
analysis of igneous rocks, comparative studies of orogenic belts, and geochemical investigations are becoming increasingly useful.

RAMSAY, ANDREW CROMBIE, 1880, On the recurrence of certain phenomena
in geological time: British Assoc. Adv. Sci., 50th Meeting, Rept., pp. 1–22.
". . . whatever may have been the state of the world long before geological
history began, as now written in the rocks, all known formations are comparatively so recent in geological time, that there is no reason to believe
that they were produced under physical circumstances differing either in
kind or degree from those with which we are now more or less familiar."

RASTALL, ROBERT HERON, 1943, Terminology in the geological sciences:
Nature, vol. 151, no. 3828, pp. 294–295. The decline of popular interest
in geology is partly due to "the volume and complication of the nomenclature now current . . . By far the greater part of the trouble arises from
the activities of the palaeontologists . . . It is commonly understood that
modern palaeontology is supposed to be founded on evolutionary lines,
but it really seems that the present tendency to hair-splitting distinctions

and infinite multiplication of new names is exactly contrary to the true principle of evolution . . . these modern developments are mainly due to museum specialists; people with the Civil Service mind, who spend all their time indoors, surrounded by mountains of monographs instead of mountains of rocks, and appear to delight in making everything as complicated as possible."

Ravikovich, A. N., 1961, Uniformistskoye uchenie Layella i ego istoricheskie korni (Uniformitarian teaching of Lyell and its historical roots): Akad Nauk, SSSR, Inst. Geol., Ocherki po istorii geol. znanii, vol. 9, pp. 48–83. In uniformitarian thinking, von Hoff and Hutton were the forerunners of Lyell.

Read, Herbert Harold, 1937, Certain aspects of metamorphic geology: Liverpool Geol. Soc., Pr., vol. 17, pt. 2, pp. 103–114. "Time because it means history, and in one aspect life, is the most fascinating aspect of metamorphic studies. We shall some day read a long and complex history at a glance in a single section of a metamorphic rock, and shall know even the minor episodes of its dark and turbulent past."

2——1943, Geology in the war and in the peace: Junior Institution of Engineers, London, J. and Record of Tr., vol. 53, pt. 7, pp. 179–187. "Any man looking out of any window sees a geological laboratory in constant and full-scale operation."

3——1957, The granite controversy: London, Thomas Murby, xix and 430 pp. "The study of history of any kind depends upon documents and records. For the history of the earth's crust, these documents are the rocks and their reading and interpretation are often difficult operations. It is true that for certain classes of rocks, made at the earth's surface, the uniformitarian method is valid and sufficient . . . But many important rocks were clearly made deep in the crust and no uniformitarian key can unlock their secrets."

Rensch, Bernhard, 1960, The laws of evolution, pp. 95–116 in Sol Tax, ed., Evolution after Darwin, vol. 1: Chicago, Univ. of Chicago Press. The laws of evolution are of three kinds: laws of causality, laws of psychic parallelism, and laws of logic.

Richey, James Ernest, 1952, Some aspects of geological research and their practical application: Adv. Sci., vol. 9, no. 34, pp. 122–133. "A pattern of evidence may include an anomaly at variance with apparently valid conclusions reached on other grounds. Anomalies may not constitute vital objections to a conclusion: on further investigation they may yield and conform to the prior solution, or prove irrelevant. On the other hand the recognition of anomalies has frequently been a most fruitful source of discovery in geology as in other sciences."

Rios, José Maria, 1962, Limitaciónes y perfectibilidad permanente en la cartografía geológica. Problemas que plantean las tecnicas modernas: Inst. Geol. y Minero de España, Notas y Comuns., no. 65, pp. 127–138. "Por mi parte me alegro mucho de poder participar aún de la época en que la cartografía geológica es un arte y no una fabricación, en que el géologo es una persona y no una máquina."

Robertson, Thomas, 1956, The presentation of geological information on maps: Adv. Sci., vol. 13, no. 50, pp. 31–41. Geological maps are not real portrayals of Nature. "At the very start of our field investigations we abstract from geology as a whole the subject that we choose to study" and the treatment of that subject will be "based upon a theory regarding the succession and structure of the rocks." In the alternating flux of induction and deduction attending the construction of a geological map, deductions are sometimes built upon deductions "until an inverted pyramid of formidable size is balanced upon a very small base."

Rodgers, John, 1959, The meaning of correlation: Am. J. Sci., vol. 257, no. 10, pp. 684–691. ". . . in stratigraphy the term *correlation* should and in fact ordinarily does mean the attempt to determine time relations among strata . . ."

Roever, W. P. de, 1956, Some differences between post-Paleozoic and older regional metamorphism (with discussion): Geol. en Mijnbouw, vol. 18, no. 4, pp. 123–127. "There is apparently not only an evolution of life during the history of the earth, but also some change in the character of the metamorphic mineral assemblages produced during the main phases of regional metamorphism of the various orogenic epochs."

Roger, J., 1961, La documentation en géologie: B. Biblio. Fr., vol. 6, no. 1, pp. 5–15. "Des progrès considérables ont été réalisés en géologie (au sens large) depuis une trentaine d'années dans les moyens et les techniques d'observations. Par contre, dans la plupart des domaines, les généralisations, les larges hypothèses, les théories n'ont pas sensiblement avancé et souvent ne sont conservées qu'en raison de l'absence de vues satisfaisantes. Cette situation est due . . . pour une grande part à l'incapacité de réunir, dans un temps suffisamment court, une quantité considérable de données éparses dans une littérature énorme ou issues d'observations nouvelles qu'il fait souhaiter aussi abondantes et précises que possible."

Romer, Alfred Sherwood, 1949, Time series and trends in animal evolution, Chapter 7, pp. 103–120, *in* Glenn Lowell Jepsen, Ernst Meyr, and George Gaylord Simpson, eds., Genetics, paleontology, and evolution: Princeton, Princeton Univ. Press, xiv and 474 pp. "From time to time we are confronted with teleological evolutionary theories, evolved in general in the philosopher's cabinet or theologian's study, which base evolutionary events upon the 'design' of some external force—a deity, or 'Nature'—or upon some mysterious 'inner urge' of the organism or its protoplasm . . . In general, the paleontologist can dispose of such theories by the application of Occam's razor."

2——1959, Vertebrate paleontology, 1908–1958: J. Paleont., vol. 33, no. 5, pp. 915–925. ". . . divisions between disciplines are tending to become faint. Physics merges into chemistry; chemistry and physics merge into biology and geology; paleontologists, invertebrate and vertebrate alike, bridge the gap between geology and biology."

ROSSITER, *Mrs.* P. M., 1937, Basic for geology, Psyche Minatures, gen. ser. no. 90: London, Kegan Paul, Trench, Trubner, 164 pp. "There is no danger now that the theories of geology will seem to be against true religion, little that such forces as the *vis plastica* will be made the 'causes' of effects, even less that the printed word will not get into the hands of workers in far countries. The danger with which the present-day worker is faced is that the printed word may not make sense when it gets there."

RUSSELL, ISRAEL COOK, 1907, Concentration as a geological principle: Geol. Soc. Am., B., vol. 18, pp. 1–18. One of the important net results of physical and chemical changes affecting the earth throughout geological history has been the concentration of mineral substances which originally were widely disseminated.

RUSSELL, RICHARD JOEL, 1958, Geological geomorphology: Geol. Soc. Am., B., vol. 69, no. 1, pp. 1–22. "Never before has the earth been so well armored [by soils and vegetation] against processes of weathering and erosion. Effects of this armoring must exist in sedimentary deposits to a degree which makes it a bit hazardous to press too far any interpretation of the remote past on the basis of the present."

RUTTEN, MARTIN GERARD, 1955, Mathematics in geology and the former extension of the Pre-Cambrian (with discussion): Geol. en Mijnbouw, vol. 17, pp. 192–193. ". . . every geological phenomenon is determined by an almost immeasurable number of variables, horrifying in their complexity and in the number of their interrelations. Every formula that uses a limited number of variables is therefore but an extreme simplification."

2——1957, Origin of life on earth, its evolution and actualism: Evolution, vol. 11, pp. 56–59. "There was, of course, at one time a pre-actualistic period in the earth's history . . . These early stages have often been called pre-geologic. It seems better to speak of them as pre-actualistic, for a non-actualistic early geologic history is well conceivable."

3——1962, The geological aspects of the origin of life on earth: Amsterdam, New York, Elsevier, vii and 146 pp. ". . . the findings of geology are in complete agreement with the modern biological views on the origin of life through natural causes."

SAINT-SEINE, PIERRE DE, 1951, Les fossiles au rendez-vous du calcul, *in* Sciences de la terre, XXI Cong. Internat. Phil. Sci., Paris, 1949: Paris, Hermann, pp. 78–84. Although generally regarded as a descriptive science, paleontology is rapidly developing predictive capabilities.

SANDBERG, C. G. S., 1932, Der Grundsatz des Aktualismus und die Bestimmung gewisser Ablagerungen als glaziogene: Deut. Geol. Ges., Zs., vol. 84, pp. 636–641.

SCHÄFER, WILHELM, 1959, Elements of actuo-paleontology: Salt Marsh Conf. Pr., 1958, Univ. Georgia, Marine Inst., pp. 122–125. Actuogeology and actuopaleontology are based upon direct observation of events. "Because the work is in the present there is the possibility of experiment. The result is in all cases the knowledge of timeless laws. These laws in the hands of the geologist and paleontologist cast light on the geological occurrences of the earth's past, and they give an insight into the past life and death upon the earth and into the environments of this life."

SCHAUFELBERGER, P., 1962, Geologie und Bodenlehre: Neues Jb. Geol. u. Paläont., Mh., 1962, no. 4, pp. 179–203. Pedology draws its resources from several of the physical and biological sciences, but geology—by virtue of its concern with problems of weathering in general—is the discipline which appropriately coordinates and unifies the various approaches to soil science.

SCHEIDEGGER, ADRIAN EUGEN, 1960, Mathematical methods in geology: Am. J. Sci., vol. 258, pp. 218–221. The mathematical method is indispensable in testing the consistency of inferences drawn from different sets of geological data.

SCHENCK, HUBERT GREGORY, 1961, Guiding principles in stratigraphy: Geol. Soc. India, J., vol. 2, pp. 1–10. Compares original and modern usages relating to the concepts of superposition, horizontality, original continuity, uniformitarianism, faunal succession, strata identified by fossils, rock-stratigraphic unit, time-stratigraphic unit, and facies.

SCHINDEWOLF, OTTO HEINRICH, 1944, Grundlagen und Methoden der paläontologischen Chronologie: Berlin-Nikolassee, Gebrüder Borntraeger, 152 pp. Because fossils, taken in their natural order of succession, record an evolutionary development which is both linear and irreversible, paleontology provides the surest basis for geological chronology.
2——1944, Über die Bedeutung der Paläontologie als geologische Grundwissenschaft: Reichsamt für Bodenforschung, Jb., vol. 63 (1942), pp. 629–676.

3——1948, Wesen und Geschichte der Paläontologie; Probleme der Wissenschaft in Vergangenheit und Gegenwart No. 9, Gerhard Kropp, ed.: Berlin, 108 pp. As a historical science, paleontology has provided an empirical basis for evolutionary theory in modern biology. By the same token, paleontology is basic to systematic stratigraphy and hence to geology in general.

4——1957, Comments on some stratigraphic terms: Am. J. Sci., vol. 255, no. 6, pp. 394–399. "The sedimentary rocks, by themselves . . . do not yield any specific time marks, setting aside the old law of superposition, which can provide relative age indications only in a restricted manner and which is unfit for age correlations."

SCHNEER, CECIL JACK, 1960, History in science, Chapter 10, pp. 159–185 *in* The search for order; the development of the major ideas in the physical sciences from the earliest times to the present: New York, Harper, xvii and 398 pp. "The development of geological science, as a *historical* science, within the larger framework of the growth of natural philosophy, has a special importance that can be compared only with the development of astronomy as a descriptive science."

SCHRÖDINGER, ERWIN, 1956, On the peculiarity of the scientific world view, pp. 178–228 *in* What is life? and other scientific essays: Garden City, N. Y., Doubleday, viii and 263 pp. "This object, the vivid and colourful picture of past events is one hundred percent purely ideal . . . Should one, therefore, omit it and study only the actual remains . . .?

The picture is not only a permissible tool, but also a goal . . . it is hard to understand why that which is self-evident in the historical sciences ought to pass for heresy in the physical sciences, namely, to deal with events and situations that are inaccessible to direct observation. The historical sciences do that almost exclusively."

SCHUH, FRIEDRICH, 1937, Gedanken über die bei der tierischen Entwicklung hervortretenden Entwicklungsrichtungen: Paläont. Zs., vol. 19, no. 1–2, pp. 116–126. From an evolutionary point of view, progress is a series of psycho-organic victories over the inorganic world.

SCHWINNER, ROBERT, 1943, Ist die Geologie wirklich eine "historische" Wissenschaft?: Neues Jb. Min., Geol., u. Paläont., 1943, Abt. B., no. 5, pp. 130–136. It is misleading to call geology an historical science. History deals exclusively with man; geology is an explanatory natural science.

SCRIVEN, MICHAEL, 1959, Explanation and prediction in evolutionary theory; Satisfactory explanation of the past is possible even when prediction of the future is impossible: Science, vol. 130, no. 3374, pp. 477–482. "The most important lesson to be learned from evolutionary theory today is a negative one: the theory shows us what scientific explanations need not do. In particular it shows us that one cannot regard explanations as unsatisfactory when they do not contain laws, or when they are not such as to enable the event in question to have been predicted."

2—1961, The key property of physical laws—inaccuracy, pp. 91–101 *in* Herbert Feigl and Grover Maxwell, eds., Current issues in the philosophy of science: New York; Holt, Rinehart and Winston, 484 pp. "The most interesting fact about laws of nature is that they are virtually all known to be in error. And the few exceptions . . . seem quite likely to become casualties before long . . . but they *represent* great truths so we forgive them their errors."

SCROPE, GEORGE JULIUS DUNCOMBE POULETT, 1858, The geology and extinct volcanos of central France, 2nd ed.: London, John Murray, xvii and 258 pp. "The periods which to our narrow apprehension . . . appear of incalculable duration, are in all probability but trifles in the calendar of nature. It is Geology that, above all other sciences, makes us acquainted with this important though humiliating fact."

SEARES, FREDERICK HANLEY, 1938, The concept of uniformity, growth and reactions (Elihu Root lectures of Carnegie Institute of Washington on the influence of science and research on current thought): Carnegie Inst. Washington, Supp. Pub. 37, 50 pp. "Evolution . . . stands as the law of all the laws of science and thus symbolizes two things of interest here: the notion of pervasive recurrence and regularity in the world of phenomena— the *uniformity of nature*—and the growth of the notion of uniformity itself; in a word, the development of *the idea that the phenomena of the physical world can be described by simple laws.*"

SEDGWICK, ADAM, 1831, Address to the Geological Society, delivered on the evening of the 18th of February, 1831, on retiring from the President's Chair: Geol. Soc. London, Pr., 1826–1833, pp. 281–316. ". . . we all allow, that the primary laws of nature are immutable . . . and that we can only judge of effects which are past, by the effects we behold in progress . . . But to assume that the secondary combinations arising out of the primary laws of matter, have been the same in all periods of the earth, is . . . an unwarranted hypothesis with no *a priori* probability, and only to be maintained by an appeal to geological phaenomena."

SEEGER, RAYMOND JOHN, 1958, Scientist and theologian?: Washington Acad. Sci. J., vol. 48, no. 5, pp. 145–152. ". . . all our views are based upon an underlying assumption of the uniformity of nature, not only those views of scientists but also those of theologians, for whom dependability is a *sine qua non.*"

SEMPER, MAX, 1911, Bemerkungen über Geschichte der Geologie und daraus resultierende Lehren: Geol. Rundschau, vol. 2, pp. 263–277. "Ausserdem ist es in der Geologie gar nicht möglich, sich auf die Wiedergabe von Beobachtungen zu beschränken. Jedes Profil enthält eine grosse Anzahl von Angaben, die auf Schlüssen, auf dem Zusammenwirken von Beobachtungen und theoretischen Elementen beruhen."

SEWARD, Sir ALBERT CHARLES, 1959, Plant life through the ages; a geological and botanical retrospect: New York, Hafner, xxi and 603 pp. "It does not in the least follow that because all living species of a genus are now confined to areas with a certain range of temperature, therefore extinct species, almost identical with the living species, were equally susceptible to limiting factors."

SHERLOCK, ROBERT LIONEL, 1922, Man as a geological agent; an account of his action on inanimate nature: London, H. F. and G. Witherby, 372 pp. "Man's most permanent memorial is a rubbish heap, and even that is doomed to be obliterated."

SHOTWELL, JAMES THOMSON, 1949, Time and historical perspective, in Time and its mysteries, ser. 3, pp. 63–91: New York, New York Univ. Press ". . . though we cover all time with numbers, we do so only in order to find things in it, and to know where we are when we find them . . . In short we mark Time by events rather than events by Time."

SHROCK, ROBERT RAKES, 1948, Sequence in layered rocks; a study of features and structures useful for determining top and bottom or order of succession in bedded and tabular rock bodies: New York, McGraw-Hill, xiii and 507 pp.

SIGAL, J., 1961, Existe-t-il plusieurs stratigraphies?: France, Bur. Rech. géol. et min., Serv. d'Inf. géol., B. (Chronique Mines d'Outre-mer, Suppl. no. 297) an. 13, pp. 2–5. Distinguishes between faciostratigraphy, zoneostratigraphy, and chronostratigraphy as aspects of stratigraphy whose respective concerns are with the establishment of local stratigraphic columns, the definition of units bounded by isochronous surfaces and the understanding of earth history.

SIMPSON, GEORGE GAYLORD, 1941, The role of the individual in evolution: Washington Acad. Sci., J., vol. 31, no. 1, pp. 1–20. "Whatever happens in organic evolution, or indeed within the realm of the biological sciences, happens to an individual."
2——1950, Evolutionary determinism and the fossil record: Sci. Monthly, vol. 71, pp. 262–267. "The fossil record is consistent with historical causation that is in continuous flux, nonrepetitive, and therefore essentially nonpredictive."

3——1950, The meaning of evolution, a study of the history of life and of its significance for man: New Haven, Yale Univ. Press, xv and 364 pp. "It used to be usual to claim that value judgments have no part in science, but we are coming more and more to perceive how false this was. Science is essentially interwoven with such judgments. The very existence of science demands the value judgment and essential ethic that knowledge is good."

4——1960, The world into which Darwin led us: Science, vol. 131, no. 3405, pp. 966–974. Astronomy made the universe immense; physics and related sciences made it lawful. "To all these discoveries and principles, which so greatly modified concepts of the cosmos, geology added two more of fundamental, world-changing importance: vast extension of the universe in time, and the idea of constantly lawful progression in time."

5——1960, The history of life, pp. 117–180 *in* Sol Tax, ed., Evolution after Darwin, vol. 1: Chicago, University of Chicago Press. "All science is philosophical, and the only philosophies capable of validation are those of scientists . . . A scientist cannot so much as make an observation without reliance on a philosophical premise, such as the by no means self-evident minimal premise that there really is something to observe."

6——1961, Principles of animal taxonomy: New York, Columbia University Press, xii and 247 pp. "All theoretical science is ordering and if . . . systematics is equated with ordering, then systematics is synonomous with theoretical science. Taxonomy, in any case, is a science that is most explicitly and exclusively devoted to the ordering of complex data, and in this respect it has a special, a particularly aesthetic . . . , and . . . almost a superscientific place among the sciences."

SMALL, JAMES, 1952, The time scale of organic evolution: Irish Astronom. J., vol. 2, no. 1, pp. 21–26. ". . . we can recognize that there is, and has been, as much law and order in organic evolution as there is and has been in astronomical evolution—and on a similar time scale of millions of years."

SMILEY, TERAH LEROY, *ed.*, 1955, Geochronology: Univ. Arizona B., Physical Sci. B., 2, 200 pp. Twelve essays on scientific methods which can be applied to the dating of terrestrial events.

SMITH, JAMES PERRIN, 1900, Principles of paleontologic correlation: J. Geol., vol. 8, pp. 673–697. "The geological succession of faunas has some irregularities and anomalies . . . but the displacements of the time scale are too slight and the uniformity in various separated regions too great to lay much stress on homotaxis as opposed to synchronism."

SOLLAS, W. J., 1900, Evolutional geology: Science, n.s., vol. 12, pp. 745–756, 787–796. With the growth of knowledge about the earth, catastrophic geology was supplanted by uniformitarian geology, and this in turn by evolutional geology.

SONDER, RICHARD AUGUST, 1956, Gedanken zur theoretischen Geotektonik, pp. 381–395 *in* Franz Lotze, ed., Geotektonisches Symposium zu Ehren von Hans Stille: Stuttgart, Ferdinand Enke, xx and 483 pp. "Die in der endogenen Geomechanik anzuwendende *Methodik* muss nach dem bekannten Prinzip von '*Versuch und Irrtum*' vorgehen. Die verschiedenen Grundtheorien sind für den Theoretiker Probe-oder *Testtheorien*, die geotektonischen Thesen sind die *Testthesen*."

SPENCER, HERBERT, 1884, The classification of the sciences, pp. 59–112 *in* Recent discussions in science, philosophy and morals: New York, D. Appleton. The sequence of concrete sciences—astronomy, geology, biology, psychology, and sociology—forms a natural and intergradational series which reflects the cosmic evolution of their subject matter.

SPIEKER, EDMUND MAUTE, 1956, Mountain-building chronology and nature of the geologic time scale: Am. Assoc. Petroleum Geol., B., vol. 40, no. 8, pp. 1769–1815. "The pattern of concepts, and the consequent way of thinking that the geologist brings to his observations . . . inevitably will control the data he obtains, either by selection or in outright discernment."

STENO, NICOLAUS (NIELS STENSEN), 1667, Canis carchariae dissectum caput (The earliest geological treatise, translated from the Latin, with introduction and notes, by Axel Garboe): London, Macmillan; New York, St. Martin's Press, 51 pp., 1958. "Since the ground from which the bodies resembling parts of animals does not produce this sort of body in our time (a); since it is likely that the soil in question has been soft in former times (b), indeed, presumably has been mixed up with waters (c); why, then, should we not be allowed to surmise that these bodies are remains of animals that lived in these waters?"

STOREY, TARAS PHILIP, and PATTERSON, JOHN ROBERT, 1959, Stratigraphy— traditional and modern concepts: Am. J. Sci., vol. 257, no. 10, pp. 707– 721. "Whereas the traditional stratigrapher sets his sights high by regarding attributes of time as the guiding factor in stratigraphy, modern workers drift aimlessly about in their arbitrary philosophy that lithologic, biologic and time criteria should be treated without simultaneously relating one with the other."

STRAHLER, ARTHUR NEWELL, 1952, Dynamic basis of geomorphology: Geol. Soc. Am., B., vol. 63, no. 9, pp. 923–938. "Two quite different viewpoints are used in dynamic (analytical) geomorphology and in historical (regional) geomorphology. The student of processes and forms *per se* is continually asking, 'What happens?'; the historical student keeps raising the question, 'What happened?'"
2——1958, Dimensional analysis applied to fluvially eroded landforms: Geol. Soc. Am., B., vol. 69, no. 3, pp. 279–300. "The rational phase of science,

often associated with 'deductive science' in geology, consists of the formulation of explanations and general laws through logical steps of reasoning from a series of initial postulates which seem to be valid in the light of prior observation and experience."

STUBBLEFIELD, CYRIL JAMES, 1954, The relationship of palaeontology to stratigraphy: Adv. Sci., vol. 11, pp. 149–159. "Both palaeontology and stratigraphy are observational rather than experimental sciences, nevertheless however accurately the observations are recorded, they are but retrospective in so far as they relate to natural processes."

SUZUKI, KOITI and KITAZAKI, UMEKA, 1951, On the stratigraphical meaning of time and space: Res. Inst. Nat. Res., Tokyo, Misc. Rept. no. 22, pp. 28–35. The dualistic conception of stratigraphic classification, according to which sequences of strata may be subdivided into lithological and chronological categories which are independent of one another, reflects a misunderstanding of what geologic time actually means. Since the chronicle of earth history is based upon the arrangement of rock masses in space, lithological and chronological units are conceptually inseparable.

TASCH, PAUL, 1954, Search for the germ of Wegener's concept of continental drift: Osiris, vol. 11, pp. 157–167. Wegener's concept of continental drift may have its roots in Plato's myth of the lost continent of Atlantis.

TEICHERT, CURT, 1958, Concepts of facies: Am. Assoc. Petroleum Geol., B., vol. 42, no. 11, pp. 2718–2744.
2——1958, Some biostratigraphical concepts: Geol. Soc. Am., B., vol. 69, no. 1, pp. 99–120. "Biochronology shows the order of succession in which events occurred; a loosely fitting absolute scale comes from the radioactive methods."

TEILHARD DE CHARDIN, PIERRE, 1951, La vision du passé: ce qu'elle nous apporte, et ce qu'elle nous enlève, *in* Sciences de la terre, XXI Cong. Internat. Phil. Sci., Paris, 1949: Paris, Hermann, pp. 71–74. As our perceptions of space are affected by the geometric laws of perspective, so our perspectives of time are subject to certain natural constraints. In reconstructions of the geologic past, the slow rhythms of the universe are revealed, but the actual origins of entities which have evolved in time cannot ordinarily be resolved.

THOMAS, GWYN, 1956, The species conflict—abstractions and their applicability: Systematics Assoc., London, Pub. no. 2, pp. 17–31. Discusses differences among paleontologists, and between paleontologists and neontologists, on the definition of species, and suggests that paleontological taxonomy is, and will remain, as much an art as a science.

THORBURN, W. M., 1918, The myth of Occam's Razor: Mind, vol. 27, pp. 345–353. "The unfortunate carelessness of Tennemann and Hamilton . . . has turned a sound rule of Methodology into a Metaphysical dogma . . . It is folly to complicate research by multiplying the objects of inquiry; but we know too little of the ultimate constitution of the Universe, to assume that it cannot be far more complex than it seems, or than we have any actual reason to suppose."

TIKHOMIROV, V. V., 1959, Aktualizm v trudakh russkikh geologov nachala XIX veka (Actualism in the works of Russian geologists at the beginning of the nineteenth century): Akad. Nauk. SSSR, Inst. Geol., Ocherki po istorii geol. znanii, vol. 8, pp. 154–164. The uniformitarian, or formal, approach to actualism leads to a dead end, because, according to this approach, we cannot explain the origin of rocks whose analogues are not to be found forming at the present time. On the other hand, the outright rejection of actualism leads to agnosticism regarding the possibility of deciphering the evolution of our planet.

TOMKEIEFF, SERGEI IVANOVICH, 1946, James Hutton's "Theory of the Earth" (Hundred and fiftieth anniversary of the birth of modern geology): Geologists' Assoc., London, Pr., vol. 57, pt. 4, pp. 322–328. "Towards the end of the eighteenth century the heroic conception of human history was being replaced by one of gradual development composed of the actions and thoughts of a multitude of men and women. Condorcet was the exponent of this idea and his book was published in 1794. To the heroic conception of human history corresponded the catastrophic conception of earth's history. This Hutton replaced by what may be called gradualism."
2——1948, James Hutton and the philosophy of geology: Edinburgh Geol. Soc., Tr., vol. 14, pt. 2, pp. 253–276. Hutton's theory of the earth was based upon the principle of the uniformity of Nature; the postulate of determinism; the idea that the study of processes, rather than of matter, affords the better approach to geological problems; and the principle of integration, which assumes that small events in their cumulative result lead to great changes. Hutton's principal contribution to geology was his concept of the geostrophic cycle, which he apparently borrowed from the life cycle of organisms.

TOULMIN, GEORGE HOGGART, 1783, The antiquity of the world, 2d ed.: London, T. Cadell, xiii and 208 pp. "If something always has existed, or must have been eternal,—why not pay a deference to the magnificent and beautiful objects of whose existence we are certain? Why not grant eternity to nature? . . . Nature is invariably the same, her laws are eternal and immutable . . ."

TOULMIN, STEPHEN EDELSTON, 1953, The philosophy of science; an introduction: London, Hutchinson's University Library, 176 pp. ". . . in whatever sense we understand the Uniformity Principle, whether as assumption, as discovery or as manifesto, it has one special weakness: that of irremediable vagueness. A principle stated in such general terms can be of no practical significance . . . . So it is not Nature that is Uniform, but scientific procedure; and it is uniform only in this, that it is methodical and self-correcting."

2——1961, Foresight and understanding; an enquiry into the aims of science: Indiana University Press, 116 pp. "Those who build up their sciences around a principle of regularity or ideal of natural order come to accept it as self-explanatory. Just because (on their view) it specifies the way in which things behave of their own nature, if left to themselves, they cease to ask further questions about it."

TRUEMAN, ARTHUR ELIJAH, 1948, Geology today and tomorrow: Adv. Sci., vol. 5, no. 19, pp. 184–193. Among the principal contributions of geology to general thought are the scale of geologic time, a world view of the history of life against this time scale, and an appreciation of the insignificance of historical time as compared with the stages of human evolution and of vertebrate evolution in general.

TSILIKIS, JOHN D., 1959, Simplicity and elegance in theoretical physics: Am. Scientist, vol. 47, pp. 87–96. "Truth is usually simple, and the discovery of simple equations for the description of natural phenomena gives some assurance that simple results involve factual truths."

UMBGROVE, JOHANNES HERMAN FREDERIK, 1942, The pulse of the earth: The Hague, Martinus Nijhoff, xvi and 179 pp. "The historical succession of phenomena, their correlation and meaning, form the most attractive and interesting feature of geology."

VOGELSANG, HERMANN PETER JOSEPH, 1867, Philosophie der Geologie und mikroskopische Gesteinsstudien: Bonn, Max Cohen, 229 pp. "Wo die Gegenwart aufhört, da fängt die Vergangenheit an; die eine kann nur durch die andere erklärt werden."

VYSOTSKII, B. P., 1961, Problema aktualizma i uniformisma i sistema metodov v geologii (The problem of actualism and uniformitarianism and the system of methods in geology): Akad. Nauk, SSSR, Inst. Filosofii, Voprosy Filosofii, no. 3, pp. 134–145. Actualism and uniformitarianism are different scientific concepts. Uniformitarianism is an hypothesis of a simple cyclic development in Nature; actualism is a method of investigation, by which the study of present phenomena and processes is used as a basis for discovering the geologic past and predicting the future.

2——1961, Vozniknovenie uniformizma i sootnoshenie ego s aktualizmom (The origin of uniformitarianism and its relation to actualism): Akad. Nauk,

SSSR, Inst. Geol., Ocherki po istorii geol. znanii, vol. 9, pp. 84–125. "... as a rule, hypotheses and ideas never die; they are partly incorporated into new theories ... Lyell's periodicity does not contradict irreversible evolution; it is only one of its aspects ... The uniformitarian approach, but not the uniformitarian philosophy, is valid on small scales, so that it still remains significant—in the same sense that the decimal scale remains significant despite Einstein's theory of relativity."

WADELL, HAKON ADOLPH, 1938, Proper names, nomenclature and classification: J. Geol., vol. 46, no. 3, pp. 546–568. "Geology is unfortunate in the respect that the things pertinent to the subject are difficult to arrange into a single well-constructed and complete classification."

WALTHER, JOHANNES, 1893–1894, Einleitung in die Geologie als historische Wissenschaft: Jena, Gustav Fischer, vi and 1055 pp. "Während die Geognosie beschreibt, die Formationslehre ordnet, ist die Erdgeschichte eine erklärende Disciplin, und daher bedarf *die Geologie als historische Wissenschaft* anderer Methoden und anderer Hilfswissenschaften, um ihr hohes Ziel zu erreichen ... Diese ... Art geologischer Erklärungs-versuche, die mann gewöhnlich als Aktualismus bezeichnet, wollen wir die *ontologische Methode* nennen."

WATSON, DAVID MEREDITH SEARES, 1951, Paleontology and modern biology: New Haven, Yale Univ. Press, xii and 216 pp. "Thus even the most extended flights of morphological argument have led to predictions which ... have been verified by the description of actual fossil animals whose structure conforms exactly to expectation."

WATTS, WILLIAM WHITEHEAD, 1911, Geology as geographical evolution: Geol. Soc. London, Quart. J., vol. 67, pp. lxii–xciii. "The History of the Earth, so far as the Geologist is capable of following it through the geological systems and formations, is a history of successive geographies, and of the relations of these geographies to the living beings which successively characterised them. In the reading and restoration of these geographies there is but one unfailing guide, unceasing comparison, at every stage, of the ascertainable geological phenomena of the past with the known geographical phenomena of the present."

WATZNAUER, ADOLF, 1956, Kritische Bemerkungen zur wissenschaftlichen Begriffsbildung: Zs. angew. Geol., vol. 2, no. 2–3, pp. 64–65. "Das geologische Weltbild ist das Ziel der geologischen Wissenschaften."

WEBER, CHRISTIAN OLIVER, 1927, The reality of time and the autonomy of history: Monist, vol. 37, pp. 521–540. "... suppose that we reconstruct the world's past, by applying our present laws to the data of the world's present state. It is evident that we could never meet with a contradiction in making this reconstruction, provided that no disharmony existed between our present data and laws. Then, suppose we find deep in the earth a geological condition which shows a past different from the one we have reconstructed? Will we conclude that the laws of mechanics have evolved, and that they were different in the past? No, for the scientist can always say that our present laws of mechanics are faulty, and must be modified to cover the new facts. This amounts to saying that scientific laws do not enable us to recover historical facts."

WEDEKIND, RUDOLF, 1916, Über die Grundlagen und Methoden der Bio-stratigraphie: Berlin, Borntraeger, 60 pp. "Das grundlegende Prinzip jeder Zeitmessung lautet: *Die gleichen Ursachen bedürfen des gleichen Zeitintervalls, um am gleichen Objekt die gleiche Veränderung hervorzurufen.*"

WEGMANN, EUGÈNE, 1950, Diskontinuität und Kontinuität in der Erdgeschichte; ein Nachwort: Geol. Rundschau, vol. 38, no. 2, pp. 125–132. The tension generated between catastrophists and uniformitarians continues to stimulate investigations and discoveries.

2——1951, L'analyse structurale en géologie, *in* Sciences de la terre, XXI Cong. Internat. Phil. Sci., Paris, 1949: Paris, Hermann, pp. 55–64. In reconstructing a succession of shapes which have led to the development of a geological structure in its present form, structural geology accomplishes one of its main objectives without appeal to "causes" or "forces." This manner of explanation is appropriate to geology, which is above all an historical science.

3——1958, Das Erbe Werner's und Hutton's: Geologie (Berlin), vol. 7, no. 3–6, pp. 531–559. "Die Herstellung der geologischen Geschichte ist eine Art Zusammensetzspiel in Zeit und Raum. Viele Stücke dieses 'Puzzles' fehlen und zwingen uns, um die Lücken herum zu bauen. Die Art des Zusammenfügens der einzelnen Bausteine hängt weitgehend vom Leitbilde ab."

WEIZSÄCKER, CARL FRIEDRICH VON, 1949, The history of nature: Chicago, Univ. Chicago Press, 191 pp. "Since practically every event in nature produces heat—though often very small amounts—every event is in the strictest sense irreversible. Every pendulum comes to a stand-still. Even the motion of the planets around the sun is constantly slowed down ever so little by interstellar gas. Hence no event in nature is repeated exactly. Nature is a unique course of events."

WESTGATE, LEWIS GARDNER, 1940, Errors in scientific method—glacial geology: Sci. Monthly, vol. 51, no. 4, pp. 299–309. "Geology differs from most sciences in that its investigations are geographically determined . . . It was no accident that stratigraphic geology took its rise in central England . . . and . . . in the Paris Basin . . ."

WHEELER, HARRY EUGENE, 1947, Base of the Cambrian system: J. Geol.,
    vol. 55, no. 3, pp. 153–159. "... how can we continue to indulge in a
    concept which regards the base of the Cambrian system as a time horizon
    but determines that base by physical criteria that are not amenable to
    interregional correlation?"
2——(and Beesley, Edward Maurice), 1948, Critique of the time-stratigraphic
    concept: Geol. Soc. Am., B., vol. 59, no. 1, pp. 75–86. "This variation in
    age of lithogenetic units is ... a fundamental truth in stratigraphy, nearly
    equal in significance to the laws of superposition and faunal succession,
    and is ... designated therefore as the *principle of temporal transgression*."
3——1958, Time-stratigraphy: Am. Assoc. Petroleum Geol., B., vol. 42, no. 5,
    pp. 1047–1063. "... just as rock units of one kind or another are defined
    to fill all space occupied by the determinable present geologic record,
    time-stratigraphic units of one kind or another must be conceived or
    designated to account for all interpretable space-time."
4——1959, Stratigraphic units in space and time: Am. J. Sci., vol. 257, no. 10,
    pp. 692–706. "Time has no meaning in stratigraphy unless it is tied to the
    spatial record and then substituted for its vertical dimension."

WHEWELL, WILLIAM, 1858, History of scientific ideas, being the first part of
    the philosophy of the inductive sciences, 3rd. ed., vol. 2: London, John S.
    Parker, xv and 324 pp. "I conceive that the assertion of an *a priori* claim
    to probability and philosophical spirit in favour of the doctrine of uni-
    formity, is quite untenable. We must learn from an examination of all
    the facts, and not from any assumption of our own, whether the course of
    nature be uniform."
2——1872, History of the inductive sciences from the earliest to the present
    time, 3rd. ed., 2 vols.: New York, D. Appleton. "The effects must them-
    selves teach us the nature and intensity of the causes which have operated;
    and we are in danger of error, if we seek for slow and shun violent agencies
    further than the facts naturally direct us, no less than if we were parsi-
    monious of time and prodigal of violence."

WHITE, ANDREW DICKSON, 1930, A history of the warfare of science with theol-
    ogy in Christendom: New York, D. Appleton, 2 vols. Chapter 5, "From
    Genesis to Geology" sketches the contest between geological and theo-
    logical views of nature to near the end of the nineteenth century.

WHITTARD, WALTER FREDERICK, 1953, The enigma of the earliest fossils:
    British Naturalists' Soc., Pr., vol. 28, pt. 4, pp. 289–304.

WIENER, NORBERT, 1961, Newtonian and Bergsonian time, Chapter 1, pp.
    30–44, *in* Cybernetics, or control and communication in the animal and
    the machine, 2nd. ed.: New York, M. I. T. Press and John Wiley, 212 pp.

"Bergson emphasized the difference between the reversible time of physics, in which nothing new happens, and the irreversible time of evolution and biology, in which there is always something new . . . The record of paleontology indicates a definite longtime trend, interrupted and complicated though it might be, from the simple to the complex."

WILLIAMS, HENRY SHALER, 1893, The making of the geological time-scale: J. Geol., vol. 1, pp. 180–197. "Chronological time periods in geology are not only recognized by means of the fossil remains preserved in the strata, but it is to them chiefly that we must look for the determination and classification on a time basis."

WILLIAMS, JAMES STEELE, 1954, Problems of boundaries between geologic systems: Am. Assoc. Petroleum Geol., B., vol. 38, no. 7, pp. 1602–1605. Discusses criteria that have been used to determine the boundary between the Devonian and Carboniferous systems in Missouri, and concludes that it is rarely possible to establish intercontinental correlation of thin units near boundaries between systems.

WILLISTON, SAMUEL WENDELL, 1914, Water reptiles of the past and present: Chicago, Univ. Chicago Press, vii and 251 pp. ". . . it is also a law in evolution that the parts in an organism tend toward reduction in number, with the fewer parts greatly specialized in function, just as the most perfect human machine is that which has the fewest parts, and each part most highly adapted to the special function it has to subserve."

WILMARTH, MARY GRACE, 1925, The geologic time classification of the United States Geological Survey compared with other classifications, accompanied by the original definitions of era, period and epoch terms: U. S. Geol. Survey, B. 769, vi and 138 pp.

WILSON, JOHN ANDREW, 1959, Stratigraphic concepts in vertebrate paleontology: Am. J. Sci., vol. 257, no. 10, pp. 770–778. "Type sections in stratigraphic classification should have no more significance than name bearers. They are one dimensional samples of three dimensional bodies of rock."
2——et al., 1961, Geochronologic and chronostratigraphic units, Note 25 of the American Commission on Stratigraphic Nomenclature: Am. Assoc. Petroleum Geol., B., vol. 45, no. 5, pp. 666–673. ". . . time can be logically thought of, in geology, as being coincident with space."

WILSON, JOHN TUZO, 1952, Orogenesis as the fundamental geological process: Am. Geophys. Union, Tr., vol. 33, no. 3, pp. 444–449. "Now if, as is believed to be the case, geologists accept the assumption that the general laws of physics and chemistry apply to the earth and that no other exclusively geological laws are necessary, then the fundamental processes arrived at from physical reasoning must be the same as those arrived at from geological reasoning."

2——1959, Geophysics and continental growth: Am. Scientist, vol. 47, no. 1, pp. 1–24. "A belief that the earth does operate in a manner which can be generalized in some simple way is justified because that is usual in nature."

WILSON, MORLEY EVANS, 1956, Early Precambrian rocks of the Temiskaming region, Quebec and Ontario, Canada: Geol. Soc. Am., B., vol. 67, no. 10, pp. 1397–1430. "'No vestige of a beginning' is as true of the earliest Precambrian rocks of the Canadian Shield as it seemed to Hutton of the Highlands of Scotland in 1785."

WINTER, JOHN GARRETT, 1916, The prodromus of Nicolaus Steno's dissertation concerning a solid body enclosed by process of nature within a solid: an English version with an introduction and explanatory notes, with a foreword by William H. Hobbs: Univ. of Michigan Studies, Humanistic Ser., vol. XI, Contributions to the History of Science, Pt. II, pp. 165–283; New York, Macmillan. "If a solid substance is in every way like another solid substance, not only as regards the conditions of surface, but also as regards the inner arrangement of parts and particles, it will also be like it as regards the manner and place of production . . ."

WOLMAN, M. GORDON, and MILLER, JOHN P., 1960, Magnitude and frequency of forces in geomorphic processes: J. Geol., vol. 68, no. 1, pp. 54–74. "Analyses of the transport of sediment by various media indicate that a large portion of the 'work' is performed by events of moderate magnitude which recur relatively frequently rather than by rare events of unusual magnitude."

WOODFORD, ALFRED OSWALD, 1935, Historical introduction to geology: Pan-American Geol., vol. 64, no. 1, pp. 1–7.

2——1956, What is geologic truth?: J. Geol. Education, vol. 4, no. 1, pp. 5–8. ". . . complicated problems can usually be broken down into simple parts. Then each element can be attacked by one of several more or less rigorous methods . . . A solution, if found, may be (1) mathematically rigorous (2) the sole surviving hypothesis, after exhausting other possibilities (3) intuitive but fitting an extensive series of known facts, or (4) more or less doubtful."

3——1960, Bedrock patterns and strike-slip faulting in southwestern California: Am. J. Sci., vol. 258-A (Bradley Volume), pp. 400–417. When two slip-solutions for faults are possible, "tentative choices may be made by use of the rule *Disjunctiones minimae, disjunctiones optimae* . . . This rule may be considered a quantitatively parsimonious relative of Ockham's law . . ."

WOOLNOUGH, WALTER GEORGE, 1937, Fact and theory in geology, with special reference to petroleum, salt and coal: Australian and New Zealand Assoc.

Adv. Sci., Rept. 23rd Meeting, pp. 54–79. "I desire very diffidently to suggest . . . that a set of physiographic conditions has existed from time to time in past geological eras of which we have no true example at the present time; and that *variants* of these conditions *may* serve to explain at least some of the difficulties with which we are faced in an endeavour to explain the origin of oil, salt, and coal."

WRIGHT, CHARLES WILL, 1958, Order and disorder in nature: Geologists' Assoc., London, Pr., vol. 69, pp. 77–82. Geology comprises a group of sciences unified chiefly in their concern with time and process. The geologist should occasionally review his store of purely factual information, for the order and regularity of nature are in the last analysis assumptions.

ZEUNER, FREDERICK EBERHARD, 1952, Dating the past; an introduction to geochronology: London, Methuen, xx and 495 pp. Describes methods and principal results of geochronology, "the science of dating in terms of years those periods of the past to which the human historical calendar does not apply."

Index To Bibliography

limitations: Bunge
metalogical: Tsilikis
metascientific: Feuer 1; Hawkins 1
methodologic principle: Feuer 1; Thorburn
origin: Thorburn
postulate: Gold
related to cosmolysis: Blanc
relationship to uniformity: Barker 2; Hooykaas 2
wishful thinking: Jennings
Smith, William
contributions to systematic descriptive geology: Whewell 2
stratigraphical nomenclature: Whewell 2
Soil science (*see* Pedology)
Soil stratigraphic units
definition: Amer. Comm. on Strat. Nomenclature
Space
concept: Spencer
relation to time in stratigraphy: Suzuki
space-time analysis: Amstutz
Space-with-time continua
in stratigraphy: Wilson, J. A. 2
Species, inorganic
individuality: Niggli
mineral species: Orcel
Species, organic
Simpson 6
artificiality: Arkell 1; Haldane 3; Kermack
chronospecies: Thomas
conflict in neontological and paleontological viewpoints: Thomas
geographical and chronological subspecies: Joysey
morphospecies, monotypic vs. polytypic: Thomas
multidimensional: Mayr 2
nondimensional: Mayr 2
philosophic basis: Mayr 2
typological: Mayr 2
varieties of concepts among paleontologists: Thomas
Stages, stratigraphic
development of concept: Stubblefield
Stagnancy
landscape evolution: Crickmay
Statistical analysis
geologic data: Fisher 1; Krumbein 1
geosciences: Griffiths
Steno
laws of: Steno (*see* Winter)
postulate of: Woodford 2

Structural geology
    analytic, dynamic and synthetic terms: Wegmann 2
    geotectonic theses: Sonder
    interpretations in spirit of dialectic materialism: Popov
    relation to stratigraphy: Billings; Wegmann 2
    scope: Galbraith
    tectonic stage and style: Wegmann 2
Stromer's law
    Simpson 2
Studies, geologic
    depersonalization of: Rios
    examples: Krumbein 2
Superposition
    basis of geologic science: Spieker
    law: James Jeletzky 1; McLaren; Moore 3; Richey; Rutten 3; Schindewolf 4;
        Wheeler 2; Wilson, J. A. 1; Woodford 2
Symbols
    geologic cartography: Robertson
Syngenesis
    Amstutz
Systematics
    definition: Simpson 6
Systems, stratigraphic
    development of concept: Stubblefield
    terminology: Wilmarth

Taxa
    evolutionary basis: Simpson 6
Taxonomy, animal
    principles: Simpson 6
Teleology
    Davis 5
    biologic thought: Beckner
    theories of evolution: Romer 1
Temporal transgression
    principle of: Wheeler 2
Terminology, geologic
    ambiguity: Watznauer
    genetic vs. descriptive: Baulig 1
    geomorphic: Baulig 1
    origin of terms for eras, periods and epochs: Wilmarth
    overelaboration: Chamberlin 4; Watznauer
    proper names: Wadell
    stratigraphic: Wheeler 3
    structural: Wegmann 2

Notes on the Contributors

Donald B. McIntyre was born in Edinburgh and was trained there in the famous university that has produced so many outstanding geologists. For six years he was a member of the faculty at the University of Edinburgh, where he supervised studies of structural geology and petrology. In 1954 he migrated to California to join the faculty of geology at Pomona College. In addition to his present duties as departmental chairman, he is engaged in geochemical investigations and is particularly interested in the application of computers to all aspects of geological research.

A native of Connecticut, **Wilmot H. Bradley** completed graduate studies at Yale University in 1927. His career with the United States Geological Survey has been long and distinguished. As an administrator he has served as Chief of the Military Geology Unit and as Chief Geologist. As an investigator, he is well known for his contributions to paleoecology, paleolimnology, and geochronology. Dr. Bradley is a member of both the National Academy of Sciences and of the American Academy of Arts and Sciences. In 1947, Yale awarded him the honorary D.Sc.

George Gaylord Simpson is Alexander Agassiz Professor of Vertebrate Paleontology at Harvard University. His training was at Yale, where as a graduate student he began the studies of vertebrate paleontology and evolution that have since been acclaimed through awards of medals, prizes, and honorary degrees from several countries. His work has resulted in an improved classification of mammals and a better understanding of evolution and ancient migrations.

Following undergraduate studies at the University of Pennsylvania, **David B. Kitts** enrolled at Columbia University, where he received his doctorate in Zoology in 1953. After a year's teaching at Amherst College, he joined the faculty of geology at the University of Oklahoma. Presently he is an Associate Professor of Geology and of the History of Science at Oklahoma. He has published papers on Cenozoic mammals and on the geology of western Oklahoma. During the past five years his interests have broadened to include the history and philosophy of science.

A graduate of Syracuse University, **Vincent E. McKelvey** completed graduate studies at the University of Wisconsin in 1947. As a member of the U. S. Geological Survey since 1941, he has been concerned primarily with studies of physical stratigraphy and with the economic geology of sedimentary mineral deposits. Dr. McKelvey is now Assistant the Chief Geologist for Economic Geology.

Upon completing his graduate studies at the University of California, **A. O. Woodford** returned to Pomona College, his alma mater, where he taught courses in chemistry and geology until his appointment as Emeritus Professor in 1955. That same year he received the Miner Award, in recognition of his

accomplishments as teacher and scientist. Although he lists sedimentary petrology as his principal research field, his interests range across the spectrum
of the geological sciences.

J. Hoover Mackin is a New Yorker by birth, a Washingtonian by virtue
of long residence, and a Texan by recent adoption. After completing graduate
studies at Columbia University, he joined the faculty of geology of the University
of Washington in Seattle. During World War II he took leave of academic
duties and worked with the U. S. Geological Survey in field studies of strategic
mineral deposits. Recently he accepted a distinguished professorship at the
University of Texas, where he continues his studies of geomorphology and engineering geology. Dr. Mackin is a member of the National Academy of
Sciences.

A graduate of Pomona College, **Mason L. Hill** received the doctorate from
the University of Wisconsin in 1932. After three years of teaching at Coalinga
Junior College in California, he entered the petroleum industry through the
geological department of the Shell Oil Company. In 1937 he joined the staff
of the Richfield Oil Company and is at present Manager of Exploration.
Dr. Hill is a former Councilor of the Geological Society of America and is
past-President of The American Association of Petroleum Geologists.

Charles A. Anderson is Chief Geologist of the U. S. Geological Survey.
He is a graduate of Pomona College. Following the completion of graduate
studies at the University of California, he became a member of the faculty and
taught there for twelve years. He joined the Geological Survey in 1942, and
served as Chief of the Mineral Deposits Branch prior to the appointment to
his present position. Dr. Anderson's recent field studies have been concerned
mostly with the intricacies of Precambrian geology, with special reference to the
structural associations of ore deposits in these most ancient rocks.

Luna B. Leopold is Chief Hydrologist with the U. S. Geological Survey.
Prior to the completion of his studies for the doctorate at Harvard in 1950—a
year after he joined the Geological Survey—he had worked with the Soil Conservation Service, Department of Agriculture, Corps of Engineers, and Bureau
of Reclamation. He had also served as Head Meteorologist for the Pineapple
Research Institute of Hawaii. In 1958 he received the Kirk Bryan Award
for distinguished contributions to geomorphology.

After graduating from Cooper Union in 1931, **Walter B. Langbein** began
his professional career as a construction engineer. In 1935 he joined the U. S.
Geological Survey, with which he is presently affiliated as Hydrologist. For
his studies of rivers and lakes, and their responses to climatic changes, he has
received both the Distinguished Service Award of the U. S. Department of
Interior and the Horton Award of the American Geophysical Union.

Frederick Betz, Jr. was an undergraduate at Columbia and completed graduate work at Princeton. Throughout a career of varied activity he has maintained an interest in problems of communication and use of scientific knowledge.

The experience of living and working in Europe for a long period gave him a special insight into the problem of language barriers. Scientific communication is now one of his main activities. He is also a specialist in problems of terrain evaluation and is one of the few experts in the history of military applications of earth sciences.

Following the completion of his advanced studies at Yale, **James Gilluly** became a member of the U. S. Geological Survey. Except for an interval of twelve years when he served as Professor of Geology at the University of California at Los Angeles, he has been an active member of the Survey. During World War II, Dr. Gilluly was attached to the Military Geology Unit and served as a consultant to the Chief Engineer of the Southwest Pacific area. A member of the National Academy of Sciences, he was awarded the Penrose Medal by the Geological Society in 1958.

J. M. Harrison is Assistant Deputy Minister (Research) of the Geological Survey of Canada. His training was in Canadian universities, with undergraduate studies at the University of Manitoba, and graduate studies at Queen's. After several years of work as an industrial chemist, he joined the Canadian Survey in 1943. Dr. Harrison's principal interests are with Precambrian stratigraphy and structural relations of ore deposits, iron ores in particular.

A native of New Jersey, **Arthur F. Hagner** did his undergraduate work at New York University and his graduate work at Columbia. He taught at the University of Wyoming before joining the faculty of the University of Illinois, where he is now a Professor of Geology. His field studies have been conducted mainly in the Appalachian highlands and Adirondack Mountains and in the Laramie Range of Wyoming. Dr. Hagner's principal interests are with petrology and the study of mineral deposits.

Robert F. Legget is a Civil Engineer, holding his Master's degree from the University of Liverpool, LL.D. *honoris causa* from McMaster University, and D.Sc. *honoris causa* from the University of Waterloo. After four years' practical experience in Scotland and London, he came to Canada in 1929 and was engaged in heavy construction work until 1936, when he joined the staff of Queen's University, Kingston, Ontario. He went on to the University of Toronto in 1938, remaining there as teacher and consultant on soil and foundation problems until 1947. He was then invited to come to Ottawa to start the new Division of Building Research of the National Research Council of Canada, of which he has since been Director.

Claude Albritton is Hamilton Professor of Geology and Dean of the Graduate School at Southern Methodist University. Following graduate studies at Harvard, he joined the faculty at SMU, where previously he had done his undergraduate work. During World War II he was on leave with the U. S. Geological Survey, engaged in studies of military geology and strategic minerals. His present research interests are in the history of early man in North America, and in the history and philosophy of the geological sciences.

Subject Index